Construction
Disasters

The Engineering News-Record Series

Construction Disasters:
Design Failures, Causes, and Prevention

Steven S. Ross

An Engineering News-Record Book

McGraw-Hill Book Company

New York   St. Louis   San Francisco   Auckland   Bogotá
Hamburg   London   Madrid   Mexico
Montreal   New Delhi   Panama   Paris   São Paulo
Singapore   Sydney   Tokyo   Toronto

Library of Congress Cataloging in Publication Data

Ross, Steven S.
    Construction disasters.

    Includes index.
    1. Structural failures. I. Title.
TA656.R67 1984   624.1'71   83-16215
ISBN 0-07-053865-4

4 5 6 7 8 9 0 BRBBRB 8 9

ISBN 0-07-053865-4

The editors for this book were Joan Zseleczky and Georgia Kornbluth,
the designer was Jules Perlmutter, and the production supervisor was
Teresa F. Leaden. It was set in Century Schoolbook by University
Graphics, Inc.

In reprinting articles from *Engineering News-Record* for this book,
material was occasionally omitted to avoid repetition or improve
continuity. In those cases, the omitted material was replaced with
ellipses (. . .).

Sometimes, relevant information such as the final death toll or cost of a
disaster was made available only after the article was originally published.
Sometimes, errors were noted in articles after publication. Such corrections
and new facts are enclosed in brackets: [   ].

In order to present a realistic picture of the development of
construction engineering over the past half-century or more, the
articles reprinted here have been left in their historical contexts.
McGraw-Hill policy is not to discriminate on the basis of gender.
However, since the engineering profession as a whole has traditionally
been dominated by men, the work of male engineers is necessarily the
primary or exclusive focus of this book. No sexual bias is implied or
intended.

To the staff of *Engineering News-Record*
and to
Robert L. Davidson,
without whom this book
would not have been possible.

Contents

viii   **Contents**

Preface

Why *Engineering News-Record* Reports Failures

ENR policy is to report both failures and successes. We report both for the same reason: to give readers the information they need in their own businesses, so that they can avoid the failures and emulate the successes.

Every week ENR editors and correspondents report on the ingenuity of the construction industry—design innovations, clever approaches to building, new developments in materials and equipment, new ways to manage companies, coups in bidding and winning contracts. These are all success stories.

Some weeks we also have to report the failures of people and companies and the things they plan, design, make, or build: financial failures such as bankruptcy, personal failures such as crime and corruption, planning failures such as a downtown renovation that doesn't work, disasters that are caused by natural phenomena like earthquakes and floods. There are also structural failures such as dam collapses and system failures such as hotel fire-safety assignments that fall apart in a fire.

ENR pays a great deal of attention to accidents that kill and injure people—people who build as well as people who use and live or work in or near structures that fail. The importance of this attention is threefold: First, it is the responsibility of the building trades to constantly improve and refine design, as well as construction materials and methods, so as to prevent unnecessary failures and minimize damage from those that cannot be averted. Second, fatalities and injuries often receive much publicity in the general press, which adds to the pressure. Third, the expenses and legal consequences of fatalities and injuries can create serious problems for ENR readers.

In addition, ENR reports many failures that do not harm people physically—potholes, cracks in facades, leaking roofs, tunnel machine entrapments, popping windows, and so forth. We also try to dig out expert opinions or professional judgments on why these things happen. Readers frequently let us know that they expect and want us to do this. In fact, readers constantly contribute to and supplement our reporting, and many letters from readers are included in this book.

Engineering News-Record could run only upbeat stories, and success stories are usually easier to get than the truth behind the failures. But that policy would not serve readers' best interests. Our readers need to know what is really going on, and we try our best to tell them.

In this book, more than two dozen of the worst disasters of the past half century are reported in detail, using words (and often pictures) that originally appeared in the pages of ENR. The reports are often sobering. But brought together in this way, they also reveal the progress the building industry has made during those years and point to the progress it is continuing to make.

The Editors

Construction Disasters

1

Introduction

A poorly constructed apartment house collapses in a mild earthquake in Manila, and 400 people die. An offshore drilling platform capsizes and more than 100 are lost. A little dam in Connecticut washes away and a neighborhood is inundated.

Such happenings numb the minds of the general public: so many killed here, so many maimed there, so many millions of dollars of property destroyed. For most engineers, architects, and contractors, however, the numbers are not mere statistics. The numbers leap off the pages appended to the lives of real people—not only the immediate victims, but the people who conceived, designed, and built the structures that failed.

Structural failures are remarkably uncommon, considering the number of structures standing today, and the number added every year. Nevertheless, the number of minor failures is large enough so that insurance companies report about one architectural or engineering firm out of every three is involved in a claim for financial damages *every year*. The number of highly visible, major disasters in which heavy property damage results or lives are lost is large enough so that there is hardly an engineer, architect, or contractor alive who does not personally know of a colleague who has been touched by tragedy.

This book gives details of many of the major construction disasters of the past half century. All of these disasters have led or are leading to changes in the way buildings are designed and built. Over the span of 50 years, it is remarkable how much we have learned—and how much knowledge we have applied—about fire, wind, earthquake, and the physical properties of construction materials.

Nevertheless, many patterns continue to be repeated. Our structures continue to fall prey to natural and man-made disasters. Partly this is due to unforeseen problems that have arisen as we have stretched technology to bridge wider rivers, cope with higher building costs, or build on marginal sites. Among such problems discovered in the past 50 years: wind-induced resonant vibrations that destroyed the Tacoma Narrows Bridge, lamillar tearing in welded steel joints, and reservoir-induced earthquakes behind ever-larger dams.

Careful study of such disasters has helped keep the number of recurrences

Figure 1-1   The South Canadian River Bridge on U.S. 75 near Calvin, Oklahoma, fell on May 21, 1976. Drivers of two semitrailer trucks were killed. The expansion joints at each pier apparently locked, so that all expansion and contraction accumulated at one joint. When the span "walked" off the pier at that point, it dragged other spans with it. *(United Press International.)*

remarkably low. Unfortunately, another class of problems has been less amenable to study and solution. Simply put, these are the disasters caused by the unforgiving nature of many modern construction materials and methods. Today's public, a public quite used to the wonders of technology, feels betrayed, hurt, and angry when something goes wrong—especially if the "something" interferes with the use of a highly visible object like a skyscraper or a bridge.

This public attitude has been growing slowly over the past century. James B. Eads, for example, had to go to great lengths to assure the public of the safety of his proposed great bridge at St. Louis. At the bridge's inauguration in 1874, he said, "the peculiar construction of [the bridge's superstructure] is such that any piece in it can be easily taken out and examined, and replaced or renewed, without interrupting the traffic of the bridge. . . . In completing the western span two of the lower tubes of the inside ribs near the middle of the span were injured during erection, and were actually uncoupled and taken out without any difficulty whatsoever, after the span was completed, and two new ones put in their place in a few hours."

In October 1969, a tugboat knocked away a section of the lower chord of one of the arches. There was no progressive collapse, thanks to Eads's overdesign. The gap was jacked and new structural members were inserted. In those days the construction of a great bridge was as immense and as visible an undertaking as a space shot is today. At a time when few buildings had more than 4 or 5 floors, Eads, Roebling, and their contemporaries could build structures that would take people 150 feet or higher above a river. Bridge towers—the height of a modern 20-story building—dominate early photos and prints of post-Civil War America.

Today's construction sites are rarely policed with the care of a space shot, however. Thus daring concrete structures can sometimes fall prey to a hidden flaw: poorly placed reinforcing rods. Composites find ways to corrode from within unless perfectly waterproofed. Facades and roofs fail with distressing regularity.

The public has come to expect and demand daring design, rather than to be suspicious of it. Computers have made many once-difficult calculations easy, allowing designers to reduce the thickness and strength of structural members but narrowing the margin for error in actual construction.

How many people are aware that different codes and different design practices may allow the designer to calculate needed strengths in different ways? More to the point, how many potential clients understand that a concrete beam designed under code assumptions of "ultimate strength" can cut the need for steel reinforcing by anywhere from 5 to 20 percent compared to the same beam

Figure 1-2 This overloaded loft building on Duane Street in New York City collapsed late in 1944. The facade was mass-produced cast iron, made to look like stone, which was popular in New York before the turn of the century. *(ENR File.)*

designed under "working-stress" assumptions—but that conditions may demand working-stress assumptions even if the "code authority" allows ultimate-strength design?

Likewise, how many clients understand the possibilities for error when modifying a structure that is already being occupied and used? There is hardly a report about any major disaster that does not note a myriad of minor deficiencies in design, construction, or modification of the structure involved. It is a tribute to the code writers that such deficiencies do not usually erase the margin for safety that is designed into structures that comply with codes in the first place.

Under the pressure of economics, however, those margins have been steadily reduced. How far can we go, and continue to build and use structures with old organizational forms?

"The use of such terms as 'ultimate design' for a method which is not in fact ultimate design at all, the magic of load factors, and a misleading complexity of complicated formulae do not in any way justify the extremely low safety factors. Use of computers for solutions with programs developed by some analyst who has never seen concrete only speeds up the application to further failures," said C. D. Williams, president of Southeastern Architects and Engineers, in a 1971 letter to *Engineering News-Record.*

Even when a design is adequate and capable of being built safely by average construction crews, unforeseen delays can always spell trouble. If the concrete trucks are late arriving at a continuous pour, are the workers down at the face of the last lift, shoveling out keys and trenches? Is the clever, prefabricated formwork designed so that such emergency work is even *possible?*

There are tens of thousands of parts, tens of thousands of design calculations, in even a small structure today. Those parts must be made to work together, those calculations must be constantly updated, as the work on the structure proceeds from architectural concept through engineering to detailing of working drawings (by specialists in such matters as rebar placement and steel joints) to the construction site and fabrication shop. And no matter how carefully the plans are detailed, there is hardly any structure that can be built exactly as designed. Who can imagine all the possible places in a structure where ductwork, wiring, plumbing and structural members might interfere with one another—until some hapless construction worker perched 40 feet up tries to fit some piece into a space that "isn't there"?

The solution offered by most of the experts is "better inspection." ENR put it this way in the issue of March 2, 1967:

In the long, complicated chain of events that produce a building— from the owner's first decision to build, through checking shop drawings and finally issuance of a certificate of occupancy—inspection is still the weakest link.

Figure 1-3 Many Americans consider the partial meltdown of the Three Mile Island nuclear power plant as the greatest man-made disaster of all times. Repairs to the damaged core (under the containment dome at right center in this photograph) will take at least 5 years and cost more than $1 billion. But no immediate loss of life occurred, and the accident forced electric utilities to train employees better. *(AEG.)*

Almost every week ENR reports news of one kind of failure or another, and these are, of course, the small minority of failures we hear about. Sloppy field work nullifies elaborately calculated designs too often to allow any complacency about inspection. . . .

The 1966 caisson trouble at the John Hancock Center in Chicago dramatized deficiencies in inspection. This $95-million structure was designed and its construction scheduled by the most sophisticated techniques of the industry. Its architect-engineer and contractor are among the most prominent in the U.S. Yet in one caisson foundation, designed for the tremendous load of a 100-story column, a 14-ft, earth-filled void was discovered in the 8-ft-dia concrete shaft. Its top shifted under the trivial weight of a 12-ton column section. An investigation revealed serious defects in other caissons, and the ensuing repairs and delay could cost millions of dollars— probably for lack of a pair of watchful eyes.

It would be too much to say that good inspection can be creative, but at its best, it can do more than merely insure conformance with the plans and specifications. A well-qualified inspector can catch errors in shop drawings or even design. But even in its checking function, good inspection provides insurance that more than pays for its relatively low cost.

EVOLUTION OR REVOLUTION

Basically the problem of inspection requires a reallocation of construction industry resources, and this, of course, means more money. Both types of inspection available today—by private consultants and public agencies—suffer from lack of money. Municipal and county building departments can't afford the salaries required to attract top-notch talent, and even if they could, the vast volume of construction would still overwhelm them. And the widespread refusal of owners to pay the price required for consultants' private inspection often precludes this form of inspection.

Most proposals for reform stay within the traditional structure of the industry, seeking merely to improve existing practices. They would, in effect, siphon the needed funds into inspection by legislation—state licensing of inspectors, or mandatory inspection by design engineers. Construction's perennial gadfly. New York City consulting engineer Jacob Feld, however, thinks the industry needs stronger medicine. According to Feld, the U.S. construction industry should adopt a system that has proved successful in three European countries: comprehensive structural insurance, similar to fire insurance, with a technical control bureau reviewing and inspecting all phases of construction.

INSPECTOR ELEVATOR

The recommendations of the Advisory Commission on Inter-governmental Relations, a 26-member group comprising representatives from federal, state, and municipal governments should gratify states' rights advocates: The ACIR urges a program of state licensing of inspectors, state inspector training programs, and state-set minimum requirements for building inspector staffs in all local government jurisdictions.

These proposals make sense. By raising inspector qualifications to quasiprofessional status, the states could raise the caliber and salaries of inspectors whose median salary appears to be about $7,000 [in 1983, about $20,000 for people] with up to 20 years experience. Minimum state staffing requirements for local governments would supplement quality with quantity. Since the minimum staffing requirement could place a financial burden on small towns, ACIR suggests several ways to handle the problem—such as joining with several other towns for building code administration.

A more appealing approach in one important respect, is that of cities like Phoenix, which has attempted to place the financial responsibility for inspection on building owners, where it belongs. The Phoenix building code requires a registered engineer or architect to "certify that to the best of my knowledge, the structural requirements of the approved plans for which inspection is required ... have been complied with." The mandatory inspection should insure the engineer's getting a decent inspection. . . .

Figure 1-4 Sometimes a financial disaster—mismanagement—can hurt an industry far more than any loss of life ever could. These pipes, valves, and turbines are awaiting installation in a Washington Public Power Supply System nuclear plant that may never generate any electricity. The cost of the system's canceled plants could rise to a staggering $15 billion. *(Washington Public Power Supply System.)*

STARTING FRESH

But efforts to improve inspection quality through conventional means are mere palliatives, according to Feld, who has probably investigated more failures than anyone in the world. For some years he has tried, unsuccessfully, to interest U.S. insurance companies in offering owners the kind of comprehensive structural insurance available in France, Belgium, and Holland. In those countries, technical control bureaus financed by the insurance companies review and approve the structural design, soil testing, choice of materials, field practices and other key phases of construction. On the basis of the technical bureau's certificate of approval, insurance companies underwrite a policy insuring the owner against partial or total structural collapse for a period extending 10 years following a project's completion. This coverage includes formwork or steel erection collapses resulting from faulty construction practice as well as structural collapses resulting from poor design. Inspection fees in Belgium average about 0.9% of total cost; insurance premiums are less.

The great advantage of technical control appears to be the way it focuses responsibility. The love of money is the root of all evil, according to St. Paul, but the fear of losing it is the root of good inspection, according to Feld. Technical control bureaus represent insurance companies that must pay off in cold cash for any failure—from total collapse to minor cracking. As a natural consequence, says Feld, the inspector's greater responsibility inspires keener vision.

The French and Belgian technical control bureaus were created in response to serious construction accidents during the late 1920s. The technical control bureau appeared as a practical way of avoiding the red tape of governmental supervisory agencies, while enforcing public safety. As a private organization, the technical control bureau can proceed with an efficiency often lacking in a governmental agency.

Technical control has many other advantages, according to Feld. By the same principle that enables subcontractors with many jobs to make more efficient use of skilled workmen, technical control bureaus can make more efficient use of engineering personnel by centralizing a trained pool of technical talent.

Despite some complaints that it delays project completion, the French technical control bureau (SOCOTEC) is still growing and expanding its services. It takes on some 12,000 projects a year, representing one-third of France's total construction volume. The majority of its 11,500 employees are engineers. Now operating from 90 French branch offices, SOCOTEC is opening branch offices in Spain, and its staff skills are expanding from basic construction services—such as inspecting concrete, soils, and foundations—into such mechanical services as heating and airconditioning.

Why couldn't the consulting engineer perform this same service? Because no owner, unless he has learned from sad experience, is willing to pay the price, says Feld, and he is skeptical of mandatory inspection provisions. Public agencies generally limit inspection fees to reimbursement of "productive" inspection payroll cost plus overhead limited to 100%. They should allow for 200% added to the productive payroll, or 2½ times actual payroll costs. Properly done field supervision by a resident engineer costs more than design, drafting, and specification writing, according to Feld.

Feld is joined by Philadelphia structural engineer David Bloom in calling inspection, at best, unprofitable work. Bloom takes inspection work on his projects in self-defense, as insurance that his designs are carried out correctly in the field. Many testing laboratories retained for inspection are "inadequate, or worse," says Bloom. And even though inspection work helps in the continuing education of designers, it is not the highest use of their skills. A reliable technical control bureau could allay conscientious engineers' fears that their designs were not being executed properly.

Even apart from the obvious problem of safety, erection accidents and structural failures are inspiring increasingly complex legal difficulties, especially for architects and engineers. The unification of designer-builder responsibility offered by technical control could lighten designers' risks.

Figure 1-5 A failure of concept is evident in the half-wrecked Pruitt-Igoe public housing project in St. Louis. The impersonal superblocks became an instant slum, part of which has since been torn down. (*A Globe-Democrat photograph by J. M. Carrington.*)

Meanwhile, other efforts to improve inspection can continue without fear that they are being wasted in this complex task of strengthening construction's weakest link.

This call for better inspection—more time spent at the job site by better qualified personnel—has in part been heeded. But quality-assurance specialists in other industries know that it is impossible to "inspect in" quality. The whole system—from architect to builder and client—must organize itself to produce a quality product from a design that helps assure quality in the first place. Given the complexity of modern design, inspection sophistication may not have even kept pace in recent years.

But how is the change to come about? Increasingly, the courts have made designers and architects responsible for defects in the finished structure. This has been so, even though the fatal flaws often come about in the construction process and not in the design. Simply put, the architects and designers are more likely to carry heavy insurance policies. And injured employees, barred from suing their own firms because of workers compensation laws, collect the often-inadequate workers compensation insurance, then turn around and sue the

Figure 1-6 Modern construction can be remarkably immune to fire—although loss of life and damage to interior furnishings can be substantial. Here, the basic soundness of framing at 1 New York Plaza is evident after a 1970 blaze. *(Alfred H. Miller Co.)*

deepest pockets they can find. They are usually joined by the very same workers compensation insurance carrier, seeking to recover from the designer's insurance company the pittances paid to the workers.

Designers and architects, in turn, are more likely than ever before to insist upon blind conformance to the construction drawings. Is this a healthy trend? Or should the contractor be a real partner in the process of design and specification? Perhaps there should be greater emphasis on prequalifying bidders for specific jobs, especially where the design calls for construction methods that are uncommon in a given locale.

Then, at least, the builders could be made to fully understand the function of a complex joint—whether it is for expansion or to deflect moisture, whether it is in tension or compression—and not make foolish materials substitutions under the pressure of construction deadlines. Contractors could also be better trained to understand the behavior of structural members under cycling stresses, and how such stresses can induce fatigue in a structure that appears perfectly designed to withstand static loads that can be much greater.

If designers insist on absolute compliance with plans, then the plans themselves must be perfect. Yet the checking of drawings is often carried out by the lowest-level person in the shop—or is not done at all because each person in the design and construction chain assumes someone else will catch any errors.

Luckily, errors in design are often caught by the experts who are usually hired to detail the position of reinforcing rods or the stiffening of wide welded webs.

Perhaps especially critical details—details that will cause major structural damage if not built absolutely perfectly—should be marked with a special, universal symbol. One obvious class of details that could be marked this way is structural members for which there is no backup—members the failure of which will automatically cause collapse.

Clients should have to pay for as-built drawings for any reasonably complex projects, and safety systems such as fire walls and critical trusses and webs should be clearly marked on such drawings. Of course, a legal disclaimer would have to be included warning the client that modification of other things in the structure could also cause failure. But at least the biggest potential trouble spots would be flagged.

Codes must take into account the reduced safety margins being designed into modern structures. Many (if not most) building codes, for example, call for roofs to withstand a "25-year" storm. Buildings are usually meant to withstand the elements for a lot longer than a 25-year useful life. Stated another way, a 25-year storm has a 4 percent risk of occurring in any given year. No client would willingly agree to those odds. But clients and building tenants—and local

Figure 1-7 Formwork failures are among the most common of all construction disasters; formwork design is often left to nonprofessionals. This collapse occurred in Japan in 1978. *(Kyodo.)*

authorities—have come to rely on large safety factors that once were built into just about every structure. The "25-year load" design will withstand a 50- or 100-year storm—or at least it used to.

This does not mean that we have to overdesign every structure, rewrite every code. For example, the collapse of the Firth of Tay Bridge (discussed briefly in Chapter 5) led to absurdly stringent requirements for wind loading in England—requirements that remained in effect for a half century, until the construction needs of World War I showed British engineers that they had been overcautious. It does mean, however, that the construction industry and its clients and regulators must understand the *philosophy* behind the requirements, and follow that philosophy so that safety is not degraded.

Philosophy is not something that can be computerized. Thus, engineering will always be more than the rote preparation of plans and specifications. There will always be a bit of art in the science and technology of construction. That art is born of mature experience—of heeding the lessons learned from our failures as well as our successes.

Nature well understands that process, and relentlessly attacks even the smallest flaws in our handiwork. Is it asking too much of the public—and our clients—to expect some flaws but not attack so relentlessly?

CHAPTER

2 Earthquakes

Introduction

Until a half century ago, people all over the world believed that earthquakes were heaven-sent, the damage they did was proportional to their intensity, and there wasn't much anyone could do about it. If television had been available back then, peoples' living rooms would have been saturated with news of earthquakes causing major losses of life perhaps six or eight times a year. Television does not exhibit such suffering today.

Major earthquakes still occur, of course. But these days it takes a quake of very great intensity to tumble buildings in urban areas. Even in rural communities, where scientific construction is less well practiced, losses to life and property are much lower than once occurred, on the average.

The change can be traced to California. The state's residents had quickly forgotten the lessons of the 1906 San Francisco earthquake. In their haste to rebuild, they repeated most of the design errors that had contributed to loss of life and property. The great Tokyo earthquake of 1923, however, heightened awareness of the potential disaster that lurked beneath the shores of the Pacific basin. Many Californians of Japanese descent maintained family ties with Japan— a coincidence that brought the suffering close to home.

Then, in 1925, a mild quake centered near Santa Barbara, California, caused greater-than-expected damage. Poorly designed, unreinforced brick and concrete walls tumbled. Poor-quality mortar and concrete were exposed. Californians began to realize that, though there might be little defense against a really big earthquake, the damage from smaller quakes would be reduced and loss of life minimized.

In the wake of the Santa Barbara quake, California communities passed rudimentary earthquake design codes. Professionals began presenting papers and circulating design ideas. On March 10, 1933, the Long Beach earthquake gave them an opportunity to see how well their ideas worked. The verdict: Buildings designed in accordance with new ideas about earthquakes fared bet-

Figure 2-1 Santa Barbara's Hotel Californian, an unreinforced brick structure, after the mild earthquake of 1925. The other two walls of this building did not collapse, but show a network of cracks. *(International Newsreel.)*

ter than did older structures. But there was still a long way to go before comprehensive earthquake design codes could come into being.

In the 5 years following the Long Beach quake, *Engineering News-Record* carried a score of major design reports covering all types of construction and all types of buildings: schools, offices, hospitals, auditoriums, bridges, and homes. One previously unrecognized technical finding was that resonance between the earthquake's period and the natural vibration period of a building can cause more damage than simple high acceleration from the quake's gross movements.

Such findings led to immediate changes in the state's earthquake code. The first revision, in fact, was passed only 2 months after the Long Beach quake. The California Seismic Code, along with major revisions in 1936, served as a model for other earthquake codes around the world. It has saved tens of thousands of lives, and continues to save new lives almost weekly. Beginning in the 1950s, teams of engineering experts have been sweeping in to inspect and catalog damage from any major quake, no matter where it occurs. Recent quakes in Italy and Nicaragua, along with quakes in Yugoslavia, Alaska, Mexico City, and elsewhere, have helped refine construction techniques.

Western earthquake experts were less successful in exploring the wreckage of two great quakes in China during the 1970s, however. And what is more important for the safety of the public in future earthquakes, new knowledge has been applied only in certain expensive structures in known earthquake zones.

As a result, progress has slowed considerably from the pace set starting in 1933, although new buildings generally have structural framing that resists the forces of moderate quakes.

This chapter traces the knowledge gained from earthquake damage, starting with the Long Beach quake of 1933 and continuing through the Mexico City quake of 1957, the massive Anchorage quake of 1964, and the San Fernando Valley quake of 1971.

The various articles describe earthquake intensities according to two scales—the modified Mercalli (a measure of felt intensity) and the Richter (based originally on the maximum trace amplitude of a seismogram written by a horizontal-pendulum seismograph with a 0.8-second natural period). The Mercalli scale ranges from 1 (not felt), through 4 (vibration like that of passing trucks), to 8 (damage to masonry, falling stucco) and on up to 12 (damage nearly total, ground massively displaced, etc.).

The Richter scale more accurately defines the energy released by an earthquake. It is based on the logarithm to the base 10 of the ratio of an observed quake's amplitude to the "standard" maximum trace described above. The distance of the seismograph from the quake is also taken into account. All earthquakes that occurred between 1900 and 1950, for which seismograph traces are available, lie between 0 and 8.6 on the Richter scale. Because the scale is logarithmic, a Richter 7 quake releases 10 times as much energy as a Richer 6 quake and 100 times more than a Richter 5 quake.

Long Beach Earthquake, 1933

March 10, 1933, at 6 P.M. The rumblings start slowly. The public, remembering deaths caused by collapsing buildings in the 1925 Santa Barbara quake, knows only one thing: Get outside, get outside quickly. People race out of homes, shops, and restaurants—and in the crowded streets 120 die. Most are victims of flying glass and falling debris, rather than of outright structural failure.

The affected area extended about 15 miles along a north-south line running from Long Beach to Los Angeles, and 20 miles along an east-west line from Long Beach to Santa Ana. Along the line of maximum movement, north-south, lateral forces were moderate—about a tenth that of gravity, sometimes more—and roughly equivalent to the Santa Barbara quake of 1925 in intensity.

The Los Angeles section of the American Society of Civil Engineers quickly appointed a committee (headed by California Institute of Technology Prof. R.

R. Martel) to study the quake's effects. The initial inspection revealed little damage among large, steel-framed buildings; the quake was not strong enough to reveal defects in their designs. There was a great deal of damage among small structures, however, including stores; low-rise, brick-clad apartment buildings; and single-family dwellings.

Most important, however, the initial tally revealed a score of school buildings that had failed structurally. In fact, if the quake had occurred at 3 P.M. instead of at 6 P.M., thousands of schoolchildren might have perished. Fortunately, the schools were empty when the shaking started.

The Long Beach quake was particularly useful to designers for another reason: For the first time, detailed accelerometer measurements were made of an earthquake from points near its epicenter. The accelerometers and displacement meters that made the measurements had been installed by the U.S. Coast and Geodetic Survey, as part of a network of such devices in California. Accelerations of as high as 1 g, accompanied by a vibration period of 0.1 second, occurred for a few seconds at the beginning of the quake, followed by movements ranging from 1 to 2 seconds with accelerations that were much smaller— 0.04 g. Because most of the damage occurred after the major first shocks had passed, scientists and engineers concluded that the small slow shocks were in resonance with the damaged buildings' natural frequencies of vibration.

The weaknesses in school design were discussed in ENR's first comprehensive report of the quake, on April 13, 1933. Also noted was the role of poor workmanship in leading to collapse of many brick walls.

Long Beach Earthquake Emphasizes Known Facts

Although teaching a few new lessons, the recent California earthquake largely substantiated existing knowledge and concentrated its damage on structures lacking unity and strength and the benefit of sound structural design.

Walter L. Humber   *Consulting Engineer, San Francisco, California*

The earthquake which damaged or destroyed many structures in the region of Long Beach, Compton and portions of Los Angeles on March 10, 1933, brings out a few new lessons, but more particularly does it emphasize the lessons derived from other earthquakes.

It is not surprising that practically all earthquake reports are to some extent exaggerated. This is often wholly unintentional. The tendency is, however, to describe or to photograph the abnormal which, in these instances, is the building or structure that has failed or has suffered perceptibly. Its neighbor next door, which may have been built in accordance with sound engineering principles and thereby escaped practically unharmed, gives the same appearance as it did last week or even last year and is therefore not the subject of much interest at the moment, particularly to the lay observer or photographer. Thus, a record is left which is more or less complete so far as damage is concerned, but very incomplete in respect to the well-built structures that were unharmed.

The performance of well-built buildings of both steel and reinforced concrete construction, ranging in height up to some fifteen stories, is very reassuring. Instances of these are shown in the illustrations of the Villa Riviera Apartments, the Security First National Bank Building and the Heartwell Building (ENR, March 23, 1933, p. 378), which were, when photographed a few days after the earthquake, but little the worse for their experience. Many other examples could be cited.

The condition of these buildings should be compared with those constructed of ordinary light brick bearing walls supporting floor and roof joists. While buildings of the latter type are not dependable for resistance to earthquake stresses, while they have furnished the most spectacular examples of complete wreckage, and while I do not advocate this type, I do not wish to leave the impression that their complete destruction was by any means general. There are many examples of strongly built masonry walls that survived with little damage. . . .

BRICK-WALL FAILURES

The inability of many brick-wall buildings to resist the stresses imposed by earthquakes lies in poor workmanship and improper materials. . . [as exemplified by] a partly collapsed lodge building in Compton. [There] is a 13-in. brick wall with pilasters upon which roof trusses are supported. Header courses are quite unknown; whole stories are laid up without them. Often mortar does not fill the vertical joints. To these conditions . . . the reader needs only to add that the mortar itself is in most instances a lime mortar with little adhesive quality, which can easily be powdered in the hand, and he will have a complete picture of the reasons for failure of these walls under earthquake stresses. In the design of these buildings probably no thought was given to the resistance of lateral forces due to earthquake. The contrast between this masonry and that which I examined a few years ago at Charleston, S.C., and which had survived the Charleston earthquake of 1886, is marked indeed. Certainly the art of masonry construction has deteriorated under the urge of competitive speculative building. The builders of the splendid masonry construction of early Charleston would be horrified at present-day practices. I would not, however, limit my criticism of present brick masonry construction to that of Los Angeles County. Similar construction is now found in practically every American city and only needs a catastrophe to expose it.

DESTRUCTION OF SCHOOLS

Unfortunately, the schools throughout the afflicted area were very generally constructed of inferior masonry bearing walls supporting long-span timber joists and roof trusses. The almost complete destruction of many of the school buildings is one of the outstanding developments. Had the earthquake occurred during school hours the loss of life and injuries would have been appalling. It is to be hoped that from the lesson derived better construction of school buildings and places of public assembly will result. The public memory is short, however, and is often dulled by false ideas of economy. The fault here lies with the administrative officials who, knowingly or unknowingly, choose this type of construction for public buildings; it lies also with those who follow, if they do not actually direct, the program by preparing the plans; and with the builders who in many instances have been responsible for poor workmanship and improper materials. Again, these faults of school buildings are not peculiar to Los Angeles County—they are very general in other localities.

After the Santa Barbara earthquake of 1925 a study of reinforced-concrete frame buildings disclosed many instances where concrete girders of long span proportioned for heavy bending moments were supported on comparatively small columns designed only to resist the vertical loads of low buildings. The two members were constructed monolithically. The stresses induced by the earthquake caused the heavy girders to rupture the lighter concrete columns. Instances of this kind are not so evident at Long Beach, although they may be disclosed in connection with some of the repairs.

In the Y.W.C.A. Building certain long-span concrete girders were designed to act with their supporting columns as rigid frames. . . . Although subjected to some of the most violent effects of the shocks, this construction shows no damage whatever. The damage to this building, which has brick walls supported on a concrete frame, is limited to the displacement of certain bricks where a 4-in. layer is carried up past a concrete spandrel beam at the roof level and to certain other cracking of face bricks. It is of interest to note that on this building brick parapet walls were constructed by carrying the columns above the levels of certain roofs and decks and joining them by a 6 x 4 x ½-in. angle carried in the top of the brick walls. These parapets are intact. . . .

More details, particularly concerning school construction and the behavior of reinforced concrete framing, were forthcoming in the ENR issue of May 4, 1933:

Reinforced Concrete in the Long Beach Earthquake

Damage, although slight, revealed some weaknesses that can be remedied—Beneficial bracing effect of concrete walls is notable.

Norman B. Green   *Consulting Engineer, San Francisco, California*

The Long Beach earthquake of March 10, 1933, affords engineers an excellent opportunity to study the effects of a destructive shock upon all the different types of modern American construction. The following observations relate largely to reinforced-concrete construction.

The author also discusses brick and steel-frame construction, but this part of the report is omitted because it largely repeats what has been published previously in our issues of March 16, 1933, p. 353; March 23, p. 378; and April 13, pp. 474 and 476.   —Editor

There are a considerable number of reinforced-concrete buildings in Long Beach, of varying height, shape of floor plan and type of floor framing. An analysis of the damage that they sustained indicates a general similarity of action, from which certain conclusions can be drawn. It was very noticeable that whereas the columns in many instances had suffered severe injury, the floor framing was usually intact, with the exception of occasional cracks in spandrel beams, particularly where they meet the corner columns. This is true of the California Garage, a three-story concrete beam-and-joist structure 150 ft. square, with 13-in. brick curtain walls, in which nearly all the columns in each story showed evidence of a varying degree of flexural failure. The Artaban Apartments, 40 x 150 ft. in plan and eight stories high, with beam-and-joist framing and 8-in. tile curtain walls, exhibited cracks at the junction of the first-story wall columns with the second-floor wall beams, even though the beams were seldom cracked. The Ambassador Apartments, of four and five stories, with beam-and-joist framing and 13-in brick curtain walls, also illustrated the same effect, with horizontal tension cracks visible in many of the interior columns that were exposed as well as in some of the first-story wall columns at the soffit of the second-floor beams. In this building there is also an elevator pent house, all four columns of which failed top and bottom in tension, with the beams uninjured.

It seems probable that in a reinforced-concrete structure the column bending moment is distributed laterally to a considerable width of floor system. Thus, unless the column is specifically designed to resist lateral bending, it will fail, while the floor may show no sign of distress. On this supposition, wall beams would be more apt to crack than would interior

Figure 2-2 Tile curtain walls often failed in the Long Beach quake, even though reinforced concrete framing behind the walls showed little or no damage. *(Dwyer Studio.)*

beams, since the former can be relieved of stress by distribution of the moment in only one direction, while with interior beams it can travel laterally both ways from the column. In only one or two instances was there evidence that the failure of the column could be attributed to a plane of weakness at a construction joint, while the cracks in nearly every case were irregular, and spalling revealed what was apparently sound concrete.

BRACING EFFECT OF WALLS

The great value of reinforced-concrete walls as bracing against lateral forces was everywhere very evident. A valuable comparison illustrating this fact may be made between the California Garage already described and the Loynes Garage, which is three stories and basement of beam-and-joist construction, but with 6-in. concrete curtain walls instead of brick walls. The former building had wide diagonal cracks in the east and west walls and suffered extensive structural injury as already described. On the other hand, the injury in the Loynes Garage was confined to the exterior walls, where there was considerable broken wire glass, with an occasional bent or broken steel sash bar and narrow diagonal or vertical cracks extending from the corners of many of the windows. A similar comparison can be made between the Artaban Apartments, already described, and the eight-story Professional Building, which is 50 x 150 ft. in plan, of concrete beam-and-joist construction, but with 6-in. reinforced concrete curtain walls. In this structure the north and south walls, which are cross-wise of the building, were extensively cracked from the corners of the windows, but these walls took most of the lateral load so that the structural columns were apparently entirely uninjured, while injury to the partitions was mainly confined to the first story, where there were x-cracks in a north and south direction. In the case of the Artaban Apartments, however, the 8-in. tile walls were badly cracked and broken out in the lower stories, and evidently added little or no stiffening to the building so that the frame itself was injured.

An examination of the cracks in the rear wall of the Professional Building demonstrated that it acted as a portal frame, with horizontal and vertical members formed by the piers and spandrels. In this case the damage was the reverse of that sustained by the usual concrete frame, since the spandrels were cracked but not the piers, indicating probably that the spandrels, by reason of their relatively great stiffness, received little support from the floor framing. The damage was confined to the outer bay on each side, and every spandrel up to the eighth floor was cracked clear across where it meets the corner pier. This indicated that the outer piers probably resisted the same lateral shear as the interior piers, in which case the resulting moment was resisted by one spandrel intersection instead of two, with a crack as the result. A uniform lateral-shear distribution between end and interior piers of equal width is what would be expected in a frame having short and wide members, in which shear deformation is predominant. Evidently outer spandrels should be given special reinforcement and particularly where they meet the corner pier. When, as in this wall, the windows are placed in pairs with a relatively narrow pier between, the spandrel should be considered as a single member under this window unit, since horizontal shear cracks due to flexure, where they occur, are always continuous for this length of spandrel.

It was very noticeable in all concrete walls that there was a plane of weakness at the floor line and sometimes also at the ceiling line, due of course to the existence of a construction joint at this location. In almost all multi-story buildings with reinforced concrete walls, these were cracked horizontally for the length of the spandrels in many places, and often these cracks constituted the only damage to the wall. It is certain that some better bond should be provided at construction joints than is the usual practice, and particularly is this true where the wall is intended to act as lateral bracing. Since the deformation is evidently that of shear along the plane of the joint, requisite keys should be provided to transmit this stress.

CONCRETE-JOIST FLOORS

It has been argued against the concrete-joist type of floor construction that it is inadequate to distribute heavy lateral forces properly, and there was some evidence that this objection may be well founded. The Campbell Apartments, a ten-story steel-frame structure, 55 x 160 ft. in plain and oriented with its long dimension north and south, afforded a good test of this contention. The building has concrete joists running east and west and 6-in. reinforced-concrete curtain walls, which, being much stiffer than the interior bents, should have forced a horizontal load distribution. A careful examination of the under side of the second-floor slab revealed narrow diagonal cracks entirely across some of the bays adjacent to the rear wall and transverse cracks perpendicular to the joists and extending entirely through many interior panels. These are such cracks as would be produced by the floor system acting laterally as a horizontal beam. It is possible that with the joists running in the opposite direction the floor would be stronger.

BENDING FAILURES IN COLUMNS

The fifth story of the Ambassador Apartments and the third story of the California Garage illustrated the fact that great care should be exercised in designing concrete columns that support a long-span roof system, when these columns form part of a continuous structure and are not free to swing with the earth shock. In such cases adequate bending resistance should be provided, particularly in the direction in which concrete tie beams are not practicable. In the garage building the third-story columns are tied together in an east-and-west direction by reinforced-concrete tie beams, but in the opposite direction the framing consists of heavy timber trusses on a 50-ft. span. Every column in the story, with the exception of those in the east wall, failed at the base due to a rocking motion in a north-and-south direction. Most of the columns spalled out at the floor on the north and south faces so as to expose the reinforcing steel, which in some cases buckled outward. The fifth story of the Ambassador Apartments is an open loft, 50 x 75 ft. with wood trusses of 50-ft. span extending east and west and resting on concrete wall columns. Every column that was visible failed in tension due to flexure in a north-and-south direction.

It is believed that the quality of the concrete employed in Long Beach was in general quite good. An exception is the four-story Board of Education Building, a beam-and-joist structure in which both the front and rear concrete walls were badly shattered, damage directly attributed to very weak concrete.

CONCRETE CORRIDORS IN SCHOOLS

So much damage was done to public schools in the earthquake region that it seemed almost as though these had been singled out by fate as an object lesson. The destruction of these buildings, erected with brick bearing walls and wood floor and roof framing, has been described in previous reports in these pages. One type of design, however, has not been commented upon. This is illustrated by schools that employ a corridor with reinforced-concrete floors supported on concrete columns, in combination with external brick bearing walls and wood floor and roof construction for the class rooms. While this construction was originally intended simply to provide a fireproof exit through the corridors, it proved to be earthquake-resistant as well, since the stiff corridor framing provided excellent support for the exterior walls when these were properly anchored to it. The Huntington Beach Union High School ... is of this type, and it was uninjured except for an occasional slight crack. The Lowell Elementary School in Long Beach ... on the other hand, although having such a fireproof corridor was badly damaged because it was constructed with two 13-in. brick bearing walls along the line of the corridor and a concrete slab spanning between them. These walls offered little or no bracing, so that the building suffered accordingly. Other examples of schools with concrete corridors which stood almost intact are the Lindbergh and the U. S. Grant schools, both in Long Beach.

EARTHQUAKE ACTION

When an effort is made to determine the nature of the earth motion in this earthquake, by the observation of its effect upon structures, the usual anomalies appear. It seems reasonably certain, however, that in Long Beach that part of the motion having a magnitude and frequency of acceleration (which gave a destructive combination for most buildings) was in general in a north-and-south direction. The cracks and spalling in the columns of the California Garage all showed clearly a destructive flexure in this direction, as did also the cracks in the columns of the Ambassador Apartments. In the Professional Building the north-and-south first-story partitions were heavily x-cracked, but those running east and west were undamaged. The front wall of the Long Beach Polytechnic High School and the rear wall of the Board of Education Building each face west and were obviously parallel to the direction of the destructive shock. In the case of the last-named building the side walls were practically uninjured.

Such evidences of a major north-and-south motion can be multiplied indefinitely. However, there is also some evidence of destructive damage due to an east-west acceleration. For example, an 8-in. brick wall 8 ft. high that extended along the north, east and south sides of an athletic field at the Woodrow Wilson School was broken off at the ground level and thrown down. This wall was laid with good lime-and-cement mortar; and if a modulus of rupture of from 100 to 200 lb. per sq. in. is assumed, the requisite acceleration ranges from 0.4 to 0.8 gravity. This instance is believed to be typical and indicates that there was probably a secondary motion in both directions of high acceleraton and high frequency, which affected only relatively stiff structures such as this wall. As another instance of this same effect may be cited the case of the north wall of a four-story reinforced-concrete flat-slab building at 4th and Pine Sts., Long Beach. This entire length of wall for 160 ft., including the heavy wall columns, was sheared through along a horizontal line at the window heads. On the other hand, the two street fronts, having narrow piers and a much greater flexibility, were uninjured except for broken plate glass. It is probable that there was a laitance joint along the line of the window heads, which had the effect of rendering this wall weak, while not affecting its stiffness.

In conclusion, it seems that any effort at an interpretation of the structural damage in terms of acceleration alone brings the usual contradictions, due to the equal importance of period of acceleration and stiffness of the structure.

About 10 weeks after the quake, local officials released a detailed report, carefully separating and grouping buildings by age, type of construction, and amount of damage. The report was meant to build public support for tougher earthquake codes. It succeeded. Looking back, it is easy to see how: Complex technical detail was rendered clearly in plain language.

Officials moved quickly because they did not want a repeat of what had happened in the wake of the 1906 San Francisco quake. Analysis of buildings that had been wrecked in that disaster had concluded that structures designed to withstand lateral forces of at least 30 pounds per square foot would be sufficient to protect occupants. While the 1906 disaster was fresh in everyone's mind, the engineers had prevailed and the 30-pound standard was inserted into San Francisco's building code. Within 3 years, however, the standard had been reduced to 20 pounds, then 15, and finally 0 for structures less than 10 stories high.

The technical community's strategy after 1933 was to have the lateral load requirements embedded into state law rather than local ordinances. The engineers got their statewide law, but one that called for buildings to withstand 20 pounds of lateral force per square foot rather than 30. In short, the new law would protect against most quakes, but not quakes with the force of the one that hit San Francisco in 1906.

The editor's note at the beginning of the article below (from the May 25, 1933, issue of ENR) was originally published with the article itself.

Earthquake Damage Analyzed by Long Beach Officials

Grouping all damaged buildings into five classifications and separating old structures from those erected under 1930 code reveals greater inadequacy of old buildings—Basic code changes suggested for existing as well as for future buildings

C. D. Wailes, Jr.　　　　　　　　　　　*Chief Building Inspector, Long Beach, California*
A. C. Horner　　　　　　　　　　　　*Consulting Engineer, San Francisco, California*

This article has a particular significance not reflected by its title. In one sense it is the official report of the damage caused in Long Beach by the earthquake of March 10. In all respects it presents the most comprehensive factual information to come out of the earthquake, and gives the only figures available that show the true relation between the number of damaged and undamaged buildings. The analysis of damage given is based on a survey of all buildings irrespective of the amount of damage sustained by each one. It shows that a relatively small per cent was substantially damaged. It indicates that "old code" structures were most vulnerable and that increasingly better code supervision is necessary. In the opinion of the authors, who are well qualified to judge, certain code changes are advisable. These changes are outlined.

—Editor

Following the Southern California earthquake of March 10, 1933, the spectacular damage revealed in a comparatively few buildings occasioned a demand, voiced largely in the public press, for immediate revision of building laws and for new laws designed to make buildings earthquake-resistant in the future. In large measure this demand was based on conclusions drawn from hastily gathered data. . . . [Before] any changes in the building laws could be recommended, the character of the damage to all buildings had to be analyzed.

In order to assist in arriving at a basis for new legislation and to check the adequacy of the existing building code in Long Beach, an analysis was undertaken by the writers, based on the reports turned in by a group of special inspectors, supplemented where necessary by personal inspection of damaged buildings. The group of special inspectors was made up of a number of engineers and architects who volunteered their services and worked under the direction of the Long Beach building department in inspecting damage to individual buildings for the purpose of determining whether or not they were reasonably safe for immediate occupancy. The survey reported herein was not designed primarily for the purpose of learning the reasons for damage to buildings, but rather to disclose the relative degree of damage with respect to: (1) types of construction, (2) occupancy of the building (as it might affect structural security), and (3) the building regulations under which buildings were erected—that is, their age.

TABLE 2-1 Earthquake Damage to Buildings, Other than Dwellings and Schools, Costing over $1000 (Equivalent to $40,000 in 1982 Dollars) and Erected in Long Beach after March 10, 1930, When the Code in Effect at the Time of the 1933 Earthquake Became Effective

Damage Classification*	Type I Buildings (Steel or Concrete Frame)		Type III Buildings (Masonry Walls)		Type V Buildings (Wood Frame)		Total Buildings	
	Number	Percent	Number	Percent	Number	Percent	Number	Percent
A	7	88	34	44	122	94	163	76
B	1	12	26	34	6	4	33	15
C			14	18	2	2	16	7
D			2	3			2	1
E			1	1			1	1
Total	8	100	77	100	130	100	215	100

*See Table 2-4 for definitions.

SOURCE: *Engineering News-Record,* May 25, 1933.

TABLE 2-2 Earthquake Damage to Buildings, Other than Dwellings and Schools, Costing over $1000 and Erected in Long Beach since March 10, 1930, Summarized According to Occupancy and Type of Construction

Damage Classification		Apartments, Hotels, Etc.			Stores, Banks Offices			Public Garages		
		I	III	V	I	III	V	I	III	V
A	Number		4	72	2	19	25		1	
	Percent		45	95	67	46	92		9	
B	Number		3	4	1	14	1		7	
	Percent		33	5	33	34	4		64	
C	Number		2			8	1		1	
	Percent		22			20	4		9	
D	Number								1	
	Percent								9	
E	Number								1	
	Percent								9	
Total	Number		9	76	3	41	27		11	
	Percent		100	100	100	100	100		100	

SOURCE: *Engineering News-Record,* May 25, 1933.

BASIS OF THE ANALYSIS

All building permits issue in Long Beach from March 10, 1930 (the date when the present code became effective), to Jan. 1, 1933, were examined, and a list was made of all new buildings (other than dwellings and schools) costing over $1,000. One- and two-family dwellings were excluded because of the comparatively large number and because it was believed that their inclusion would not add greatly to the value of the analysis. Schools were excluded because their supervision has been performed by other than city officials.

In assigning a degree of damage to a building the damage classification shown in the accompanying tabulation was used. The classification was developed to meet the requirements of this analysis and is intended to represent the total range of damage experienced by all buildings in the city. The results of this portion of the survey are shown for the 215 buildings erected since March 10, 1930, in [Tables 2-1 and 2-2].

In order to obtain a comparison of damage to buildings erected since the adoption of the present building code with damage to buildings erected prior thereto, the reports of the special inspectors were examined, and the damage to each building was classified. Although these reports did not cover the entire city, they did cover all buildings in the principal business and mercantile sections of the city. By subtracting from this latter tabulation the number of buildings involved in the previous tabulation a list of buildings with the damage thereto was obtained (Table 2-3) for buildings erected prior to March 10, 1930. Some error is doubtless introduced in using this method, but it is unimportant in view of the comparatively large number of buildings involved in the second group.

Storage Warehouses			Factories, Industrial Buildings			Assembly Churches, Amusement			Total			
I	III	V	I	III	V	I	III	V	I	III	V	Total
	2	2	3	4	12	2	4	11	7	34	122	163
	67	67	100	50	100	100	80	91	87	44	94	76
		1		1			1		1	26	6	33
		33		13			20		13	34	4	15
				37				9		18	2	7
	1									2		2
	33									3		1
										1		1
	3	3	3	8	12	2	5	12	8	77	130	215
	100	100	100	100	100	100	100	100	100	100	100	100

TABLE 2-3   **Earthquake Damage to Buildings, Other than Dwellings and Schools, Costing over $1000 and Erected in Long Beach before March 10, 1930**

Damage Classification	Type I Buildings (Steel or Concrete Frame)		Type III Buildings (Masonry Walls)		Type V Buildings (Wood Frame)		Total Buildings	
	Number	Percent	Number	Percent	Number	Percent	Number	Percent
A	29	45	232	14	1,268	73	1,529	45
B	19	29	476	30	332	19	827	24
C	15	23	556	34	105	6	676	20
D	1	1½	274	17	10	1	285	8
E	1	1½	85	5	14	1	100	3
Total	65	100	1,623	100	1,729	100	3,417	100

SOURCE: *Engineering News-Record*, May 25, 1933.

CHARACTER OF LAWS AND INSPECTION

Conclusions to be drawn from these data are affected by the code provisions under which the various buildings were built and by the efficiency of inspection that the construction received.

In the past twenty years Long Beach has had three building codes, one adopted in 1913, one adopted in January, 1923, and the present code, which became effective on March 10, 1930. With particular reference to masonry buildings, the 1913 code permitted a straight lime mortar for all walls, except that isolated piers, foundation walls, parapets and chimneys above the roof line were required to be laid up in 1:3 cement lime mortar. During the period when this code was in effect much of the sand used for both mortar and concrete was a dirty fine material comparable to beach sand. The walls were laid up with dry wall and head joints (contrary to code stipulation), and workmanship was decidedly inferior.

The 1923 code required a mortar of 1 part cement to 10 parts of lime mortar, the lime mortar requirements being 1 part lime to 5 parts of sand. Workmanship under this code showed the same dry wall and head joints and was of inferior quality.

The 1930 code requires a mortar consisting of 1 part cement, 1 part lime, and 6 parts clean sharp sand. For all isolated piers, mullions and work below ground line a 1:3 cement mortar is required. The workmanship calls for full shoved joints using wet brick. This 1930 Long Beach code is essentially the same as the Uniform Building Code prepared by the Pacific Coast Building Officials Conference.

The character of inspection in Long Beach during the past three years is believed to be comparable to that permitted by the average appropriation of money allowed for building inspection by the average city administration. It is probably fair to assume that the quality of building inspection (considered without regard to personnel) in Long Beach, as in other large cities, has been slowly improving for the past six or seven years.

OLDER BUILDINGS SUFFERED MOST

Buildings erected according to the provisions of the present Long Beach code withstood the earthquake much better than those erected prior to the adoption of the present code. This was true for every type of construction. A comparison of the figures in [Table 2-1] with those in [Table 2-3] is as follows: Buildings classified as sustaining A damage constituted 76 per cent of the "new" buildings (erected since March, 1930) and 45 per cent of the "old" buildings (erected prior to 1930); buildings with B damage, 15 per cent of the new and 24 per cent of the old; C damage, 7 per cent of the new compared to 20 per cent of the old; D damage, 1 per cent of the new compared to 8 per cent of the old; and E damage, about 1 per cent of the new compared to 3 per cent of the old. If buildings grouped under the A and B damage classification are combined, the survey shows 91 per cent for new buildings and 69 per cent for old buildings. Stated differently, this means that 9 per cent of the buildings erected since March, 1930, suffered damage classified as C, D or E and that 31 per cent of the buildings erected prior to that date suffered similar damage. Most of the buildings in Long Beach having been erected in the past 25 years, it was assumed that deterioration was not an important factor in the different showing of old and new buildings.

This damage analysis, supplemented by facts gained from personal observation, leads the writers to conclude that the problem of obtaining reasonably adequate public safety in buildings should be resolved in two parts: (1) design provisions for new buildings, and (2) alteration provisions for existing buildings.

NEW BUILDINGS

Viewed from the standpoint of public safety alone, it seems reasonable to assume that new buildings should be required to be so designed that they would not sustain more than class A damage. The analysis shows that less than one-half of the buildings inspected in Long Beach escaped with A damage.

Considering only the newer buildings, in [Table 2-1], only 44 per cent of the type III structures escaped with A damage; this is not a good enough record from the standpoint of public safety.

To confine future earthquake damage in buildings hereafter erected to an A classification, it is believed that the minimum requirements are:

1. Adequate enforcement of an existing building code equal to the 1930 Long Beach code.

2. An ordinance requiring that all new buildings be designed for a lateral force approximating that induced by an earthquake having an intensity equal to the maximum earthquake recorded in similar geologic and geographic regions.

3. Additions or revisions to existing building codes, such as the present Long Beach code, covering certain specific details of construction.

There is abundant evidence to show that otherwise well-designed and constructed buildings in many cases were seriously damaged because lateral forces were given no consideration. The practical aspects of building-law enforcement lead the writers to believe that the enforcement of both the lateral-force requirement and the specific requirements as to details of construction are necessary.

EXISTING BUILDINGS

Existing buildings in seismically active areas should be examined, and all parapet walls, ornamentation or other objects found to be inadequately supported or attached to the building should be removed or otherwise made safe. It may reasonably be assumed that such action, had it been taken in Long Beach prior to the March 10 earthquake, would have resulted in a different damage classification, i.e., a change from B to A for all types I and III buildings surveyed. The percentages of A and B damage for all buildings of these types, regardless of age, are 17 and 30 respectively. From this we may deduce that if B damage could be eliminated, 47 per cent of all now existing types I and III buildings might be considered reasonably safe in a future earthquake of similar intensity.

These figures serve to call attention to the pressing necessity for legislation affecting existing buildings. Replacement and repair due to obsolescence and deterioration may be expected to bring about gradually some improvement in the situation. For a few years, however, the existing-building problem is the hardest one to meet, and the minimum attempt should include the strengthening of parapet walls, ornaments and other similar semi-detached portions of buildings, combined with such alterations to street fronts of buildings, as are necessary to make both the exits and the adjoining streets safe for use.

SPECIFIC CODE CHARGES

Notwithstanding the better performance of buildings erected under the present Long Beach code, certain revisions and additions to this code and to other similar codes are desirable and necessary, in addition to a lateral force requirement. The mortar used should be a rich cement-lime mortar approximately 1 part of portland cement to ½ part of lime putty to 4½ parts of

TABLE 2-4 Earthquake Damage Classification, Long Beach, California

	Type I and Type III Buildings*	Type V Buildings*
A	Includes buildings not damaged; buildings showing plaster cracks or other minor damage not affecting structural safety. Parapet walls and brick walls at corners may show cracks but have not been materially weakened. In general damage to building estimated at less than 3 percent of value of building.	Includes buildings not damaged and buildings showing plaster cracks which are not indicative of structural failure. Also includes rupture of upper parts of chimneys.
B	Parapet walls thrown down; extensive interior partition damage; rupture of brick or tile filler or partition walls, which will require minor replacements and extensive plaster repairs; separation of veneer from backing; minor damage to structural frame of building.	Exterior wall cracks at or near foundation; extensive chimney damage; loosening of exterior plaster or brick veneer; shifting of porches and other appendages but not of building as a whole.
C	Rupture of masonry walls below roof line; bond failures in concrete; in general, failure of structural parts (walls or frame) necessitating major repairs to or replacement of somewhat less than 50 percent of exterior walls or framework.	Buildings moved on foundations; general damage to plaster and walls; racking of structural framework, doors, partitions, etc.
D	Extensive damage to walls necessitating replacement of more than 50 percent of wall area. Corresponding extensive interior damage to partitions, floors, foundations or roof. Failure of structural frame requiring considerable replacement.	General damage to building more extensive than in type C but not requiring complete demolition.
E	Building demolished to an extent making repairs impracticable.	Building demolished to an extent making repairs impracticable.

*Long Beach code classification according to type of construction:

Type I   Fire-resistive (concrete or steel frame)
Type II Mill (heavy timber frame and masonry walls)
Type III Ordinary masonry (wood joists and masonry walls)
Type IV Steel frame (steel framework with incombustible walls)
Type V   Wood frame (wood framework—stucco, wood siding or brick veneer walls)

The number of type II and type IV buildings was so small that they were not included in the analysis

SOURCE: *Engineering News-Record,* May 25, 1933.

clean sharp sand. All joints in unit masonry should be solidly filled with mortar, and each masonry unit should be thoroughly wetted and shoved into place. Header courses should be required in at least every fourth course, and this should apply to veneering and face brick as well as to the backing. Careful consideration should be given to the approval of any types of ties, other than header courses as above suggested, for some methods of anchorage now permitted will not adequately resist earthquake stresses; this is particularly true of ties for masonry veneer on wood-frame buildings.

Hollow walls of masonry, clay tile, concrete blocks and similar construction, whether in bearing walls or in panel walls, should be required to be reinforced with steel in all but the small one- or two-story dwelling. Masonry around and above openings should be tied to the steel lintels.

Careful consideration should be given to anchorage of floor and roof systems to walls. The usual form of joist anchor installed on every fourth joist has proved inadequate. Roof trusses should not only be required to be braced vertically between trusses, but there should be an adequate system of horizontal X-bracing in the plane of the lower chord. Reinforced horizontal belt courses at all floor and roof levels and reinforced vertical ties at the corners and at proper intervals between should be required. Masonry arches should be avoided. The height of parapet or other walls laterally unsupported at the top should be restricted, and such walls should be reinforced and surmounted by horizontal ties of steel or concrete.

Chimneys should be required to be reinforced from the foundation continuously to the top. Wood-frame and steel-frame buildings should be fastened to the foundations with suitable anchor bolts. Where underpinning is used in wood-frame buildings between the first floor and the foundation, it should be diagonally braced in both directions. Clay roof tile should be required either to be wired or nailed to the roof sheathing.

A study of [Table 2-2] will indicate some interesting trends, although the number of buildings surveyed hardly justifies any conclusions regarding additional legislation.

CONCLUSION

The results of this survey indicate that 53 per cent of all existing buildings may be damaged in a future earthquake to an extent equal to B, C, D or E damage. The minimum action recommended herein as to existing buildings would result in the elimination of B damage in future earthquakes, which would reduce the 53 per cent to 30 per cent. Even this leaves much to be desired from the standpoint of public safety. The ideal objective would be to confine all future damage to such as is included in the A classification. To do this would require the complete removal of some existing buildings and more or less extensive reinforcing of others. This would involve such an enormous expenditure in seismically active areas that there seems to be little hope of reaching the objective, although a bond issue for such a purpose has been suggested in Long Beach.

The reduction of *B* damage, which could be brought about by applying the minimum suggestions referred to above, involves comparatively little expense and should be given at least as much attention as the preparation of new laws providing for earthquake safety for new buildings.

If the legislation outlined above is enacted and enforced, there should should be no loss of life or serious injury to persons or property from failure of buildings *hereafter erected* in any future earthquake, the intensity of which does not exceed the intensity of those that have occurred in Long Beach, Santa Barbara and San Francisco.

The official reports formed the basis of emergency legislation, enacted less than 3 months after the Long Beach earthquake, in the closing days of the state's legislative session. The goal was simple: to apply minimum design standards to many new buildings as possible, and to allow state enforcement of building codes in unincorporated areas of California. This summary of the new law was published in the June 1, 1933, issue of ENR:

New California Building Law Makes Lateral Force Design Mandatory

Resistance for a lateral force equal to 2 per cent of the total vertical load or a 20 lb. wind load (the larger to control) must be provided in the design and construction of all buildings built in incorporated sections of the state of California according to a bill passed by the legislature as a direct result of the Long Beach earthquake. The combined vertical and horizontal stresses are not to exceed one and one-third (1⅓) times the allowable working stresses provided by the local ordinance. The few exceptions provided are for small buildings in rural communities or buildings already started. The bill has not yet been signed by the governor but as an emergency act will become effective immediately upon his signing.

The bill originated in southern California with the purpose of controlling reconstruction following the earthquake of March 10. Opposition was mainly in regard to the provisions of the bill and not to its intent. Questions as to making the bill uniformly applicable to the entire state, some sections of which have no record of serious seismic disturbance, and of reconciling it with the results of the long study made by San Francisco engineers in connection with a new city ordinance on the same subject formed subjects of controversy.

After some slight changes in the original measure it developed that, in the rush of closing legislative action, any attempt to amend the bill further would kill it and, in the interest of having the measure as it stood or none, opposition was withdrawn.

Principal provisions of the act are as follows:

Section 1. Every building of any character, and every part thereof which is hereafter constructed in any part of the State of California, including every incorporated city, incorporated city and county, and county except such buildings as are hereinafter expressly excepted from the operation of this act, shall be designed and constructed to resist and withstand horizontal forces from any direction of not less than either two (2) per cent of the total vertical design load or twenty (20) pounds per square foot wind pressure on the vertical projection of the exposed surface, the horizontal force used to be the one that produces the greater stresses in the building.

Sec. 2. For the purposes of computing the resistance of any building to such horizontal forces as required by section 1 hereof, the computed stresses resulting from the combined vertical forces and horizontal forces shall not exceed one and one-third (1⅓) times the allowable working stresses as hereinafter provided.

Sec. 3. For the purposes of this act, allowable working stresses shall be those specified in the ordinances governing the erection and construction of buildings in the city or city and county in which the building is to be constructed or if in unincorporated territory then of the county wherein the work is done.

If no such ordinance is in effect at the place at which the work is done then the allowable working stresses shall be those specified by the Division of Architecture of the State Department of Public Works, which is hereby fully authorized and empowered to specify such allowable working stresses for the purposes of this act as to any city, city and county, or county in which no such ordinance is in effect.

Sec. 4. This act shall not apply to the following buildings:

a. Any building not intended primarily for occupancy by human beings and no part of which is located within the limits of an incorporated city or incorporated city and county.

b. Any building designed and constructed for use exclusively as a dwelling for not more than two families and no part of which is located within the limits of an incorporated city or incorporated city and county.

c. Any building on which work has actually been commenced prior to the effective date of this act.

Enforcement is placed under municipal buildings departments and where these do not exist the state division of architecture is to control.

The act, as evident from the wording, is general in provisions and questions of interpretation are many. Further, the requirements are minimum and for various sections of the state known to be subject to seismic disturbance these provisions will be exceeded by local ordinance, especially for poor ground conditions. In the case of larger buildings there is the question as to whether the designer will be permitted to put lateral stresses into frame or walls or both and in what proportion. For smaller structures of brick or timber definitely without structural frame new problems of analysis are involved.

Mexico City Earthquake, 1957

It would be hard to imagine a more perfect laboratory for earthquake design than Mexico City. First, the city is located in a seismically active area. Second, the central city area sits on a filled-in lake. The loose fill magnifies the effects of earthquakes that occur there. Finally, the city contains a wide diversity of building designs featuring flamboyant architecture. On July 28, 1957, this laboratory suffered its first earthquake experiment of modern times. Mexico City was shaken by a high-intensity quake—between 7 and 8 on the Mercalli scale. Of the 10 million people who lived in the city and its surrounding communities, only 125 died. Some observers called it a miracle. Some cited good design. And some—mainly Mexican engineers—said loss of life and property would have been even less if existing building codes had been properly enforced. As it was, nearly 1000 buildings were damaged at a cost of more than $25 million.

In the year that followed, Mexican engineers got their wish. A new seismic code was enacted. It called for tighter limits on torsional deflection of tall buildings and better connections between frames and building facades. Even more important in the long run, the Mexico City quake coincided with the growth in computational ability among earthquake experts. No longer would designs based on static calculations be enough. Dynamic analysis would slowly become the norm for just about any new building in seismic zones built anywhere in the world.

The biggest single failing among tall buildings in Mexico City was their flexibility. Few buildings actually fell, but some moved so violently during the shaking that they suffered major structural damage involving partitions, elevator shafts, and windows.

Here's how ENR reported the quake in its August 1, 1957, issue, just a few days after the event:

Mexico City Buildings Hit by Earthquake

The high intensity earthquake (estimated at 7 on the Mercalli Scale of 12), which rocked Mexico City in the early morning hours of July 28, tested the strength of one of the world's most notable collection of modern multistory buildings. Many passed the test but a number did not. About a dozen buildings, including two large ones, collapsed, and many others were damaged to such a severe extent that an undetermined number may have to be demolished.

Such features of the local architecture as cantilevered balconies, columnless facades and exterior stairways will have to be re-examined in the light of frequent failures, which littered sidewalks with debris. Long-span theater framing also showed up as a weakness. The problem of enough separation between buildings with differing modes of vibration to keep them from banging against one another also appeared as a result of the quake damage.

Prevalent, too, as a result of the whipping back and forth of the tall buildings, were out-of-plumb elevator shafts and broken plumbing risers. A number of buildings, giving the appearance of being relatively undamaged, will, in fact, be subject to costly repairs from these causes.

The fact that the city's tallest building, the [43-story] Latin American Tower, did not even suffer broken windows may be attributed to the fact that, alone among the city's buildings, its pile foundations go deep to hardpan under the old lake bed on which Mexico City is built.

Felix Candela, prominent Mexico engineer and architect, well known for his concrete hyperbolic paraboloid roofs [ENR, May 16, p. 36], reported to ENR that none of these shell structures fell or even cracked.

All hotels, and most buildings generally, suffered plaster and window breakage. The Continental Hilton suffered perhaps the most among the hotels. Sprung elevator shafts and broken plumbing practically put the establishment out of commission. This new building did not crack, as news stories reported, but separated from the adjacent old Continental Hotel to which it was connected. The crack started at the base and widened to measure about a yard across the roof line.

Of the two buildings that completely collapsed, an apartment house of six stories less than six months old was reported to have exhibited the use of poor materials in that the concrete crumbled into a sandy mass with evidence of insufficient cement. The other building, also six stories high, had a steel frame, and was under construction, with the floors but not the walls in place. A movie theater may also be considered as completely collapsed, since only the concrete walls which supported the steel roof trusses remain standing.

The epicenter of the earthquake was west and south of Mexico City, between Cuernavaca and Acapulco. In some areas it is said to have reached 10 on the Mercalli Scale.

Amazingly, the city's tallest building, the 43-story Latino Americana Tower, suffered absolutely no damage in the quake. Not one pane of glass popped, not one partition cracked. Or perhaps it wasn't so amazing after all. Knowing that the structure would be placed on a site subject to quakes, the

Figure 2-3   The complete collapse of this 6-story apartment house in Mexico City caused the death of thirty-three people. This was about half the city's death toll in the earthquake. *(ENR.)*

designers (including Prof. Nathan M. Newmark of the University of Illinois and Leonardo Zeevaert of Mexico City) exercised great care. The client, Latino Americana Seguros de Vida, S.A., a life insurance company, insisted on elaborate precautions no matter what the cost, because the structure was nearly twice as high as any other in Mexico City. Prospective tenants would have to be doubly reassured of its safety.

The building is approximately 120 feet square at street level, and 70 feet square above the fourteenth floor. The roof is 456 feet above the street and holds a television tower that adds another 138 feet. Four basement levels extend 44 feet below the street.

Because the foundation soils are so poor at the site, the building was designed to float on a concrete box that, in turn, rests on 36 button-bottom piles driven to compact sand 117 feet below the surface. Western Foundation Company drove the piles; Bethlehem Steel fabricated and erected the 3600-ton steel frame. The building's weight is divided equally between the piles and the buoyancy of the concrete box. But even if the box were not there, the piles would be capable of taking the building's weight with strength to spare. Tests showed the piles capable of loads of 90 tons each without deforming. They normally are called upon for 35 tons each; without the buoyant box, the load would be 60 tons each.

The base of the box—the foundation over the piles—is a grid of concrete girders as much as 13 feet deep and 14 feet wide, reinforced with as many as

110 bars 1½ inches in diameter. To make the tower as rigid as possible, the 3½-inch-thick concrete floors were connected to the main steel frame with steel channel shear connectors. Reinforcing rods in the floor slabs were welded to steel hoops around the columns to resist horizontal torsion.

The Mexico City building code had specified that the tower be analyzed for lateral static loads using a 2.5 percent shear coefficient, so that "the horizontal force at any elevation may be computed by the product of this shear coefficient and the total dead and reduced live load applied to the structure above the elevation."

Zeevaert and Newmark felt the code did not go far enough, especially for a building so much taller than anything else that had been attempted in Mexico City up to that time. In a paper presented at the June 1956 World Conference on Earthquake Engineering and published in the August 8, 1957, issue of ENR, they wrote:

In the preliminary design of the building, the first estimate of the seismic shears for the design was made on the basis of a uniform seismic coefficient of 5%.... Since previous buildings had successfully withstood earthquakes and were designed for shears corresponding to a 2.5% uniform seismic coefficient, it was felt that owing to the increased height of the building the shearing stresses might be increased roughly in proportion to the height (nearly double that of the city's next highest at the time).

The base shear was based on preliminary estimates of the weight of the building. The building at that time was to be only 40 stories in height. A rough preliminary design of the building was made, and fabrication of the steel was

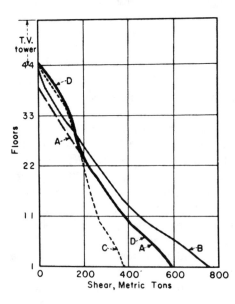

Figure 2-4 These curves show the shears, in metric tons, expected in a major quake and allowed for in design of the 43-story Latino Americana Tower. The "44th" floor is the roof of the top floor. *(ENR.)*

begun. However, at this time it was decided to add three stories to the structure as well as a television antenna. The increase in height and weight of the tower made it necessary to consider the design of the building again. It was at this stage of the problem that the first dynamic analyses were made.

The results of the various bases for the design of the building are shown in the accompanying graph. In this figure, the curve marked A is the shearing capacity of the various stories for the original 40-story building. The curve marked B shows the shears computed on the basis of seismic coefficient applied uniformly, of 5%, considering the same structure as A but with the increased height and taking into account the weight of the television tower. The curve marked C is the result of the dynamic analysis based on the most probable dynamic shears, for a base shear coefficient of 2.5%.

It can be seen by comparisons of Curves A, B and C that the upper part of the building would be overstessed and the lower part understressed, under dynamic conditions. The shearing strength for the final design of the building is shown by curve D. Only the upper part of the building was strengthened, from the 28th floor to the top. This strengthening was done so as to provide the resistance indicated by the requirements of the dynamic analysis, with a slightly greater resistance provided in the region just below the television tower.

Because the steel was already fabricated, the building has an increased strength below the 28th floor, compared with the indicated design values from the dynamic analysis. The final strength of the building, shown by Curve D, is the same as that indicated by Curve A below floor 28.

It is therefore apparent that the structure above the 28th floor is actually designed for a dynamic shearing condition corresponding to a base shear of 2.5% of the total weight of the building.

However, the lower part of the building is actually designed for a shear coefficient of approximately 4%.

The effective shear coefficient for the base of the tower is about 19%, for the 41st story 14%, for the 39th story 10.5%, for the 35th story 7%, for the 27th story slightly more than 4%. For the upper part of the structure, these shears are at least 20% to 75% greater than those required by the Uniform Building Code, and somewhat greater even than this factor in relation to the provisions of the joint committee. . . . For the lower part of the building, the design is conservative by any standards, the base shear being about twice that specified by the joint committee code.

The designers estimated from previous quakes that since Mexico City is built over deep lacustrine clay deposits, the vibration period would be between 1.5 and 2 seconds. They designed the building to vibrate with a fundamental frequency that is much longer—3.66 seconds. Nevertheless, the buildng's second vibration mode is 1.54 seconds, allowing (unavoidably) some resonance between the structure and the quake. History was a good teacher. The actual vibration period in the 1957 quake was between 1 and 1.8 seconds.

A quake with a period of roughly 1.5 seconds and an intensity of 7 on the Mercalli scale would give a ground velocity of roughly 8 cm per second. The velocity would be as much as 16 cm per second for the worst earthquake that could be expected to hit the city. The base shear for ground movement of 8 cm per second would be 207 metric tons, and for 16 cm per second it is 413 metric tons. Zeevaert and Newmark stated, then, that

> It appears that the structure is adequately safe for the maximum probable earthquake in Mexico City and has a factor of safety of about two for the maximum earthquake which has occurred in the period from 1900 to 1946, based on working stresses. The actual factor of safety is, of course, considerably greater.

[In the July 28 temblor the shears in metric tons were computed to be as follows:

	Relative Movement, Inches		
	1st–2d Floors	25th–26th Floors	39th–40th Floors
Deflection, 1 inch	0.25	0.23	0.18
Actual shear (metric tons)	500	211	82
Design shear	381	189	93
Action/design ratio	0.76	1.12	0.88

Dividing the base shear, 500 tons, by the total dead load plus 20 percent of the live load, 15,228 tons, yields a seismic coefficient of 3.3 percent.]

The partitions were undamaged because they were anchored to the floor but the tops were connected to the upper slabs with flexible hangers. The glass windows remained uncracked because the ordinary size panes, 4½ x 6 ft., had ½ in. clearance in their frames, and the big first story windows had 2½ in. clearance. Vertically pivoted windows had extra large pivots to prevent them from coming out when the frame was distorted.

FACTORS AFFECTING BEHAVIOR

In evaluating the performance of the 43 story tower, several important design details should be borne in mind:

1. The deep, pile-supported foundation was effective in resisting overturning.
2. Columns were closely spaced, only 20 ft. apart.
3. Moment connections are heavy. Made with split wide-flange beams, some are so large they could not be placed against the column webs but had to be attached to the edges of the column flanges. From the 28th floor up, the girders were reinforced by the welding to the bottom short lengths of steel beams, forming haunches at both ends. All other connections are riveted.
4. The building gets no help in resisting lateral forces from its external walls or partitions. As mentioned previously, the partitions are free to move at the top. The facade, cantilevered about 5 ft. beyond the outer columns, consists of continuous glass windows with no mullions, 2 ft. high, blue structural glass panels below the windows and 30 in. high aluminum panels

above. The backup is a 3 in. thick concrete wall projecting 30 in. above and below the floor.

Adolfo Zeevaert is chief engineer for the owner, and Eduardo Espinosa, chief designer.

Many other buildings in Mexico City were, of course, not as fortunate. Further, carefully studying the effects of the quake, engineers concluded that even the Latino Americana Tower might not escape damage in future quakes. Some of the findings were detailed in the August 15, 1957, issue of *Engineering News-Record:*

Earthquake Revealed Defects in Design and Construction

Frederick S. Merritt   *Senior Editor*

The earthquake that shook Mexico City in the early morning of July 28 affected principally the taller buildings. Few under five stories high were

Figure 2-5 A gap formed when sidewalks settled in the Mexico City quake, but the adjoining building, on piles, did not settle. *(ENR File.)*

damaged if they had good foundations and were not pounded by adjoining buildings.

Authorities are not yet finished counting the number of structures over five stories that need extensive repair or should be demolished.

Examination of many tall buildings in the business and hotel district, which was shaken severely, reveals that faulty design and construction practices were responsible for much of the damage. Nevertheless, there are several reasons for believing that the buildings that were designed to the highest of current standards and escaped this shock unscathed—including a 43 story skyscraper—may not be as fortunate in future earthquakes.

One important reason is the considerable variation in intensity of shock in the Mexico City region. It appears highly probable that due to peculiar subsurface conditions the shock was many times as severe on some buildings as on structures only a few hundred feet away.

Another significant factor is the period of the shock waves. There is much evidence that the peak vibrations of the ground in this quake coincided with the natural frequencies of many of the tall buildings that were damaged severely. Thus, with ground and structures moving simultaneously in the same direction, the forces acting on the buildings built up rapidly and almost tore them apart. It is possible that many of the tall buildings that escaped the earthquake did not have the same natural frequency as the ground movements; in a severe future shock with resonant frequency they might not be so fortunate.

BUILDINGS WERE FOUNDED ON WATER

It would be hard to find, outside of Mexico City, more difficult foundation conditions for a building solely under static loading, let alone seismic forces. One Mexican engineer estimates that poor foundations were responsible for the damage in about half of the hard-hit buildings.

The city is located between high mountains in a wide, flat valley about 1,400 ft. above sea level. Most of it is on land reclaimed by filling in Lake Texcoco. The rest is on natural islands which offer firmer subgrade. In addition, the older fills are more consolidated than the newer.

Throughout the filled-in areas, the water level is within a few feet of the surface. However, pumping of this water for community use has been lowering the water table, causing these areas to settle, in some places at the rate of more thn 12 in. per year.

Buildings on spread footings may sink at the same rate as or faster than the city streets. But the structures resting on piles stay at a nearly constant level, and within a few years their ground floor may be several feet above the street. Furthermore in very few cases do the buildings settle uniformly.

To counter the settlement, several buildings in Mexico City have been

Figure 2-6 A joint between sections of this long apartment house in Mexico City opened wide, and settlement of the 7-story wings dropped floors out of alignment. *(ENR File.)*

designed with concrete box foundations to float in the subsurface "soup." In addition, provision is included to right them if they should tilt while settling. The National Lottery Building and the 43 story Latino-Americana tower, which survived the quake unharmed, are two outstanding examples of this type of construction.

VARIABLE SUBSTRATA

In the downtown area, where most of the tall buildings are congregated, the fill or archeological deposits extend to depths of from 4 to 20 ft. Below to a depth of about 30 ft, are a series of alluvial and volcanic sediments. Under that, to 100 ft below grade are thick layers of soft clay with bentonitic characteristics, separated by strata of volcanic solids. The clay has a very high water content—up to 300% (weight of water to solid matter). In this state, it is easily compressed and almost impermeable.

At about 100 ft below ground level, is a 25 ft thick layer of fine sand and gravel, cemented with calcium carbonate and clay. Many buildings are supported on bearing piles driven into this layer.

It is worth noting at this point that Mexican practice in the past with timber piles left much to be desired. The piles were driven in two or more sections with a 6 x 8 in. tip and 10 to 12 in. butt. The sections were spliced with a simple dowel in the center, or a dowel and a metal ring around the outside of the splice. There is some evidence of settlement due to buckled piles, and several Mexican engineers suspect the splices.

Below the layer to which piles are usually driven is about 30 ft more of highly compressible clay. At greater depths is a series of alluvial deposits of sand, silt and andesitic gravel.

WHY THE SHOCK VARIES

With islands of firm ground interspersed in the saturated clay and with various layers of subsoil at different depths, the shock wave of an earthquake does not travel freely through the ground. It undoubtedly bounces back and forth between strata, reflected and refracted.

In some places, the vibrations may cancel out. In others, they reinforce each other. Emilio Rosenblueth, consulting engineer, Mexico City, believes the magnification factor may reach 12 or more. This can explain why some buildings may have escaped damage while comparable structures nearby suffered severely. In one case, a building previously condemned as unsafe came through the quake without additional injury.

MORE QUAKES TO COME

The July 28 earthquake originated outside the Mexico City Federal District. In fact, Chilpancingo, 55 miles northeast of the Pacific Coast resort of Acapulco and 145 miles from Mexico City, was hit even harder (estimated at 10 on the Mercalli scale).

While at Acapulco, the top story of a 13 story, reinforced concrete hotel under construction at the time for the Hilton chain collapsed.

Some geologists have reported that the quake was caused by the formation of a new volcano on the southwest coast of Guerrero near Chilpancingo. They predict additional shocks (some with intensity of up to 5 on the Mercalli scale occurred last week), with perhaps another violent one in the not too distant future.

BIGGEST QUAKE

The shock that hit Mexico City is estimated to have had an intensity between 7 and 8 on the Mercalli scale. Equivalent maximum acceleration is figured by several Mexican engineers to be between 0.05g and 0.10g. And the waves had peak periods of about 0.9 sec and 1.8 sec.

This is the worst shock the city has had since records were kept beginning in 1900 [at Tacubaya]. The Mexico City seismographs did not function during the quake.

Previously, there had been no reports of shocks of intensity 8 or higher in Mexico City. Three are believed to have been of intensity 7, and there were several hundred of weaker intensities.

As a result of this experience, and because until recently there were few buildings in the city over 12 stories, Mexico City engineers believed there was little reason for paying special attention to seismic design. However, they became more concerned about ten years ago when an 18 story reinforced concrete building partly collapsed in a quake.

WHAT THE CODE REQUIRES

The Federal District Building Code dates back to 1942. It contains provisions for seismic design. However, tall buildings, which were erected in great numbers in the last 15 years, are designed according to the judgment of consulting engineers.

The code requires that joints between different structural elements be designed to resist at least as much as the elements they join. Each structure should be designed and built to oscillate as a unit. (However, many buildings that were damaged in the July 28 temblor were built with spaces between sections covered with masonry or thin plates, which were destroyed.)

Foundations are required to be designed so that the structure will not slide or overturn and so the joints between piles and foundation girders or slabs will not fail. No pile should be overstressed in a quake by more than 33%. Nor should any point of the bearing area of the ground or the foundation elements and joints be overstressed more than one-third.

Buildings need not be designed for simultaneous action of wind and earthquake. Seismic design computation must be made for structures over 50 ft. high or with a height-width ratio over two or intended for use by large groups of people.

The code provides seismic design coefficients varying from zero for unimportant structures to 0.10g for various types of occupancies. For most office buildings, factories, hotels and houses the coefficient is 0.025g, constant for every story. (In contrast, codes of U.S. cities in seismic zones, based on dynamic analysis, increase the coefficients for upper stories.) The seismic shear at any level is the coefficient times the dead plus live loads for all floors above that plane.

The July 28 earthquake demonstrated that the code provisions are inadequate.

INVESTIGATIONS UNDER WAY

The Federal District government, following the quake, took immediate steps to protect the public by cordoning off hazardous areas and shoring up damaged structures. It also appointed an investigating commission, headed by Federnando Hiriart, Federal District Water Works Director.

The commission, in turn, established 22 committees of three men each. These committees are now at work examining the taller and more important of the damaged buildings. Only a few reports have been submitted.

As of August 5, Mr. Hiriart reported that none will be condemned. However, he believes that in several cases the owners will find demolition and reconstruction less costly than repairs.

A separate commission also was appointed to determine whether the Benito Juarez housing project of 4, 7 and 10 story buildings should be condemned. These structures, built of reinforced concrete, are long and narrow and have brick walls above the second floor.

Each of the taller buildings has an inside, centrally located elevator and an outside stairway, with steps cantilevering from and circling a vertical concrete shaft.

During the quake, one of these shafts collapsed, toppling the stairs to the ground. The stairs of several others became partly detached from the buildings but did not fall over.

The pile-supported tall buildings in this group settled at the ends. Because of the skew, elevators jammed in their shafts. The lower buildings, probably on spread footings, sank 12 in. or more, tilting adjacent sidewalks about 45 deg.

Long, narrow buildings subdivided by joints were damaged when the sections pounded each other during the quake and were left with a permanent lean. However, surface examination of exposed structural members and masonry end walls reveals little damage to these components.

HOW LOW BUILDINGS FARED

Probably because of the difference between the period of ground vibrations during the quake and their natural period of vibration, nearly all low buildings in Mexico City came through with no serious damage. Eduardo Espinosa, consulting engineer, Mexico City, believes the older low buildings survived because the walls acted as shear walls.

It is also noteworthy that almost all the one-story, thin-shelled buildings, including Felix Candela's hyperbolic-paraboloid umbrella roofs [ENR, May 16, p. 36], escaped unharmed.

Three or four buildings about eight stories high collapsed. From all reports, these failures were due to faulty design or construction. For example, one reinforced concrete apartment house is said to have had its columns turned with the axis of smallest moment of inertia parallel to the narrow dimension of the building.

Another, of flat-plate construction, with light exterior steel columns and interior reinforced concrete columns, may have failed because of inadequate shear transfer between slab and columns. There was no evidence of special provision for shear of the concrete columns, and the steel members apparently had for the purpose only a channel with web attached to the column and flanges protruding into the slab.

The floor had been cast on precast concrete boxes, and during the shock some of the boxes fell out. The question may well be raised as to whether such waffle-slab design offers sufficient resistance against horizontal torsion.

Among the low buildings of importance that were seriously damaged is the 5 story, reinforced concrete Registro Publico de la Propriedad (Hall of Records). Seated on "controlled" piles (with built-in jacks to adjust for settlement), this structure has heavy masonry walls above the second floor, no walls in the first story. The heavy mass of the superstructure rests on two rows of large-diameter tapered columns, between which, in the narrow dimension of the building, span relatively shallow haunched girders. The haunches are heavily reinforced. However, a sizable portion of the large-diameter, bottom reinforcing bars terminate at the end of the haunch.

The result of the heavy mass oscillating on the relatively flexible stilt-like columns during the quake was two-fold. First, the ground was cracked all around the buildings. Secondly, the concrete at the intersection of the haunch and horizontal part of girders spalled, exposing the hooked haunch bars; diagonal cracks extended upward from the intersection toward the nearby column. Stirrups appeared to be ineffective against the cracks.

Similar stilt-like designs used for the low concrete buildings at the University of Mexico, founded on an old island, suffered no damage. However, different details were used for those buildings, and there is no evidence that the shock was as intense at this location.

TALL BUILDINGS HIT HARD

Since the official investigating committees have not yet completed their reports, it is impossible to estimate with accuracy the dollar value of the damage to Mexico City's tall buildings.

One lesson is obvious from inspection of the city. The quality of construction and the degree to which use is made of current knowledge of seismic design are far more important in determining the ability of a building to survive an earthquake than whether the structure has a steel or reinforced concrete frame or whether the walls are masonry, glass or tile. This is proved by several high buildings that were hard hit.

Many tall buildings in the downtown area suffered only broken windows, spalling of the facade and slight plaster-partition cracking. In some lobbies with marble facings, the marble was shaken off or badly cracked. Yet, there are tall, narrow steel-frame buildings with no broken glass in floor-to-ceiling windows.

In nearly all cases where interior or exterior facings spalled off the backup, there was no evidence that the facing had been held in place by metal anchors—only by mortar.

Many examples are evident of reinforced concrete walls sheared through at floor level. In many cases also, the walls in addition, cracked away from the columns. Frequently, whole wall panels fell out. There were no dowels between walls and structural framing. If the shock had not occurred at night, when the city was asleep, the falling debris would have taken a heavy toll of lives.

Several tall buildings in the downtown area sank 4 to 6 in. during the quake. Many tilted out of plumb more than 1 ft horizontally in 100 ft of height, although in some cases the tilt was not all due to settlement but because the frame was too flexible. Sometimes, the streets tilted with the buildings; often gaps were seen between sidewalks and buildings, as structures and streets settled different amounts.

It is significant that none of the tall buildings overturned, despite poor foundation conditions.

Adjoining buildings of different height slammed against each other and ended up considerably out of plumb with wide V-shaped cracks between

Figure 2-7 This reinforced concrete column in the International Building in Mexico City failed. *(ENR File.)*

them. This also happened to tall buildings subdivided by joints. But the damage was particularly severe when the floor levels in adjoining buildings did not line up and the floor slabs hammered against the columns. In some cases, reinforced concrete columns were knocked out of alignment.

There is also an outstanding example of the disadvantage of not tying together two sections of a building at an angle. One office building consists of two wings forming an L, with a masonry wall at the intersection to cover the 3 ft. wide junction. The upper part of that wall was destroyed; the lower sections were badly cracked.

EXCESSIVE FLEXIBILITY PROVES BAD

Many buildings turned out to be too flexible as evidenced by popping out of external walls, broken windows and severe partition cracking. However in some cases the structural framing did not escape unscathed.

One twelve story apartment house appeared to have steel columns that are much too light for the height of the building. Several of these buckled badly in the second story. Bulging of masonry wall at upper levels may be a sign that higher column tiers may also have buckled.

A 13 story, reinforced concrete office building suffered serious plaster partition damage from the first to eighth floors, some failures of the exterior walls and many broken windows. Diagonal tension failures of stairwell beams and spalling of columns were evident.

A reinforced concrete building with a 17 story tower and 10 story wings not only suffered in the same way as others with joints between sections but also received severe structural damage. Founded on timber piles, this edifice had been badly injured in a previous temblor. It was later repaired by spraying a thin shell of concrete around the columns, which had been cracked, and adding haunches on the beams. In the July 28 quake, this reinforcement failed badly.

A column sheared through completely between the seventh and eighth floors. At upper and lower levels above, this column was badly cracked. Stairwell columns were severely damaged and [a] 4 in. thick reinforced concrete exterior wall around the circular stairwell cracked open vertically in several stories. Between the second and fifth floors the haunched beams spalled severely at the ends of the haunches. Diagonal cracks extended from the spalled areas upward toward the columns.

In contrast to these badly damaged structures, the 43 story, steel-frame Latino Americana tower stands as a symbol of the value of painstaking attention to detail in aseismic design (see below). It suffered only minor partition damage. Yet, there is evidence that the shock intensity at the building may have exceeded 7 on the Mercalli scale. Built-in recorders noted the relative deflections of floors at several levels.

It is noteworthy that the peak periods of the ground vibrations, 1 and 1.8

sec, straddle [a] natural vibration period of the structure ... estimated at 1.5 sec. So there is still the unanswered question as to how the building would fare if a future earthquake should have a period of 1.5 sec.

AFTERTHOUGHTS

Mexican consulting engineers naturally are studying the earthquake effects intently and busily reviewing their past design practices. They are almost unanimous in the conclusion that the building code needs revision, and in particular that strict enforcement of its provisions is necessary.

Javier Barros-Sierra, director of the National School of Engineering, University of Mexico, says the code should be modified to require dynamic analysis or higher empirical seismic coefficients, especially for important buildings. Also, a minimum distance between buildings should be specified, to prevent them from striking each other in a temblor.

Adolfo Zeevaert, chief engineer for the owner of the Latino Americana

Figure 2-8 Among the few structures that collapsed in Mexico City was this waffle-slab building with steel and concrete columns. It may have lacked adequate provision for shear transfer from slab to column. *(ENR File.)*

tower, also is sold on dynamic analysis—a technique used for the design of that skyscraper.

Emilio Rosenblueth recommends that the following be considered in future code revisions:

1. Walls should be securely anchored to floors and columns.
2. Buildings should be made stiffer than required by the present code.
3. Higher lateral forces should be used in seismic design. (However, the effects of damping of vibrations by walls, partitions, etc., should be included.)
4. A distinction should be made between different foundation conditions in imposing design seismic forces.
5. The relative deflection of floors should be limited.

Jose A. Cuevas, consulting engineers, Mexico City, warns that in the future it will be necessary to give more consideration to buildings adjoining a new structure. In particular, foundation conditions will have to be checked; also the height of the floors, to prevent floor slabs striking columns. Stability of buildings will have to be investigated.

Mr. Cuevas strongly urges that an experiment station for seismic studies be established—perhaps under the auspices of the United Nations—to develop improved design criteria.

Less than 3 months after the quake, Mexican officials had strengthened the city's building code, requiring greater resistance against lateral forces. The code did not, however, require dynamic analysis of new building designs. The extra sophistication for dynamic analysis would have to await the lessons of future quakes—and the ease of new computer-based calculating methods. *Engineering News-Record* reported on the controversy surrounding the new code in its October 17, 1957, issue:

How to Reduce Seismic Damage

Earthquake provisions in the building regulations for the Mexico City area are being changed as a consequence of the July 28 temblor. The new requirements are much more conservative than the old ones, which were promulgated in 1942.

The revision calls for higher design coefficients for computing seismic shears and assumes linear variation of accelerations in determining shears at various levels. It places limits on the deflections. It incorporates provisions for torsional resistance. In addition, it requires that consideration be given to subsurface conditions, type of occupancy, height of building and type of construction in selecting seismic coefficients.

POST-QUAKE ACTIVITY

The cities of Mexico, Acapulco and Chilpancingo were badly shaken by the July 28 earthquake. Most of the damage occurred in Mexico City [ENR, Aug. 15, 1957, p. 38], which has grown at such a rate in recent years that it has become nearly synonymous with Federal District. (Mexico City operates under the Federal District building code.)

MANY CONSULTED ON REVISION

In working out new criteria for a seismic design the Federal District Office of Public Works consulted its permanent building committee, as well as a number of consulting engineers and research professors of the Institute of Engineering, National University of Mexico.

In addition, committees were formed to gather and appraise data on the earthquake effects. Their early findings served as a basis for code modifications.

Figure 2-9 This steel-framed building was under construction near the heart of Mexico City when the 1957 earthquake hit. A night watchman was killed when it collapsed. *(International News.)*

When the old code was drafted in 1942, it was up to date according to standards of that time, except that many engineers considered the seismic design coefficients adopted too low. However, the only severe quake the committee on regulations was aware of was that of 1941, which was weaker than the July 28 temblor. Also, there were fewer tall structures in Mexico City then.

EMERGENCY RULES

The OPW calls the new regulations "Emergency Rules to Verify the Stability of Buildings Subjected to Seismic Action." In a preamble the OPW states:

> Due to the earthquake that occurred July 28, 1957, important damages were sustained in a very high number of structures of different types, found mainly in the low part of the city, where the subsoil is formed by materials of low resistance and high compressibility. Having in mind seismic experience in other regions of the world and the preliminary analysis of the damages caused by the earthquake, as far as distribution and magnitude of the more probable accelerations in structures is concerned; the influence of the mechanical properties of the subsoil on the extent and duration of ground vibrations; existence of a predominant frequency in the soft subsoil; contribution of partitions to the rigidity of structures and their action as energy dispersers; breakage of structural components due to the collisions between adjacent structures that vibrate in different periods; and the possibility of destructive earthquakes striking buildings supported on bearing walls where the ground is rigid and yields very little, the Office of Public Works has formulated the following rules. . . .
>
> These are of a provisional nature and will be applied until they are replaced by more adequate and complete specifications, which will result from a careful and well documented study of the behavior of the structures that were subjected to seismic action.

The emergency rules apply to all buildings, including one-story dwellings, whereas the old code exempted buildings less than 53 ft high.

Following the characteristics of the subsoil, Mexico City is divided into three principal zones—Zone A, lake bottom; Zone B, transition; and Zone C, hills—as indicated on a map.

Taking into account type of occupancy, buildings are classified into three groups—**a, b** and **c.** For example, hospitals, theaters, schools and other important buildings are included in group **a,** small houses in **c.**

In addition, buildings are classified in accordance with structural characteristics:

Class Alpha   Concrete on steel structures with partitions that contribute to increased rigidity, properly bounded and distributed.

Class Beta   Concrete or steel structures that do not have elements foreign to the structure that contribute to increased rigidity. Bracing and concrete walls firmly attached to the structure are considered integral parts.

Class Gamma   Structures supported only by bearing walls.

SHEAR CALCULATIONS

In accordance with these classifications, seismic design coefficients are given in an accompanying table. The coefficients multiplied by the total load on the foundations (with live load reduced as permitted for columns) yield the base shear at foundation level.

In contrast to the provisions of the present building code, the new coefficients are dependent on type of structure and nature of the ground. They range from two to four times present values. In addition, to estimate the lateral forces acting at each floor level, seismic accelerations are assumed to vary linearly from zero at foundation level to a maximum at the roof, similar to the requirement in the San Francisco building code. [See also ENR, Dec. 1, 1949, p. 28.] Up to now, most Mexico City structures were designed for a constant 0.025g.

Parapets, billboards, ornaments, exterior walls and front facings, should be considered subject to a uniform acceleration of at least 0.5g. And stability of inside walls should be checked for a uniform acceleration of 0.1g.

The emergency rules restrict relative displacement between braced points of columns or walls, such as at floor levels, to 0.2% of the distance between those points. Also, a study should be made to determine the necessary separation between adjoining, independent structures or at expansion joints to prevent damage due to collisions during an earthquake.

SAFE WORKING STRESSES

Instead of the one-third increase in working stresses formerly allowed, much larger values are permitted for a combination of earthquake, live-load and

TABLE 2-5   Minimum Values of Seismic Design Coefficient, Mexico City, 1957

Group	Building Class	Zone A	Zone B	Zone C
a	alpha	0.15	0.13	0.12
a	beta	0.20	0.18	0.15
a	gamma	0.15	0.18	0.20
b	alpha	0.07	0.06	0.05
b	beta	0.10	0.09	0.07
b	gamma	0.07	0.09	0.10
c	alpha, beta, gamma	0	0	0

SOURCE: *Engineering News-Record,* Oct. 17, 1957.

dead-load stresses. For concrete, the stresses specified in the American Concrete Institute building code can be doubled, except for diagonal tension, for which the increase remains at 33%. Reinforcing bars of mild steel may be stressed to 90% of the yield point and special steel grades to 80% of the elastic limit.

Sections may be checked by limit-load theory, with a safety factor of 1.2 in flexure and 1.5 for axial load.

Structural steel will be permitted combined stresses up to 1.5 times the safe working stresses specified by the American Institute of Steel Construction. However, sections may be checked by limit design with a safety factor of 1.0 in flexure and 1.3 for axial load.

To account for accidental torsion that might occur in an earthquake, a moment should be applied equal to the product of 5% of the horizontal shear and the maximum dimension of the floor being analyzed, measured normal to the shear. For warehouse floors, the factor should be increased from 5% to 7%.

Provision is also made in the emergency rules to protect structures against torsional oscillations.

CRITICISM

Reaction to the new rules by Mexican engineers has not all been favorable. Some of the most experienced engineers consider the new coefficients too low. Others consider them too high, claiming that it is not economically feasible to design a building 12 or more stories high.

Replies one prominent consulting engineer:

This is not so. The design of several new tall buildings has been successfully achieved with no more than 2% or 3% increase in overall construction cost. Even the reinforcing of damaged buildings has been found economical in most cases, and a 30% reduction in the design coefficients puts all damaged buildings within economical repair range.

However, this engineer also points out that the methods of analysis proposed still are static, not dynamic, though the manner in which the coefficients are assumed to vary is closer to the results obtained with dynamic analysis than the assumptions of the old code.

Building officials believe that insufficient information is available at present to permit them to specify dynamic analysis; too little is known about natural vibration periods of structures and about the characteristics of strong-motion earthquakes in the Mexico City valley. Research is under way at the Institute of Engineering, National University of Mexico, with the objecive of finding a rational solution to the problem of seismic analysis.

Another prominent Mexican engineer, while agreeing with the theory of dividing the city into zones, disagrees with the method adopted. He says it

Figure 2-10 Inadequate column bracing and reinforcement allowed the floors to pancake, in this ground view of the same 6-story apartment building as shown in Figure 2-3. *(McGraw-Hill World News.)*

would be better to base the zones on the compressibility of the subsoil in accordance with soil-mechanics studies. Also, he argues, the structural classification of buildings and the seismic design coefficients should be based on dynamic analysis, considering the vibration periods.

This engineer also considers it unreasonable to allow for combined loading double the live and dead-load allowable stresses, since the actual strength of materials is ignored. He considers incongruous the provision for concrete that permits only a 33% increase for shear but 100% for other stresses. He is also critical of the rules for steel that allow a 50% stress increase, while concrete is allowed twice as much. And for spread footings, he considers the concept of bearing capacity vague, subject to the particular criterion of soil mechanics adopted.

Despite the criticism, the Federal District Department is proud of the amendments to the old building code.

Anchorage Earthquake, 1964

As the sixties dawned, the international engineering community was beginning to think that the basic theory of earthquake design was well in hand. The two problems that remained, the experts said, were lack of code enforcement (leading to poor workmanship in newly constructed buildings) and an inability to predict the force and shape of the most damaging earthquake that might occur at a given site. Around the world, large new structures on land known to be subject to quakes were being built under provisions adopted from California's Seismic Code. The Structural Engineers Association of California, which had played (and continues to play) a prominent role in revising the Seismic Code, had labeled it "interim" and subject to revision as new data appeared.

Two strong earthquakes shook urban areas within a span of 9 months, giving the engineers a chance to test the code's adequacy. In both cases, some important details were found lacking. The first big test occurred on July 26, 1963, in Skopje, Yugoslavia. Of the city's 170,000 people, 100,000 were made homeless and 1000 died. Four out of every five buildings were damaged or destroyed. Although the city contained many quite modern structures, investigative teams from the American Iron and Steel Institute and the Portland Cement Association found that the structures had been flawed by poor workmanship and by disregard of the need for bracing against lateral forces.

Unfortunately, the codes were soon to get a better test. On March 27, 1964, the worst quake imaginable shook the Alaskan coast. It measured well above 8.2 on the Richter scale, which has a maximum of 8.9. Damage in Anchorage, the largest city hit, was almost total. A three-block section of the downtown area slid sideways. A residential district broke away from a sloping hillside. The

Figure 2-11 Part of the main street in Anchorage dropped 10 feet during the March 27, 1964, earthquake. (*U.S. Army Photograph.*)

main street was cracked lengthwise. But miraculously, of the city's population of 83,000 only a dozen died. In the entire earthquake area, only 114 were killed.

Compared to earlier quakes of about the same magnitude, the low loss of life was remarkable. In San Francisco in 1906, a Richter 8.3 quake killed 452; that same year the 8.9 Valparaiso quake in Chile cost 1500 lives. A similar number died in the 8.4 Assam, India, quake of 1950, and an 8.3 quake in Chile in 1960 had killed 5700. The Tokyo quake of 1923 killed 140,000 in rubble and by fire; it has been estimated at Richter 8.2.

Engineering study teams quickly concluded that the low loss of life was not due entirely to good design or good construction technique. Considering the massive amount of landslide volume, in fact, the death toll could have been far higher, even if not a single building had been shaken apart on ground that remained in place. Said John L. Cerutti of Tryck, Nyman Hayes, an Anchorage consulting engineering firm,

Discounting all damage in the slide areas, it appears that the remaining damage occurred to only a relatively small number of structures. Damage to those structures can be attributed to many factors: avarice of the investors who want "cheap" plans and do not want to pay for the competent inspection; carelessness of contractors in conforming to plans and specifications; sloppy workmanship; lack of details on the plans or poorly written specs by architects and engineers; and lack of respect for the forces of an earthquake by all.

After Skopje and Anchorage, the Seismic Code was revised to emphasize the need for strength and ductility in building frames. Engineers and architects were also called upon to develop "a second line of defense" in their designs, should major structural members fail in a long-duration quake (the Anchorage quake lasted 6 minutes). Finally, the two quakes taught designers that they must separate parts of a structure with different properties, to keep them from banging against one another in a quake. Vertical columns, for instance, cannot be embedded in shear walls, or even run next to such walls.

Here's how *Engineering News-Record* reported the scene in its April 2, 1964, issue, just a few days after the quake:

Quake Wrecks Alaskan Cities

The earthquake that struck the southern coast of Alaska on March 27 [1964] and sent tidal waves across the Pacific caused property damage running into the hundreds of millions of dollars. . . .

First reports indicate that damage was nearly total in Anchorage, Kodiak and Valdez. The waterfront at Seward, battered by tsunami, looks as if it had been bombed, with railroad cars and engines overturned and burning, tracks twisted. And coastal cities in California, 1,000 miles away from the temblor's epicenter, also were pounded by the giant sea waves.

Estimates place the magnitude of the earthquake between 8.2 and 8.7 in the Richter scale. Charles F. Richter, professor of seismology at California Institute of Technology, says the initial reading recorded in his laboratory was 8.2. But it will take about three months of studying records from all over the world before he can report a more accurate reading.

For comparison, the maximum on the logarithmic Richter scale is estimated at 8.9, limited by the strain energy that can be stored in the rock structure in a fault before rupture occurs. The 1906 San Francisco earthquake, in which 452 died registered 8.3.

Following the main shock on March 27, Caltech's instruments recorded six large aftershocks ranging from 6.2 to 6.5, as well as numerous smaller ones. But none of these appear to have caused serious damage or additional loss of life.

The earthquake struck Anchorage at 5:36 p.m. Fissures streaked across the city. Buildings toppled. Pipelines burst. The power plant was knocked

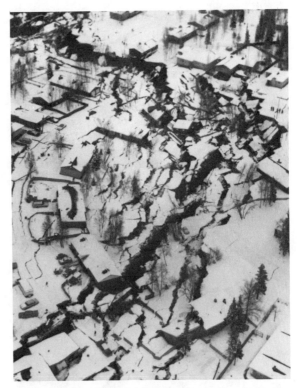

Figure 2-12 Houses tumbled downhill as fissures opened in Anchorage. *(Associated Press.)*

out. Yet, despite this devastation, in this city of 83,000, only about 10 have been reported killed and 50 injured [so far].

One fissure sliced along Fourth Ave., a main street. It dropped the buildings along one side of the street about 10 ft. An area two blocks long was ruined. Another fissure sheared a school in half.

About 75 expensive homes in a residential section along the bluff above Tumagain Arm of Cook Inlet were wrecked as fissures sheared the area. Some slid into the inlet. Others in the mile-long, half-mile-wide area tumbled downhill. Roads were cut off abruptly by newly formed cliffs about 20 ft. high.

THE CURTAIN FALLS

Massive curtain walls dropped off the five-story J. C. Penney department store in the downtown area. A six-story apartment building under construction and nearly completed, in another part of the city crashed to the ground. The 60-ft. high control tower at Anchorage International Airport also toppled, killing one man. And about 3,000 ft. of runway at the airport was torn up.

New buildings in Anchorage are required to meet the earthquake provisions of the Uniform Building Code and the International Conference of

Figure 2-13   Massive curtain walls fell off this Anchorage department store facade. *(Associated Press.)*

Building Officials. Older buildings included many of brick and concrete bearing wall construction. The city had some new buildings 14 stories high. Initial reports said they appeared sound from the outside after the quake, but they were severely damaged inside. This required confirmation, and the reports neglected the type of construction used.

The earthquake cut off the public water supply in Anchorage. Sewage systems were disrupted. Power lines fell on buildings and streets. Turning generators that supply the city with electricity, located in the Bureau Reclamation dam nearby, were knocked out of service by a landslide. Other generators, fueled by natural gas, could not be operated because the fuel supply was shut off for fear of fire. The 26-ft.-high, 555-ft.-long Eklutna Dam was not reported damaged. The power station has an installed capacity of 80,000 kw.

At least 17 bridges were wiped out in south-central Alaska.

ROCKED BUT READY

Despite minor to severe damage to Defense Department buildings and equipment in and around Anchorage, the Commanding Officer of the Alaskan Command was able to report soon after the quake, he was fully able to carry out his defense mission. A collapsing hanger with falling debris at Elmendorf was severely damaged and evacuated.

Two early warning systems with stations near the earthquake center functioned perfectly throughout the disturbance.

One of the stations, at Cape Clear, 45 miles southeast of Anchorage, is in the Ballistic Missile Warning System. The other, at Kodiak, 240 miles southeast of Anchorage, which is a part of the Distant Early Warning (DEW) Line, had to be evacuated for a time as 15-ft-high waves swept the area.

THEN, TSUNAMI

Tidal waves from the quake radiated to U.S. and Canadian Pacific Coast locations and Hawaii.

Hardest hit by the tidal wave was Crescent City, Calif., a timber town of 3,000 near the Oregon border. Estimates place damage there at from $10 million to $30 million. Some 300 buildings were destroyed or damaged, and a bulk oil and gasoline plant exploded and burned.

Four waves hit Crescent City: at 12 midnight and at 1:00, 1:40 and 2:30 in the morning. The third one caused the most damage to property and also caught many owners in the damaged area cleaning up from the first two waves. The fourth did little damage.

Crescent City's 29-block central business district suffered most of the damage. A city official estimated that three-fourths of the district was destroyed. Early reports showed that 42 small businesses were totally destroyed, 108 heavily damaged and 29 damaged to some extent. Gas mains were shut off, but water supply was reported in good shape.

Red Cross figures showed 400 families homeless, 54 homes destroyed, 13 heavily damaged and 24 damaged lightly. Buildings were knocked off their foundations. Those nearest the sea were pushed into the streets. Several motels and other structures south of the city were also damaged. Most buildings in the city are built of wood.

Crescent City's harbor is enclosed by a 1-mile-long breakwater, the first in the U.S. to be built of concrete tetrapods. The Corps of Engineers built the barrier in 1956–57 [ENR, Mar. 21, 1957, p. 46]. A spokesman for the Corps' South Pacific Division office says it was designed to protect the harbor from normal wave action, but not tidal waves.

WHY TIDAL WAVES

Tidal waves, or tsunami, as some oceanographers prefer to call them, often follow earthquakes. Theorists believe crustal movements on the ocean floor generate the waves. They travel at speeds believed to range as high a 500 miles an hour. A wave hit Hawaii last week about five and one-half hours after the earthquake had occurred about 2,600 miles to the northeast.

Tsunami have been recorded as high as 60 ft and reported as high as 90 ft. Waves last week were reported as 30 ft in Cordova, Alaska; 17 ft in Port Alberni, B.C.; 12 to 15 ft in Crescent City; and 8 ft in Vancouver, B.C.

Tsunami have the greatest destructive potential where they ride in on wide shoals, like those at Crescent City or funnel into inlets as at Port Alberni.

A few days later, ENR's San Francisco editor, Jack H. McMinn, toured Anchorage to study the damage before cleanup activities obscured it. His report appeared in the April 9, 1964, issue:

The Verdict of Anchorage: Good Structural Design Survived

Jack H. McMinn

An inspection of Anchorage, Alaska after the tremendous earthquake that leveled it March 27 indicates that good structural design saved many lives and prevented severe property damage. But unfortunately, Anchorage had many inadequately designed structures, many of them incorporating newer types of construction.

Geologists blame saturated silty clay at a depth of several hundred feet under much of the city for the intensity of the quake it felt. They say much of the area around Anchorage simply slumped when the unstable earth shook loose. This is a possible explanation for the magnitude of the damage in Anchorage, which is 150 miles northeast of the estimated epicenter of the quake. The soil, called Bootleggers Cove clay, plus steep slopes and subsurface discontinuities created slides and slumps that caused much of the major damage to buildings, pavements and utilities.

When I arrived in Anchorage last week, much of the debris had been cleared from the streets, but many of the damaged buildings, remained untouched, leaving visible the probable causes of their collapse. Structural engineers, geologists and other specialists are picking through the smashed structures to study the quake's effects.

Figure 2-14 A view, from the ground, of sliding on a steep Anchorage slope, as clay fissured and heaved. *(U.S. Army Photograph.)*

MAJOR BUILDINGS SURVIVED

Although major structural damage and a few structural failures were the most spectacular evidence of the quake, many major buildings survived with little or no damage, indicating that with good structural design a building can withstand large seismic forces. In most cases of building failure, indicated by collapse or near collapse, there was evidence of lack of frame action, and lack of adequate shear-resisting connections between building elements.

Most major buildings that collapsed incorporated newer design and construction techniques, such as precasting, prestressing and lift-slabs.

The Four Seasons Apartments, a six-story building that collapsed, was a lift-slab structure with finishing work in progress at the time of the quake. Overturning forces toppled two concrete cores housing elevator shafts. The building tumbled to the ground in a heap. Grade beams or a shear wall between the two cores could possibly have prevented this failure.

Precast concrete T-beam roofs of two automobile agency buildings, one in use and the other under construction, collapsed during the quake. And two warehouses with precast concrete walls, one in Anchorage and one at Elmendorf Air Force Base, collapsed. Better connections between precast elements might have prevented these failures.

TORSION WRECKS BUILDING

The J. C. Penney department store in downtown Anchorage suffered heavy damage. This five-story concrete building, rectangular in plan, had 10-in.-thick, cast-in-place concrete shear walls on two long sides and one short side. Concrete floor slabs spanned between these walls and interior columns. Decorative precast concrete panels, weighing over a ton each, covered the upper four stories of shear wall on one long side of the building. Similar panels formed a curtain wall on the upper four stories of the short side of the building that had no shear wall.

The quake apparently produced a torsional force in the building that sheared most of the precast panels off the building along with a large section of shear wall adjacent to the short side without a shear wall. Horizontal cracks in the shear walls at floors indicate a torsional racking in these walls and perhaps a weakness in construction joints. And some floor-to-column connections failed with attendant loss of frame action and shearing of columns and walls.

Bolted angle connections attached the precast panels to the shear walls. Dowels, welded to the angles and embedded in the panels and shear walls, fastened the angles to the concrete. Torsional forces apparently sheared the dowels near the weld, dropping the panels to the ground.

Three other buildings, including a two-story, steel-framed building and a reinforced-concrete office building of about the same height, came through the temblor with minor damage. They are still occupied.

CONTROL TOWER DAMAGE

The quake damaged the control tower at Elmendorf AFB, and the tower at Anchorage International Airport collapsed. At Elmendorf, the concrete tower was badly cracked from the base to a height of about 15 ft. At least one reinforcing bar broke. The steel-framed cab on top of the tower shows some distortion and some stretching of bolts, and the distortion broke some glass.

At the international airport, the control cab had stood on four large concrete legs, braced by concrete beams at several levels, and the cab had massive concrete floors. Under seismic load, the tower failed to act as a frame and collapsed. My inspection of the wreckage led to the opinion that vertical bars may not have been properly hooked or tied into the concrete to develop bending resistance at joints.

One man rode the collapsed tower to the ground and was injured. The wreckage crushed a second man who attempted to escape from the cab by the stairway in the tower.

TALL BUILDINGS RUINED

Two 14-story apartment buildings, similar in design and outward appearance, suffered heavy damage. The buildings, rectangular in plan, are of cast-in-place concrete construction, with load-bearing exterior walls. Built 12 or more years ago, the structures present a solid, stress-resistant appearance.

Figure 2-15 This 14-story Anchorage apartment building with concrete frame developed X-shaped cracks in its walls. *(U.S. Army Photograph.)*

The earthquake developed heavy X-cracking in spandrels and some bearing walls. It also crushed concrete near the base of some columns and bearing walls. In some cases, cracks extended completely through exterior walls. The crack pattern indicates that the quake produced major accelerations on both building axes.

The 14-story Westward Hotel building, also rectangular in plan, is a steel-framed structure with exterior concrete shear walls. Finishing work was in progress on this new building at the time of the quake.

Some steel framing was bent and some shear-wall concrete cracked when the new building struck against an adjacent six-story concrete building during the quake. Nevertheless, the building is structurally sound, says Neil McDonald, an engineer with the hotel's structural consultant, John H. Stevenson of Seattle. The contractor, J. B. Warrack of Anchorage, will proceed with repairs and expects to complete the building later this year.

The quake damaged several other major office, commercial and apartment buildings in Anchorage. Some have been evacuated, some will be demolished, but most can be repaired though in some cases at considerable expense.

STRUCTURAL LESSONS

A San Francisco consulting structural engineer, Henry Degenkolb, inspecting the Anchorage damage for the Structural Engineers Association of California, says that although the design of modern privately owned buildings in Anchorage probably conforms to the recommendations for Seismic Zone 3 of the Uniform Building Code of the International Conference of Building Officials, much of the construction is not earthquake resistant because of inadequate connections and other details, the mixture of construction materials, and the use of unit masonry for structural purposes. Also structural damage shows, on the part of designers, a lack of sensitivity to the difference between designing for lateral and vertical forces.

Mr. Degenkolb says the damage highlights two important lessons for structural engineers:

- **Importance of Inspection** Ungrouted bars in unit masonry were much in evidence. Bars were placed in hollow cells, sometimes with little or no grout. Smooth construction joints in cast-in-place concrete were common. Inaccurate bar placement also was noted.
- **Importance of details** Hooks, laps, and ties for reinforcing bars could have prevented some damage. Combinations of steel framing and concrete in bearing and shear walls should have been avoided or better designed. Use of brittle welded connections to assemble precast-concrete elements was the cause of some failures.

Schools, hospitals fared well, although a few hospital buildings in Anchorage were evacuated temporarily immediately following the quake and work in others was hampered by loss of utilities. All hospitals are now either back in operation or soon will be after minor repairs.

Of 26 schools in Anchorage, 20 either are or will be in use soon. Four were badly damaged by the quake and will need extensive repairs. Two were damaged by slides and probably will be demolished.

HOW FOUNDATIONS BEHAVED

Foundation failure was not an immediately apparent cause of damage to or destruction of any major building in Anchorage.

Failure of foundation materials, however, did damage many small commercial buildings, apartments, houses and some schools. In most cases, such damage occurred to structures located near steep slopes or bluffs. In the Turnagain residential area on a bluff overlooking Cook Inlet, several lives were lost and many homes destroyed by progressive sliding triggered by the quake. Government Hill School, on a bluff above a marshy inlet that separates downtown Anchorage from Elmendorf AFB, was undermined and destroyed by a slide.

A two-block section of downtown Anchorage that slumped about 10 ft. destroying many small commercial buildings also overlooked the same marshy inlet. Pavements and other improvements on the slope below this commercial area were heaved up and destroyed by the toe of the slide.

In another section of town, a slumped area about 50 ft. wide cut across several blocks of residential area, narrowly missing two hospitals and a five-story apartment building. Liquid action or consolidation of a weak soil deposit, possibly in an old stream channel, apparently caused this slump, since much of the area was not immediately adjacent to a bluff.

HIGHWAYS, BRIDGES DAMAGED

According to William J. Niemy, Bureau of Public Roads, regional engineer from Juneau, and Clayton B. Hawkins, BPR district engineer in Anchorage, damage to highways and structures could total $120 million. Repairs will take a year or more, but emergency traffic can use all roads now except the one between Anchorage and Seward. Emergency repairs there will take three or four months. The quake destroyed 10 bridges with a total length of 2,820 ft and badly damaged another 1,200 ft that may have to be replaced, all in a 25-mile section of highway.

Types of damage included the following:

- Fissures split a few sections of paving.
- Pile-supported bridge abutments and piers shifted and tilted, apparently due to liquid action of weak clays and silts.
- Concrete piles cast in corrugated shells driven 90 ft uplifted as much as 8 ft.
- Uplift forces pulled concrete decks and caps off wood piles and the piles pierced the concrete deck.

According to Mr. Niemy, steel bridges and concrete decks on steel bents fared best. New bridges and pavements, designed to current standards, will replace damaged facilities. But Mr. Niemy does not expect that such designs would be resistant to another quake of similar magnitude.

New bridges, ranging in length from 50 to 80 ft, will be of standard design, with steel H-piles and steel caps and girders. Composite concrete decks, designed for H-20 loading, will replace initially installed H-15 wood decks.

A spokesman for the government-owned Alaska Railroad estimates damage at $20 million to $25 million. All lines are out of service.

Repairs on the Fairbanks line will take about six weeks and on the Whittier line, about three weeks.

PORT IN OPERATION

Port facilities on the southern coast are damaged but operating. Normally closed by ice conditions at this time of year, the Anchorage port now provides the only remaining public facility capable of handling water-borne cargo for central and south-central Alaska.

George T. Treadwell, of Seattle, in Anchorage to survey damage for the port's design engineers, Tippetts-Abbett-McCarthy-Stratton, of New York City, says damage to the pier is minor. Steel cylinder piles punched through the concrete cap and deck at three bents in a finger pier at the end of the main pier. Vibration of a gantry crane, locked to the tracks in the area of the punching damage, apparently caused the punching failure.

Also, the quake opened a longitudinal construction point in the concrete deck of the main pier. Apparently, the two longitudinal deck sections pounded against each other during the quake. This caused some piles to shift, opening a crack several inches wide and several hundred feet long.

Most utilities, including drinking water, are now back in service in most areas of Anchorage. Electrical facilities are crippled, but operating on an interim basis during repairs.

The quake damaged petroleum pipelines and tankage heavily. Standard Oil Company of California reports a loss of several million dollars, but expects to resume normal operations quickly.

MILITARY DAMAGE MINOR

Warren George, chief of the engineering division, Alaska District, Corps of Engineers, reports government facilities in good condition, except for the collapsed portion of a warehouse with precast walls. The government will repair and continue to use all buildings damaged in the quake. Evacuated buildings have major utility problems but minor structural problems.

All schools at Elmendorf AFB and Fort Richardson will be reoccupied soon after minor repairs. Some small areas in certain buildings, however, will be off-limits pending major repairs. The hospital at Elmendorf is structurally sound, although the quake caused cracking and spalling at one point of two columns and on five spandrels.

The Army's docks, buildings and tank farm at Whittier, near the epicenter, are intact. Tsunami and fire destroyed all docks and waterfront structures at Seward, and tsunami damaged breakwaters at Homer and possibly at Kodiak, Valdez and Seward.

Mr. George attributes the excellent performance of government buildings to good design (mostly in accordance with the requirements of the Uniform Building Code for Seismic Zone 3), careful inspection and thorough foundation investigations. He believes that the Anchorage area can handle seismic problems by proper attention to foundation investigations and adopting good structural design practices. There may be some zoning changes, at least the possibility will get a long look, but land owners and developers probably will resist radical change.

The Corps started disaster relief immediately in Anchorage and it is starting now to survey damage to streets, utilities, waterfront facilities, and public buildings in Seward and Valdez. Cleanup is in progress in Anchorage along with reconstruction of essential facilities, such as the access road to the port terminal and utilities. Edward A. McDermott, director of the Office of Emergency Planning in Washington, D.C., has authorized this essential repair and restorative work.

An interesting aftermath of the quake is that civil defense facilities, which were on the verge of being disbanded before the quake, performed so well that they will undoubtedly be retained and strengthened.

More detailed reports of the site's geology and of the nature of the failures that did occur came later. President Lyndon Johnson established the Federal Reconstruction and Development Planning Commission under New Mexico Senator Clinton P. Anderson to coordinate federal aid for Alaska in the wake of the cleanup. The commission funded a study of the soils underlying much of downtown Anchorage, before deciding on whether to permit aid for reconstruction in the area. The verdict, by soils engineers from the Seattle firm of Shannon and Wilson: The area is extremely unstable under earthquake stresses. The report insisted upon regrading, better drainage, and buttressing before any reconstruction could take place. The engineers warned that even with such stabilization, new buildings' foundations would have to be designed to withstand large settlements, because of the clay and sand layer running only 50 feet below grade. This layer had become fluid during the quake.

In its final report, the commission went further, asking that soils be checked in all populated Alaskan areas subject to possible quakes. The report recommended that federal construction aid be withheld "wherever possible" in

Figure 2-16 This steel-framed building on Fourth Avenue in downtown Anchorage retained the shape of the last shock wave to hit it. *(American Institute of Steel Construction.)*

areas that are especially hazardous. Unfortunately, this advice has not generally been followed in the 20 years since the disaster.

Local officials have, however, followed another recommendation, that they stick close to "the requirements for seismic zone three of the 1964 Uniform Building Code approved by the International Conference of Building Officials." The commission noted that Pacific coast experience "amply" demonstrates that architects and structural engineers do not always thoroughly understand some of the design aspects of the code and how to apply them. Therefore, the commission said, local officials should hire specialists to review plans for major new structures.

The commission was also critical of the code in some respects. While the quake-proofing called for by the 1964 Uniform Building Code is "comprehensive for structural design," the commission said, the code ignored quake-proofing for a building's electrical, mechanical, and plumbing systems. The commission also asked that the code devote more attention to "interactions between certain types of multistory shear walls" in the same structure, and the "base shear distribution to upper stories on tall buildings."

Poor workmanship was also pinpointed as a cause of many problems during the Anchorage quake. The commission asked that "workers and inspectors" be "more exacting" in following drawings and specifications. A select Army Corps of Engineers study team also complained about slipshod construction and poor field inspection. The Corps found many instances of poorly bonded mortar joints, improperly placed column reinforcing, poorly welded column clip angles, and ungrouted masonry wall reinforcing. The Corps recommended that in seismic areas there be:

- A ban on precast structural members unless the proposed system has been conclusively proved to be able to resist quakes
- Revision of military design standards to strengthen partitions and reduce the hazard posed by swinging, suspended light fixtures and other elements
- Anchoring of vertical and horizontal reinforcement of masonry walls on the top and sides

The Federal Housing Administration helped finance computer studies of the behavior of a 20-story building in a theoretical earthquake. A year after the Anchorage quake, Prof. Raymond W. Clough of the University of California at Berkeley reported the results: Seismic design practices are wrong—but right. The study's calculations estimated that dynamic stresses resulting from a severe earthquake are as much as 5 times those the static calculations would call for. But the allowable stresses that are specified through static calculations underestimate the building's plastic reserve strength by about the same amount. A properly designed building—that is, one designed according to existing codes—would thus have a frame that is safe during earthquakes.

"The relatively simple code provisions cannot account for all aspects of the response of a complex building to the violent random motions of an earthquake," said Professor Clough.

Professor Nathan M. Newmark of the University of Illinois, whose Latino Americana Tower came through the Mexico City quake so well, described how tall buildings could be designed to reflect dynamic considerations. "The ideal to be achieved is one involving appropriate flexibility and energy-absorbing capacity, permitting earthquake displacements to take place without undue force being generated," he said.

One way to do this economically is to rely on ductility—to let the building's frame be flexible enough to bend permanently out of shape in an earthquake, yet still retain enough strength to keep the structure from collapsing. "It may be desirable to proportion a structure so that it suffers large distortions," he said, "short of a collapse that would involve loss of life, in a highly improbable extreme earthquake, but ... have little if any damage in the event of earthquakes normally to be expected during its life."

Professor Newmark warned that making a building slightly stronger on the basis of a dynamic calculation might make it more rigid too, and thus less likely to withstand a large quake.

Many of these new ideas on building rigidity were incorporated into the revised Los Angeles building code of November 1966. The old code had limited new construction to 160 feet or 13 stories, whichever was lower. The new code allows much taller structures, if they are designed properly. The first building to take advantage of the new criteria was the 210-foot-high Sheraton Universal Hotel of the Stars, featuring a reinforced concrete frame designed in accordance

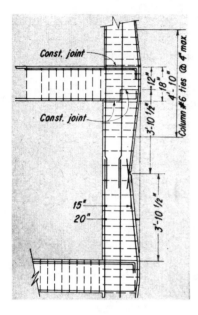

Figure 2-17 Reinforcing bars confine concrete joints in this detail from the Sheraton Universal Hotel project in Anchorage. *(ENR.)*

with the Portland Cement Association's then-new textbook, *Design of Multistory Concrete Buildings for Earthquake Motions*. The building's features were explored in an article by structural engineer Wayman C. Wing in the February 22, 1968, issue of ENR:

THE END RESULT

The 58 x 184 x 210-ft-high frame has three 19-ft bays across the building. The long dimension has fourteen 13-ft bays. An unusual aspect of the design is that in the interior 19-ft bay the beam between the columns is omitted on alternate column lines. The story height is 8 ft 9 in.

Under the Los Angeles code provisions covering this design method, energy absorption and ductility in the plastic range is designed into the frame. The ultimate-strength theory was used for design of the beams and columns under combined lateral and vertical loads. This was a basic concept because the engineers felt that it was the best tool devised so far for predicting where plastic deformations will occur.

The columns and beams were all sized, reinforced and detailed for maximum reserve strength in the frame joints. Joint details include continuous top and bottom bars and full loop stirrups in all beam-to-column connections and full loop ties in the column through the joint.

Conversely, points of contraflexure were weakened relative to the joints purposely to create flexibility. To accomplish this, the design calls for column

bar splices at mid-height rather than at the floor line. Also the exterior
columns have a reduced mid-height dimension. The designers feel that this is
a true architectural expression of the moment-resisting, ductile frame.

A basic criterion is that frame response in the plastic range should occur
at the joint but in the beam rather than the column portion to prevent
collapse of the frame. Under-reinforcement in many of the beams assures that
reinforcing steel will yield in tension before concrete fails in compression.

Steel in the columns is high-strength ASTM 432 grade with a 60,000-psi
yield strength. Intermediate grade ASTM A-15 steel reinforces the beams to
assure ductility for developing the reserve strength in the plastic range. All
concrete is lightweight with 3,000 and 4,000-psi compressive strengths at 28
days and with a splitting ratio (ratio of splitting tensile strength to the square
root of the compressive strength) of 5.5.

A design ductility factor of five (ratio of maximum design plastic strain
to yield strain) limits flexibility and avoids maintenance problems after high
winds and minor earth tremors. Total base shear is approximately 3% of the
weight of the building or 700 kips.

Flexible joint packing around precast concrete end wall panels and
around reinforced masonry walls cushions these walls against distortion of the
frame.

Congestion of the reinforcement was a problem at the connection
between beams and columns in the confined concrete area. In some places
strict interpretation of the code requirements would have made it physically
impossible to place the steel, particularly the heavy loop ties. However,
adequate practical solutions were accepted by the building code officials who

Figure 2-18 The crowded tangle of reinforcing bars at joints required
a field solution: partial prefabrication of the assembly. *(ENR File.)*

understood that over-reinforcement might cause the concrete to fail in shear before the effective yield could take place.

Large-scale layout studies of the intersecting column and beam steel with the heavy ties in the confined concrete provided reasonable assurance that congestion would not result in poor concrete.

CONSTRUCTION

In turn, the heavy reinforcement presented a field problem for Robert E. McKee, General Contractor, Inc., of Los Angeles. There wasn't room in the beam and column forms to conventionally assemble the amount of reinforcing required. The general contractor solved this by preassembling the beam and column reinforcement on the deck and lowering it, in a careful sequence to assure proper meshing of the reinforcement, into the forms for final buttoning up.

For ductile concrete frame buildings, the Los Angeles code requires continuous inspection of the work by a certified structural inspector who is responsible only to the owner or structural engineer. King-Benioff-Steinmann-King, structural consultants, of Sherman Oaks, Calif., performed this service.

Two faults cut diagonally across the building site. Thomas Clements, a geologist, and L. T. Evans, a soils engineer, found no evidence that the faults are active or that they have been active in recent geologic time.

To protect against any possible fault activity, the engineers designed the tower footings as fully continuous pads between the columns. The footings bear on the virgin conglomerate of sand, sandstone, and shale with a design pressure of 6,000 psf. Beams designed to withstand 10% of the vertical column loads tie other footings together.

Wayman Wing's structural engineering staff worked with architects William B. Tabler and John C. Mayer to design the building's frame.

San Fernando Valley Earthquake, 1971

For the first time in 38 years, a major quake hit a highly populated area of the United States. Although only about sixty people died, property damage totaled between $500 million and $1 billion. The quake shook more than buildings; as a result of the high property toll, engineers were shaken out of the complacency that had followed the Anchorage quake. One person who hadn't been complacent was Henry J. Degenkolb, president of the Consulting Engineers Association of California at the time of the quake. At the 1968 Earthquake Engineering Research Institute symposium in San Francisco he had complained about designs being "cut too thin" on the assumption that engineers had perfect information about future quakes and about their construction materials.

In particular, Degenkolb questioned the wisdom of using "ultimate-strength" design for concrete beams, and the plastic reserve supposedly available in steel. In his talk, he analyzed a column under a particular load, according to the criteria of various earthquake codes. Under the "working-strength" design method of 1964 Uniform Building Code, the beam would not be nearly strong enough; it would be stressed to 155 percent of its capacity. But it would be adequate—stressed to only 80 percent of capacity—if its strength were calculated under the 1967 Uniform Building Code or the 1967 California Structural Engineers Code.

"Are we structural engineers willing to say that [since 1964] we have learned so much about earthquakes and structural performance that we can reduce column strength by almost half . . . and who at this symposium has been able to tell us the magnitudes of the forces buildings are subjected to in a major earthquake?" asked Degenkolb. He also noted that the lack of earthquake ground-motion records is a serious handicap in making dynamic calculations of a building's strength. If the response spectrum of earthquake shocks shows that long periods predominate, rigidities based on the fundamental vibration mode of the frame may be appropriate, but if the ground motion occurs in short vibrations, the building may resonate at a higher mode and rigidities may be far different.

Early in the morning of February 9, 1971, designers got a chance to see whether Degenkolb was right. ENR carried its first major story on the quake in the February 18 issue:

New High-Rises Survive $1-Billion Quake

At 6.6 on the Richter scale, last week's Los Angeles earthquake was merely "a building-code-level shake," in one designer's words. Damage is estimated at $1 billion, but it is extreme only at isolated spots. Still, the first quake to hit a heavily populated metropolitan area on the continental U.S. in 38 years seems likely to spur advances or changes in seismic design and quake-oriented laws.

The quake, at 6:01 a.m., caused at least [64] deaths. A few hours later, it could have smashed hundreds of cars on clogged freeways, crushed children in school with rubble, and caused widespread panic among workers in office buildings.

Even so, the major damage the quake caused was dramatic. With its epicenter 26 miles northwest of downtown Los Angeles, it leveled much of the

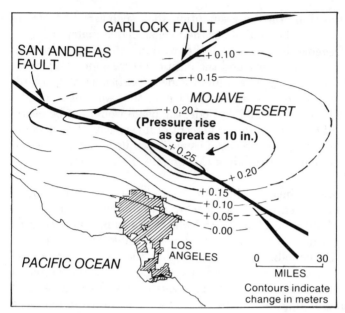

Figure 2-19 The Los Angeles–San Fernando earthquake of 1971 struck along several faults. *(ENR.)*

San Fernando Veterans Administration hospital complex at Sylmar, a few miles away. According to reports that were sometimes still sketchy by the end of last week, the three and four-story buildings' concrete walls and columns apparently gave away at ground level, causing concrete floor slabs to fall.

LIKE A BOMB'S BLAST

At Sylmar, the quake also ripped two five-story stair towers away from Los Angeles County's $24-million Olive View Health Center, which opened last October. One stair tower tipped almost onto its side. No failure occurred in the T-shaped building's upper floors, though.

A county spokesman likens damage to the reinforced concrete structure to a bomb's direct hit, and doubts it could have been avoided. "We met all the requirements that have been set up through years and years of studies on construction safety for earthquakes," he says.

In downtown Los Angeles, new high-rise buildings suffered only minor damage. On the 52-story Atlantic Richfield Towers, the under-construction, highest buildings in town, none of the granite or precast concrete exterior panels cracked or fell from the steel frames.

The city's building and safety department says, though, that 675 buildings sufered major damage. A sixth of them were posted unsafe.

Of the 114 buildings declared unsafe, 52 are within a few miles of the 28-

story Los Angeles City Hall, which sustained $500,000 worth of cracked exterior panels and interior plaster above its 15th floor. The unsafe buildings, many of them low brick or masonry structures, were all built before 1933. . . .

"GROUND MOVED SO MUCH"

On highways just north of Los Angeles city limits, overpasses fell. Ten more suffered major damage and inspections of others continued late last week. The state Department of Highways estimated damage, some of which occurred on projects under construction, at $30 million.

Some of the overpass structures that fell were concrete girders, one of them post-tensioned. In many cases, supporting columns sheared off at the top of the structures. Some sheared at grade. The state's District 7 supervising bridge engineer, Oscar Johnson, emphasizes that the structure failed not because of type, but because their foundations moved extensively.

"The ground moved so much that it caused the bridges to fail in their substructures," Johnson says. He notes that movement caused the structures

Figure 2-20 The 5-story recreation wing at Olive View Sanitarium in Sylmar, California, lies on its side. It separated from the main building (background) and fell almost as a single unit. *(Associated Press.)*

Figure 2-21 The quake effectively blocked the inland
main highway from San Francisco to Los Angeles as the
freeway overpass at the junction of Route 14 and Interstate
5 collapsed. *(United Press International.)*

to do "things they were never designed for," citing hinges as examples of
failure points. "If the hinge is designed for 10 in. of movement, and the
abutment moves out 1 ft, the thing falls off."

Johnson adds, "This ground upheaval would have caused failures or
damages to most any kind of structure, except maybe a suspension bridge."
He says many other bridges in the area "are designed just like these that fell,
and they're just sitting in perfect condition. So nothing is wrong with the
design for a normal earthquake."

Seismologists at the California Institute of Technology in Los Angeles
say the quake centered on no particular fault. It occurred instead in a maze of
faults that make the unstable base of the San Gabriel Mountains, just north
of Sylmar. The first tremor occurred on the Soledad Fault, a 3-mile rift
considered so insignificant it's not usually marked on fault maps.

By the end of the week, seismologists had counted 25 more aftershocks,
the epicenters of which extend in an elongated pattern. Slippage apparently
moved south and west.

Seismologists began repeating their estimates of timing for earthquake prediction equipment and methods, too. The optimists suggest that such work can begin in three years. Others say five to 10.

CONCERN OVER SCHOOLS

Within two days of the quake, politicians and state officials were calling for the upgrading of public buildings to resist earthquakes, especially schools. They voiced special concern over schools, seven of which were seriously damaged in Los Angeles last week.

The California Department of Education reports that 1,777 public school buildings in use in the state do not conform to standards adopted in the Field Act. The act, passed by the legislature after the 1933 Long Beach earthquake that seriously damaged dozens of schools, sets rigid structural standards for schools, but does not provide for their enforcement. However, recent legislation requires that public schools either be brought up to standard by 1975 or be abandoned.

Objections to the deadline have arisen in various quarters, largely because the cost of upgrading schools is estimated at $671 million. . . .

Figure 2-22   This ground view shows how slender, reinforced concrete columns were snapped by ground motion. *(California Department of Public Works.)*

Albert L. Kempton, education department field representative, noted last week that "we would be compiling the figures of injured or dead children right now" if the quake had occurred later. "We can't continue to rely on good luck," he says. Officials in his department add that "we have never had a major quake hit" during school hours.

Damage to the schools was particularly disturbing, considering the lessons of earlier quakes in California. Also troublesome was the failure of many hanging fixtures for lights and plumbing, in otherwise sound structures—failures that could have been predicted and prevented had the lessons of the Anchorage quake been heeded. In many cases, it appeared that the buildings in Los Angeles had been modified, with new—and dangerous—lighting fixtures added after construction.

Engineers speculated that the massive destruction at Olive View was caused by shaking that was worse than the average of Richter 6.5 prevailing elsewhere. Complete records of the quake's action had been expected, because accelerometers were required in all new buildings higher than 10 stories or larger than 60,000 square feet, under a Los Angeles ordinance passed in 1965. Unfortunately, many of the fifty-one sets of accelerometers were not operating properly at the time of the quake because their batteries had been allowed to run down. Nevertheless, the picture that emerged was far more complete than would have been the case in 1965, when only eight sets of equipment existed in the entire Los Angeles basin.

The picture was surprising in many ways, as this article from the June 24, 1971, issue of ENR makes clear:

San Fernando Quake Had Heavy Ground Motion

Evidence being amassed, principally from accelerograph readings, shows that buildings in the San Fernando (Los Angeles area) earthquake of Feb. 9 were subjected to much greater forces than are generally assumed in a moderate quake, this one registering 6.6 on the 10-point Richter scale.

Citing ground acceleration readings are the highest ever recorded, along with other readings less spectacular but still surprising, a U.S. government report says, "These records will surely lead to a careful reassessment of earthquake-resistant design criteria because they indicate ground accelerations several times greater than those commonly assumed in building criteria in seismic regions."

The 253-page preliminary report, examining 55 articles prepared in the first weeks after the quake, was issued by the U.S. Geological Survey and the National Oceanic and Atmospheric Administration (NOAA) under the departments of Commerce and Interior. . . .

At Pacoima Dam, 5 miles south of the epicenter, the earthquake accelerations were the highest ever recorded, that is, in the 0.5 to 0.75-g range with several high frequency peaks to 1 g," Maley and Cloud note.

Although the interpretation of that reading "may prove difficult because of fracturing of rock" in the dam abutment supporting the accelerograph, Maley and Cloud note that readings of about 0.4 g were logged at Castaic and Lake Hughes, 15 to 19 miles north of the quake's center.

The report says,

Ground accelerations in the Los Angeles area were predominantly 0.2 g, except in the San Fernando Valley and Pasadena, while on the top floors of taller buildings, maximum values occasionally exceeded 0.4 g but more often were in the 0.2 to 0.4 g range.

The largest values (exceeding 0.2 g) are generally observed at the stations nearest the epicenter, that is, in the San Fernando Valley and at Pasadena. Dropoff in peak values, from 0.10 to 0.15 g, is noted in the high-rise area of central Los Angeles and along the Wilshire [Boulevard] strip, although there are some deviations in this general trend. . . . Peak values in excess of 0.4 g were recorded as distant as downtown Los Angeles, nominally 26 miles (southeast of the epicenter), although the vast majority were in the 0.2 to 0.4 g range.

Figure 2-23 Inadequate ties between the vertical rebars were partly responsible for the failure of this overpass support on the Foothills Freeway. *(National Bureau of Standards.)*

FORCES MAGNIFIED

A separate report by the California Division of Mines and Geology, also citing the record Pacoima Dam reading, noted that a 1.05 g peak was "two to 10 times greater than expected at the epicenter of a magnitude 6.6 shock. . . . It has been previously estimated that magnitude 6.5 shock should produce an acceleration of 0.1 g on *better ground.*"

Another article, from the NOAA report, on performance of soils and foundations, says that soil action magnified the quake's force. L. LeRoy Crandall, a Los Angeles soils engineer, writes:

"With few exceptions, the buildings in the area of greatest damage are underlain by a varying thickness of recent alluvial deposits," described as "relatively granular, consisting primarily of sands and silts" in the immediate San Fernando area.

"It is apparent that the bedrock motions during the earthquake were amplified several-fold, resulting in much larger ground surface accelerations and amplitudes than might otherwise be expected from an earthquake of magnitude 6.6," Crandall says.

Meanwhile, a separate report released last week says that the sheer force of ground acceleration apparently accounts for the severe damage to the Olive View Medical Center's six-story reinforced concrete building, opened last October and the largest of hard-hit buildings to be designed under a recent, although not the newest, code.

Estimated ground motion, both vertical and horizontal, greatly exceeded code values, according to the special committee of the Structural Engineers

Figure 2-24 Inadequate column connections are evident in the collapsed ambulance port at Olive View medical center and in the facade of the main building, behind it. *(National Bureau of Standards.)*

Association of Southern California that prepared the preliminary report for Los Angeles County. The report is, nonetheless, critical of the building's design at the first and second-story levels, where greatest damage occurred.

"Although no seismological instruments were at the hospital, it is conservatively estimated that accelerations of at least 0.4 g were imposed on the structures" in the complex located at Sylmar near the epicenter, the report says.

The report estimates lateral resistance capacity of 0.15 g at the first level and 0.22 g at the second level, both exceeding code requirements.

Under the lateral forces exerted in the quake, the building drifted northward several inches, with extensive column damage at the first two floors.

HIGH LATERAL FORCES

Shear walls were used in the upper four stories, but not in the lower two floors, the report notes, and adds:

> The resultant abrupt change in rigidity at the bottom of the four top stories produced high lateral forces in the columns below. . . . The design criteria indicated that a lower seismic coefficient was used in the lower two stories than the upper four. The code was not specific on this point, but "hindsight" indicates that perhaps the coefficient in the lower portion should have been higher.

The report also notes that spirally wrapped columns performed much better than those that had only lateral ties because of higher ductility. The report does not compare the 1964 code provisions under which the building was designed with updated versions.

And what of the schools? At the time of the Los Angeles quake, there were 1777 school buildings within California that did not meet the code requirements established after the Long Beach quake of 1933. Engineers and political leaders jumped at the chance of raising funds for repair or replacement before the public's memory of the latest quake's damage dimmed. A $198 million bond issue for renovation of school buildings in Los Angeles itself was hurriedly placed on the ballot. Unfortunately, it fell 1 percent short of the necessary two-thirds majority for passage.

A decade later, officials of the University of California system were still awaiting funds for strengthening buildings pinpointed as "problems" after the 1971 quake. The university system asked for $300 million, of which more than a third would have gone to Berkeley for renovations to four structures—three dating from the turn of the century and one (the Moffitt Library) only from 1968.

Figure 2-25 The Moffitt Library at Berkeley—built only in 1968—could be a death trap in an earthquake unless its frame is strengthened. New, more refined calculations based on data collected in the 1971 Los Angeles quake highlighted the problem. *(McGraw-Hill World News.)*

Figure 2-26 This aerial shot of Olive View shows the localized nature of the quake's destruction. *(McGraw-Hill World News.)*

The 5-level reinforced concrete library was built with a moment-resisting frame. But studies of the 1971 quake suggested that reinforcement should be heavier and more confined than had been thought necessary. The extra reinforcing was made mandatory in new buildings as of 1973.

The 1971 earthquake also convinced the engineering community that continuous research efforts were needed to study earthquakes. Soon after the 1971 quake, the Structural Engineers Association of California founded the Applied Technology Council (ATC) to obtain grants for earthquake research. Professional engineers working on the grants are paid expenses, plus a small fee that amounts to about a third of normal professional rates. In the first 3 years of its existence, the ATC secured more than $1 million for funding four projects. These included studies of nonstructural components, ways to restore earthquake-damaged buildings, and ways to strengthen existing buildings. Another study analyzed the sharp vibrations of the 1971 quake through their entire response spectrum and issued design details for withstanding such shocks.

ATC's work, combined with devastating earthquakes that occurred around the world in 1976, spurred Congress to pass the Earthquake Hazards Reduction Act of 1977. The law pledged more than $200 million for studies of earthquakes and of better ways of enforcing new building codes in thirty-nine states with known earthquake hazards. At the first of three regional meetings sponsored by the National Bureau of Standards in anticipation of the law, Henry Degenkolb laid out the task for engineers in the years ahead. While many important lessons have been learned from observing earthquakes, he said, "there are as many lessons that are not reflected in current codes."

3 Fire and Explosion

Introduction

Among large industrial nations, the United States has by far the worst fire-safety record. In 1982, 6,147 lives were lost to fire in the United States, and $6.4 billion in property was destroyed. In contrast, Japan (with half the population of the United States), recorded only 2,000 deaths due to fire, and West Germany had fewer than 1,000.

Despite the bad American record, fire-safety experts agree that buildings are becoming more fire-safe, thanks to the lessons of the past. And deaths declined by almost 700, compared to 1981. Part of the problem: Daring new architectural designs, such as large open atriums in new hotels, make protection from fire more difficult. Nevertheless, in this century the response to disaster has been grudging—the result of public outrage after major fires, rather than a smooth evolution of standards as new needs were recognized by the experts.

In 1905, Chicago's Iroquois Theater, the city's newest and supposedly its safest, killed 602 patrons after an arc light ignited its massive stage curtain. Unmarked, blocked exits contributed to the toll.

Only 6 years later, in 1911, locked exits were the chief cause of disaster, trapping 145 employees of the Triangle Shirt Waist Company in New York.

Inadequate exits were still killing people in 1942, when 492 died in a fire and stampede at Boston's Coconut Grove nightclub. That disaster led, finally, to major changes in building exit design. Revolving doors, easily jammed in panics, were supplemented with conventional hinged doors, opening outward. Officials mandated battery-powered emergency lighting to reduce the chance of panic once fire cut power to conventional lighting.

In Boston and in many other cities, fire-safety surveys of existing buildings led to reduction of holding capacity in many public spaces. Perhaps the most famous example of that is the Boston Gardens, where the basketball Celtics and ice hockey Bruins play to packed houses. The Garden's pre-World War II seating capacity was cut from more than 17,000 to 13,909. Ten years ago, redesign of stairways and ramps, combined with exit improvements, allowed an increase in seating capacity to about 15,000—a total still well below the Garden's original design capacity.

Figure 3-1   The aftermath of the Triangle Shirt Waist fire of 1911 in New York City. *(United Press International.)*

Figure 3-2   Most of the 492 dead at the Coconut Grove fire in Boston never made it this far— they died inside the doors. *(United Press International.)*

Despite these examples, local code enforcement has not always followed national standards—or common sense. National codes themselves, in fact, have not always taken into account the increased use and variety of modern building materials. Combustible, smoky plastics, fabrics, and composite structural materials have magnified the extent of many disasters. Perhaps the best example of this is the Beverly Hills Supper Club in Southgate, Kentucky, where a 1977 fire killed 164—the biggest toll of any single building fire in the United States since Coconut Grove.

At the Beverly Hills fire, in a much-modified, labyrinthine building, paneling and other wall coverings spread flames in excess of the rate allowed in the Life Safety Code of the National Fire Protection Association. Poorly marked exits—often along corridors from ballroom areas, rather than leading directly from such rooms—added to the confusion. Some exits were blocked.

Even more recently, a rash of hotel fires—most notably at the MGM Grand Hotel in Las Vegas, discussed in detail in this chapter—has focused new attention on building design, interior finishing materials, and code enforcement. Early in 1981, major code-writing authorities offered new design standards covering large interior spaces such as atriums and football-field-size gambling floors.

Figure 3-3   Inside the modern-looking facade of the Beverly Hills Supper Club in Southgate, Kentucky, was a confusing maze of old buildings and their additions. *(United Press International.)*

Sadly, the one free-market mechanism that could help cut the toll in lives and property—fire insurance premiums—has not worked well due to inadequate research by insurance companies themselves. In 1982, for instance, business paid $7.98 billion in premiums for commercial multiple peril and general liability coverage. In turn, the insurance companies paid out $5.38 billion in claims.

One would think that "safe" buildings would command less expensive premiums than firetraps, thus providing building owners with an incentive to make their property safer from fire. That is not exactly what happens, however. Insurance costs *are* lower for buildings with sprinklers than for similar structures without them. And elimination of obvious fire hazards (such as inadequate exit capacity) can also lead to lower insurance costs, according to the Fire Insurance Research and Actuarial Association.

Unfortunately, however, the industry has never collected data in such a way that it could correlate certain building design features or operating procedures with a reduction in either the likelihood of fire or the severity of fires that do happen. The problems were examined in detail by *Engineering News-Record* in this January 29, 1981, cover story:

Compromised Codes Threaten Life Safety

Though sophisticated fire protection techniques abound and building codes are more uniform than ever, disastrous fires continue to show that something is wrong with fire protection in the U.S. After 84 died at the MGM Grand Hotel in Las Vegas, 26 at a Stouffer's Inn in Harrison, N.Y., and 30 at a New Jersey nursing home, the public wants to know: Do building codes work? Are buildings as safe as they should be?

Building owners say they are. They point to the good fire safety record of nonresidential buildings and the prohibitive cost of retrofitting them with additional safety devices.

Fire chiefs and safety groups say they are not. Recent tragedies and near-misses are evidence to them that human safety has fallen victim to neglect and financial greed.

Fire engineers working for manufacturers say one thing or the other, depending on what their companies make.

It may be true that large building fires get more than their share of attention. According to 1979 figures from the National Fire Protection Association (NFPA), 74.1% of civilian fire deaths occurred in residences, not hotels or office buildings. And yet disasters on the scale of the MGM Grand Hotel fire serve as irrefutable reminders that the potential for massive loss of life in larger buildings is real, and that a single fire, in short order, can kill hundreds and wreak damage in the millions of dollars.

Moreover, many feel that it is only chance that has kept the fire death rate in office skyscrapers and other large buildings as low as it has been. Most localities don't expect that good luck to last, and the constant evolution of building and fire safety codes around the country is evidence that communities are moving to prevent future disasters.

Denver [changed its code to require new high-rise buildings to] include refuge centers, areas where building occupants can be safe from fire and smoke without leaving the building. City officials say the code change is a "development resulting from the fire experiences of the last five or 10 years around the country."

The City of Boston is now considering an ordinance [that would] link the city's three dozen or so hotels and motels directly to the fire department. Meanwhile, a revision is in the works for the state building code that would mandate elaborate communications systems in all high-rise structures.

NFPA [published] a new version of its perpetually evolving Life Safety Code [in February 1981.] The code is used widely throughout the U.S. as a guide to human safety in fires, as distinguished from the structural safety issue that the major model building codes concentrate on. The new version, which [incorporated] "major revisions," [addresses] specifically for the first time the safety requirements for atriums. The code also includes new requirements for sprinklering and for assembly occupancies and for such specialized building types as health care facilities.

CODE LAG

One frequent complaint about fire codes is that, although they are constantly being improved, they are seldom retroactive. As the codes mature to absorb the latest technical knowledge, buildings already constructed stay as they are. A code change usually has no significant effect until years later, after buildings following the new requirements have been built.

Should the codes require that existing buildings be upgraded as well? "If we find something is a real peril, then the answer is yes," says Robert M. Dillon, executive assistant at the National Institute of Building Sciences, an organization set up by Congress to advise it on issues affecting the building community.

Retrofitting is reasonable "in some cases," agrees Jack M. Fratt, general manager of the Los Angeles Building and Safety Department. "When we feel it is important, we do pursue it." As a result of the MGM Grand Hotel fire, Los Angeles is now considering several code changes that include retrofitting provisions.

The Louisiana state fire marshal is encouraging state congressmen to push for legislation that would eliminate the "grandfather clause" in the state's fire code, an elimination that would bring all buildings under 1980 safety standards.

A code that includes retrofitting provisions more comprehensively than most is New York City's Local Law Five. . . .

The vehement criticism of Local Law Five from building owners, who felt it imposed unfair and unnecessary economic burdens on them, bottled the law up in court for a decade and reduced the potency of the brew that finally resulted. The certainty that legal bickering will accompany any movement to make life safety codes retroactive has prompted most officials to skirt the retroactivity issue entirely.

It is politically difficult to make a code retroactive, explains the chief code enforcement officer for Dade County, Fla., Thomas Black. "We realize we must be realistic and not price buildings out of the reach of people while at the same time fulfilling our primary objective in protecting the public."

CONTENTS AND DISCONTENT

Another frequent criticism of building and fire codes is that they focus their regulatory scrutiny on buildings while ignoring the often dangerously flammable contents—furniture and wall coverings in particular. In building fire protection, "the contents are the weak—almost missing—link," says Paul R. DeCicco, director of the Center for Urban Environmental Studies at the

Figure 3-4 Electrical wiring that violated New York City's code helped spread this fire from the eleventh floor of one of the World Trade Center towers. Of the 110 floors, 5 were damaged on February 14, 1975. *(United Press International.)*

Polytechnic Institute of New York in New York City and one of the main developers of Local Law Five.

The contents of a building should be the major target of fire safety officials, asserts New York City developer Melvin Kaufman, who continues to be a vigorous opponent of that law. "The building does not burn. It's the contents, from telephone wiring to coffee cups."

POOR FOLLOW-THROUGH

Yet even if all existing codes were miraculously upgraded to address the problems of retroactivity, flammable furnishings and any other weak spots, the biggest problem with fire safety standards in the U.S. would not be solved. The unfortunate fact is that in many areas of the country there is no one around to make sure the code is followed.

"A code is no better than its enforcement," says NFPA Vice President and Chief Engineer Richard E. Stevens, echoing fire experts nationwide. Although he says enforcement authorities are generally "dedicated people," Stevens claims that their departments are frequently understaffed and poorly supplied with resources and funding.

Poor enforcement was largely to blame for the MGM Grand Hotel fire, according to early reports on investigations of the blaze. The building had been altered in several locations, in violation of the applicable codes, in ways that allowed fire and smoke to spread more easily. More frequent and thorough inspections or more adamant code enforcement might have prevented some of those violations.

Stevens points out that some states lack a state fire marshal entirely and that many rural areas of the country have little or nothing in the way of fire or building codes, since there would be nobody to enforce them if the codes were adopted.

Even the better inspection departments find themselves wrapped in the straitjacket of inadequate funding. "I think Massachusetts has as good an enforcement as you'll find anywhere in the country," says Charles Dinezio, executive director of the state's building commission. "But the fact remains that it isn't economically feasible to have enough inspectors to really do all the work."

Thomas Skowronski, a fire prevention engineer in the Chicago Fire Department, would like to see hotels, hospitals, restaurants and other buildings holding high concentrations of people inspected by the department once a month. But a manpower shortage in the department makes that task impossible. "With the number of people we have, I think we do a damn good job," he says. "It would be nice if we could get into all buildings at least every six months, because a situation that looks fine one day can change radically the next day. It's virtually impossible to keep right on top of the situation."

Skowronski would also like more help from the courts, which don't prosecute consistently the code violations that are found. The legal system, Skowronski says, "frustrates" the problem "by heaping on continuance after continuance."

Former Detroit building inspector Frederick K. Morris believes the deficiency of enforcement is as much the fault of lackadaisical attitudes among building officials. "Codes have become less restrictive and the building department more permissive," he says. "The building officials don't pay any attention to the code. They talk one thing and they do another."

To drive the enforcement problem home, Morris recently led an ENR reporter through Detroit's pride, the $320-million Renaissance Center, pointing out numerous violations of the city-adopted code. He noted that emergency exits that should have been at least 44 in. wide were 38 in. wide. Some stairwells lacked emergency lighting. Ceiling areas and structural members at exits were not fireproofed as they should have been. The Detroit buildings department declines to discuss the Renaissance Center conditions until it sees allegations of code violations in writing.

SYSTEMS APPROACH

Aggravating the enforcement problem is the trend toward a systems approach to fire safety, eschewing rigid code requirements in favor of individually determining whether each building's array of fire protection pluses and minuses adds up to an adequately fire-safe structure.

The detailed, knowledgeable analyses that can be required to assess each structure individually for fire performance can make an undermanned fire inspection department feel its smallness even more.

Complicating the matter as well are the still wide variations in fire and building codes throughout the U.S., despite the increasingly widespread adoption of the three major model building codes [the Standard Building Code, the Uniform Building Code, and the Building Officials and Code Administrators] and the National Fire Protection Association's Life Safety Code. There is also broad disagreement in the field of fire technology over the relative merits of different safety systems.

APATHY

In the end, any deficiencies in the U.S. fire safety system must be blamed on an apathetic public. A concerned public would put more pressure on localities to adopt a model code or a comprehensive one of its own. A concerned public would see that its buildings and fire inspectors get the funds they need when tax money is divvied up and would encourage its legislatures to establish tax breaks for sprinklers and other fire protection devices. And these measures would put the building developer's pursuit of profit in harmony with fire safety rather than in opposition to it. Most of all, more concern by the public for fire safety would cut significantly the vast number of fire deaths that

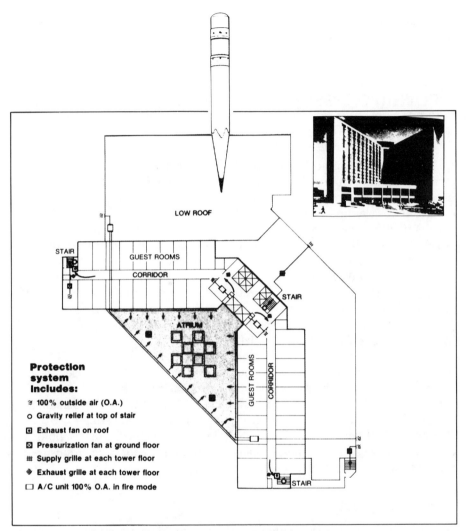

Figure 3-5 Comprehensive fire control at a new hotel in St. Louis. The building's ventilation system can remove smoke and also flush the corridors with fresh air. *(ENR.)*

occur in private residences, generally outside the supervision of fire inspectors.

"The potential for large loss of life in any property in the American community can be reduced, if not eliminated, through close attention to life safety within the buildings. Too often, however, that close attention comes only after a dramatic disaster," reports the National Fire Protection Association. "Even then, the public concern stirred by those dramatic tragedies is fleeting."

The same issue also described some of the design trends that have frustrated fire-safety efforts:

Innovative Design a Challenge

Answer: A highly refined package.

To keep up with America's appetite for innovative architecture, energy efficiency and multiuse buildings, engineers are combining the basic ingredients of fire protection—early detection, sprinklers, exits and smoke control—into ever more highly refined systems.

As buildings become more complex, they also become harder to fit into "ready-to-wear" fire-protection formulas offered by codes, says Rolf Jensen, president of Rolf Jensen & Associates Inc., Deerfield, Ill. The alternative is a "customized approach," he says, tailored to a specific building but still complying with a reasonable interpretation of a code. Jensen's firm is one of a growing number of consultants who meet this need by specializing in fire-protection engineering. Some large A-Es and mechanical-electrical engineers have set up in-house groups specializing in this field.

To make fire protection even more complicated, it can take years before provisions for new design trends—enclosed shopping malls, huge clear-span exhibit halls and now high-rise atriums—work their way into the codes. "Design is usually several years ahead of codes," says Richard R. Osman, a vice president at fire-protection consultant Schirmer Engineering Corp., Deerfield, Ill. "Every enclosed mall shopping center before 1975 was built using alternatives to fire codes," he says—it takes time for code groups to catch up as new trends become popular.

ATRIUMS ANALYZED

One current trend that [has only recently been] addressed in fire codes is the stampede towards atrium design. A. Russell Maier, senior engineer at the Sverdrup Corp., St. Louis, who specializes in fire protection, says atriums aren't really a problem because they are basically "big void open spaces with very little to fuel a fire" except at the bottom. Because an atrium could fill with smoke, Maier says, fans must be provided at the top to clear it out. The one potentially serious problem, he says, is along the perimeter where corridors intersect the atrium. In these situations, fire could leap from floor to floor. The solution there is a water curtain spray along the perimeter that would douse the fire, he says.

To assure fire and smoke control in an atrium soaring 35 stories up through the Portman hotel planned for Times Square in New York City,

Figure 3-6   A rendered interior view of the great hall of the New York Exposition & Convention Center, from the entrance. Atriums, not widely covered by fire codes, need special attention. Many cities are now considering enforcement. *(New York Exposition & Convention Center.)*

designers commissioned a study by Paul R. DeCicco and Robert J. Cresci of the Polytechnic Institute of New York. Tests used a 60:1 scale model of the hotel, and fires were simulated by injecting smoke and helium gas. The study recommended improvements in the capacity and location of emergency air-handling units, which have now been adopted.

HANDLE WITH CARE

DeCicco says atrium designs are not inherently less safe than traditional ones. But both because they are unusual and because they almost always involve high-rise, high-occupancy, multiuse structures, he believes they should receive special attention in fire and smoke protection. One advantage of an atrium is that "you can see a lot more and a fire is discoverable," he says. But since it can fill with smoke, it should have not only roof exhaust fans, he says, but also manually operated exhaust openings as a backup.

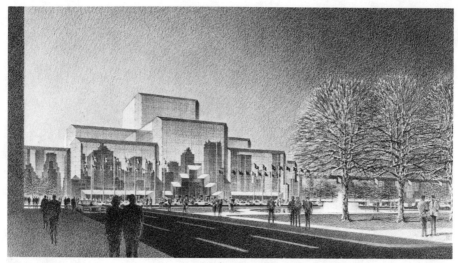

Figure 3-7   Another view of the New York Exposition & Convention Center. This exhibit hall, under construction in New York City, emphasizes sprinklers and quick exits. *(New York Exposition & Convention Center.)*

One atrium building given very special attention was the Old Post Office restoration in Washington, D.C. Bert M. Cohn, senior vice president at fire-protection consultant Gage-Babcock & Associates, Inc., Elmhurst, Ill., says the building's 200-ft-high interior court and open stairways presented problems, and, at the same time, some fire protection alternatives were ruled out because important historic features could have been destroyed.

The final protection plan includes automatic sprinklers throughout the building, the addition of three new enclosed stair towers and smoke vents at the top of the atrium. To show that the building could be evacuated before becoming filled with smoke, Gage-Babcock prepared a smoke development analysis to calculate how long it would take for dangerous carbon monoxide concentrations to be reached along the escape routes.

CHANGES CAN SNOWBALL

Peter K. Schontag, of the FPE Group, San Francisco, points out that every time a change is made in a building whether for restoration, new occupants or an energy-conservation retrofit, the building's fire protection system must be reevaluated. A structure that is well protected as a warehouse may be poorly protected as an office building, he says. And as an energy measure, for example, "If polyurethane foam insulation is added to the interior, it can drastically change the combustibility," he says.

Some engineers say that energy conservation has brought more sophisticated controls on mechanical equipment, a plus for fire protection.

But Sverdrup's Maier warns that the trend toward reducing the size of fans and air-handling equipment and minimizing the amount of outside air brought in can be a danger. "We must be careful not to minimize the ventilation system for smoke control," he says.

At the 18-story Sheraton St. Louis Hotel, for example, along with sprinklers, automatic detectors, an assured water source, emergency announcements to guest rooms and emergency power, the safety program relies on a high-powered ventilation system to remove smoke. At the same time, the system pumps in a continuous supply of outside air originating from the same points as the protected escape routes.

WIDE-OPEN SPACES

Huge volume exhibit halls also require a special approach to fire protection. Rolf Jensen says his firm developed highly individualized plans for two such projects now under construction on opposite coasts—the New York Exposition and Convention Center in New York City and the George R. Moscone Convention Center in San Francisco.

At the New York center, designed by I. M. Pei & Partners, New York City, the life-safety system includes protection of the huge steel space frame above the 1.8-million-sq-ft structure with fireproofing and sprinklers. The sprinkler system is also sized to handle the high fuel loads of double-tiered exhibition booths that may contain combustibles.

At the Moscone Center, designed by the San Francisco office of

Figure 3-8 Chicago's giant McCormick Place exhibit hall was gutted in 1967. Its steel roof trusses were unprotected against fire. *(United Press International.)*

Hellmuth, Obata & Kassabaum, Inc., fire protection is complicated because most of the exhibit space is 30 ft underground. In addition to sprinklers and smoke detectors, the building requires a special smoke removal system. Because additional structures may be built above the exhibit hall, the building couldn't be conventionally vented. Another concern was adequate exits—the hall has 18 stairways each 20 ft wide that provide a straight run to grade.

System that OK's Materials Does a Job

But it doesn't cover everything.

Building components and materials that affect fire safety have to meet acceptance criteria ranging from nothing more than buyer approval to certification of the products' behavior in specified tests.

The latter criteria are written into a great many local and regional building and fire codes that apply as a matter of law within particular jurisdictions. They are also written into various model codes such as those of the International Conference of Building Officials, the Southern Building Code Congress and the Building Officials Conference of America (BOCA).

The model codes have no legal force of their own but they have a pervasive effect on codes that are law across the U.S. The model codes are widely adopted in whole or in part by local and regional legislative bodies. This is no anomaly. Local and regional building officials, members of the model-code organizations, write the models, aided by input from other members representing test laboratories, professional and trade associations and other reservoirs of expertise.

Paul Heilstadt, deputy executive director of BOCA, says, "Model codes in toto probably make up 90 to 95% of the codes in existence." He says most sizable building-code jurisdictions in the country are represented among the members of one or another of the model-code groups.

The most widely applied fire-safety standards for materials and those with the longest history of use relate to the components of the structure—columns, walls, beams, floors, etc.—and are aimed mainly at preserving structural integrity. The reason is that fire protection has traditionally focused on prevention of property damage, where the economic imperative lay. Although structural integrity confers obvious life-safety benefits, insurance rates rose or fell according to the perceived risk of building damage rather than the risk of personal injury or loss of life.

From a purely economic point of view, this bias still exists. According to

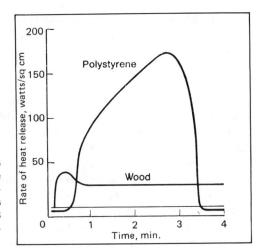

Figure 3-9 Heat-release rates of various materials differ. The rate of wood is relatively constant, while polystyrene starts burning slowly, then peaks at 3 times the burning rate of a similar volume of wood. *(ENR.)*

R. H. Wildt, structural consultant, Bethlehem Steel Corp., "Insurance on a building is usually effective only on structure and contents, not occupants. The economics of this situation, therefore, have forced much of the fire-protection [study to concentrate on] structural components and their resistance to fire."

But the personal safety aspect is becoming more persuasive. Rising social pressures, perhaps part of the great consumerism movement of recent years, are influencing the attitudes of owners, designers and code authorities more strongly in ways not related to economics. And the economic pressures may be shifting too, particularly where buildings are occupied by large numbers of people who can sue (employees of the owners sometimes can't).

The hourly fire-resistance ratings assigned to building components are almost universal. Other widely regulated fire-behavior properties of materials include heat load, a measure of the total heat the combustibles in a space would release if burned; smoke production or density; and flame spread, a measure of the speed at which flame will travel along a combustible material.

Researchers are finding evidence that these may not be enough. For example, the National Bureau of Standards' Center for Fire Research is working to refine measurement of how fast burning materials release heat. That rate, say the researchers, has more effect than total heat in producing flashover, which occurs when a room where materials are burning and heat and combustion products are building up suddenly is engulfed in fire.

When flashover occurs, says Frederic Clarke, director of the center for fire research, it immediately reduces the survival chances of occupants within several rooms of the fire. "Before flashover, extinguishment or escape is likely," he says. "After flashover, all bets are off."

The rate of heat buildup can be controlled, Clarke says, by careful selection of construction materials and furnishings.

To illustrate the differing heat release rates of two materials, the center uses a hypothetical example of two burning desks, one wood, the other polystyrene. The wood releases heat at a relatively low, uniform rate. The polystyrene rate peaks at an intensity nearly four times as high in less than three minutes. . . .

A major objective of the research supported by NBS and others is to perfect mathematical modeling of fires. Input data would include size, contents, arrangement, etc. of an actual room, and materials behavior determined in small-scale fire tests. The computerized model would then indicate what would happen in a real fire.

Bethlehem's Wildt also sees inadequacies in present building regulations. "Our codes do not recognize the way real fires burn," he says. He does not suggest reducing the two and three-hour protection provided by most occupancy requirements now, but he cites a test fire that showed "how an actual fire burns in an actual room." It peaked in 16 minutes and started to die down in 20.

Another inadequacy seen by Wildt and others in code provisions on materials arises from the rapid introduction of new materials. "During the late 1950s and early '60s," says Wildt, "a prolific growth of new protection materials and innovations overpowered the system of conceive-test-market."

Plastics in building components and contents are arousing some concern. A team of medical investigators reported in the *Journal of the American Medical Association* that in studying a series of fire injuries, they had found persuasive evidence that some fires where plastics are present produce significant quantities of cyanogens and hydrogen chloride, and that at least one fireman had died from exposure to the gas.

Plastics are getting the rap for other things, according to Jerome F. Carroll, director of safety, Society of the Plastics Industry. "Manmade materials are not all that different from natural materials in fires," he says. Carroll cites a study done of actual fires in Boston by the Harvard School of Public Health with grants from SPI and the National Fire Prevention and Control Administration. Among the conclusions were that carbon monoxide and acrolein were the most hazardous substances in those fires. Carroll says carbon monoxide is the primary toxic gas in fires whether or not plastics are involved.

The NBS fire research center supports Carroll's view. The bureau's publication *NBS/Dimensions* reported in 1979: "CFR-supported research indicates that carbon monoxide—a combustion product from nearly every burning object—is the predominant toxicant in fire injuries and death." And it is the toxicants that kill, says the bureau, in the same article. "Most fire-related fatalities are associated not with burns, but with the inhalation of toxic combustion products in smoke."

Therein lies an important limitation of codes from a life-safety viewpoint:

Figure 3-10 It could have been worse. No one was killed and only a half dozen were injured when fire erupted on the sixteenth floor of an office building on Park Avenue in New York on June 23, 1980. Many office workers were trapped above the fire floor of this 42-story structure, however. *(United Press International.)*

They don't—and probably never will—regulate much of the combustible material that might be brought into buildings. Furniture and furnishings are largely unregulated, and enough potential generators of those "toxic combustion products" can be installed to make the smoke-producing properties of the building components irrelevant.

So beyond complying with the mandatory provisions of building and fire codes, owners and occupants must exercise choices of their own that affect life safety. However, they need not be unaided. The same research and testing community that provides the data used to rate building components produces a wealth of information on test methods and fire behavior of materials. And building and fire officials counsel as well as enforce.

New York City's fire department, for example, compiles nonbinding "advisory provisions" on office furniture and furnishings that spell out the recommended fire properties of furniture (down to waste baskets, coat racks and chair webbing), draperies, curtains and carpets. The document identifies the recognized tests used to determine the properties so that a buyer or consultant can use the information to specify requirements in terms understood everywhere in the country.

New London School Explosion, 1937

Pause a moment and let the number sink in: 455 dead. Almost all of them schoolchildren. Most of the high school population of an entire rural region of Texas killed instantly as a gas explosion ripped through a seemingly solid, well-cared-for building only 4 years old.

It happened March 18, 1937. And except for the number of deaths, the incident was not all that unusual. All over the United States, communities were beginning to convert from "town gas," mainly methane from sewage treatment and the coking of coal, to the use of cheap, newly available natural gas. Many explosions and fires occurred as plumbing and fixtures designed to handle town gas were called upon to contain a natural gas mixture that included more energetic ethane and other hydrocarbons. Ventilation systems that easily dispersed methane often allowed the heavier gaseous hydrocarbons to collect unnoticed, until a spark set off an explosion.

Two months before the New London disaster, the school had been switched away from a gas utility. Instead, the separate gas heaters in each classroom were hooked to a new supply—a nearby oil field "gas stripper." The stripper pulled dissolved natural gas out of crude oil, so that the oil could be more safely shipped. The change seemed like a good bargain from all sides, since the school received fuel at low cost and the oil drillers got rid of an unwanted by-product. Otherwise, the gas would have been "flared off" in the field.

Figure 3-11   Not much was left of this New London, Texas, high school after a gas explosion that killed 455. *(ENR File.)*

Unfortunately, the natural gas right from the field did not contain any artificial odorants that would have warned of unwanted leaks. The school's basement—an area almost 300 feet long—was served by only four small vents. Evidently, this system had been adequate to prevent the buildup of methane, but it was unable to deal with the heavier natural gas. The result was detailed in ENR on March 25, 1937:

Gas Explosion in Texas School Wrecks Building, Killing 455

After a week of questioning by a Texas National Guard court of inquiry, the events and conditions which preceded the explosion that wrecked the New London, Texas consolidated rural high school on March 18, killing 455 persons, are being fitted into a logical pattern. The school, an E-shaped assembly of buildings in which the center stem was three stories high and the wings one and two stories, was heated with individual gas-fired radiators in each room, the gas being piped in from a nearby oil field.

Formerly the gas had been purchased from a utility company, but in January a connection was made to a waste gas line from a natural gasoline stripping plant. In some manner this gas escaped, and, being odorless, accumulated undetected in some confined space. The latest testimony inclines toward the theory that the collection chamber was an unventilated subbasement some 300-ft. long beneath the three-story center building and that an electric switch on a sanding machine in the manual training department, near a trap door into this space, supplied the ignition spark.

An earlier theory, advanced by E. O. Schoch, professor of chemistry at the University of Texas and a member of the court of inquiry, was that the gas accumulated in the hollow tile back-up walls. This was held to be possible since each of the 52 individual radiators was vented into tile conduits in the wall leading up to the roof loft. Although the conduits were plastered, it is held that breaks in the plaster at the joints would have permitted gas to escape into the adjacent hollow tile.

The buildings were of steel frame construction, wall columns supporting the roof trusses. The floors were concrete slabs and the walls hollow tile faced with brick. The architect of the school, which was about four years old, was T. Roy Ainsworth of Houston.

Officials moved swiftly and surely to investigate the tragedy and apply its lessons. Within 2 weeks, Dr. David J. Price, an explosion expert from the old federal Bureau of Chemistry and Soils, had delivered a preliminary assessment to Texas Governor Allred. The preliminary report called for malodorants to be used in all gas supplies, and the "application of gas indicators to detect presence of escaping combustible gases at percentages below the lower limit of explosibility and development of alarm systems and warning devices for school houses and public buildings."

Dr. Price also called for inspection of heating and lighting devices that used gas—many public and private buildings had not yet been converted to electric lighting, especially in rural areas—and the careful inspection and ventilation of basements and other storage areas. Three weeks later—only a month after the accident itself—all the experts handed in their final reports. They were summarized in ENR's April 22, 1937, issue:

Gas in Basement Caused Blast

All investigators agree New London school explosion caused by gas leak in basement.

All reports of investigators of the explosion that wrecked the high school at New London, Texas, on March 18, resulting in the death of 455 persons, agree that the primary cause was the ignition, from a spark of an electric switch, of a mixture of gas and air in the unventilated basement. Experts of the U.S. Bureau of Mines further conclude that the gas leaked from gas lines and their fittings suspended in this basement beneath the first floor and that the gas did not seep through the soil from the surrounding gas and oil field. This latter point was determined by sinking 71 test holes to rock and subjecting the atmosphere in them to gas detector apparatus.

In the final report of the U.S. Bureau of Chemistry and Soils (preliminary report, ENR, April 8, 1937, p. 535), it is pointed out that the most explosive mixture possible with the gas used would have contained only 6.5 per cent gas and 93.5 per cent air. The Bureau of Mines points out that since the ignited gas was in an enclosed and substantially confined space, little or no opportunity existed for expansion at low pressure. Hence maximum opportunity was afforded to build up a high pressure as the explosion wave progressed, resulting in widespread destructive effects. It also concludes that the results would have been the same regardless of the composition of natural gas present.

In an extensive review of the various investigations made, the Texas Inspection Bureau, representing fire underwriters, states that "the much publicized theory of accumulated gas in the hollow tile walls was started through ignorance of the conditions, since there was no way in which free gas could enter the walls and, further, it was not a wall explosion. Also, while the whole question of the heater installation is subject to criticism, it had no bearing whatever on the explosion."

According to the Texas Inspection Bureau, Dallas, Texas, the school building was of good construction and planned for reasonable safety but the excessive area of concealed space under the building (254 × 58 ft.) filled with gas pipes and electrical circuits and without ventilation, was a serious fault. The four small vents in this area were not only too small and too few but were so far apart that they could not create circulation.

> While the gas heater vents did not contribute to the disaster ... the evidence shows disregard for the hazard of non-ventilated gas fires in crowded schoolrooms. In this respect, the school officials, architects and heater salesmen were equally at fault. The few attempts to ventilate into the dead space of a blank wall, where no flues existed, were obvious deceptions to cover up an omission. ... Practically all faults of construction and installation in the building were due to lack of supervising power such as would apply in communities having city ordinances. It serves to focus attention to the need of state laws on standard construction as well as approved standards for the installation of heating systems and electrical equipment in public buildings.

The Bureau of Mines report also urges a state supervising body to inspect public buildings lying outside the corporate limits of cities and towns, stating that the inspection should extend not only to the construction, but also to plans and designs of such buildings, and including the structural features as well as the details of heating and ventilation.

The reports, combined with the public attention and the magnitude of the tragedy, led to numerous changes in local building codes across the United States. The most common provisions called for better ventilation of closed spaces.

Some localities also took note of the need for better ventilation of gas space heaters. Today, unvented gas heaters are almost universally banned. This is not the case, however, with unvented kerosene units. Such heaters are enjoying renewed popularity, thanks to the high cost of heating oil. Already there have been reports of explosions caused by the improper use of such heaters—particularly the use of gasoline rather than kerosene to fuel them. The gasoline readily evaporates, creating a highly explosive mixture in unvented spaces.

Fire at Livonia, 1953

The huge General Motors transmission plant at Livonia, Michigan, seemed impervious to fire. After all, it was framed in steel, with brick and steel walls. Inside, 4200 workers handled the casting, stamping, and assembling of metal

Figure 3-12   Fire fighters could do little but let the General Motors plant at Livonia, Michigan, burn; their hoses couldn't send water far enough into the huge building to make any difference. *(General Motors.)*

pieces, not dangerously combustible chemicals. On August 12, 1953, fire proved the experts wrong. The 4-year-old plant, all 1,500,000 square feet of it, was totally destroyed. Fortunately, only three workers lost their lives. But the damage—$55 million—set an all-time record for industrial fires. If a similar fire occurred today, the damage would be well over $200 million.

A welding torch had ignited a pan of oleum, used to clean and preserve the parts before shipping. The oleum in turn ignited cutting oils. Workers tried fighting the fire with carbon dioxide extinguishers, and then with water, which only spread the oil-fed flames. The plant's wood-block floor, which had soaked up oil from machining operations, burst into flames as well.

The intense heat quickly buckled the unprotected steel framing, sending burning tar from the roof to feed the inferno. Metal chips turned red-hot and burst into flames.

When it was all over, General Motors would comment only that the plant had been built in conformity with applicable codes and operated in conformity with fire-safety regulations and insurance company guidelines. Livonia fire chief Calvin Roberts agreed, noting that the plant was as well protected as "90 percent of industrial plants."

Numerous safety inquiries were made into the cause of the fire and into measures that might be taken to keep such disasters from happening again. Perhaps the most complete was the investigation of the National Fire Protection Association, summarized in ENR October 15, 1953:

Findings Made on General Motors Blaze

Lack of fire walls, sprinklers held responsible for huge loss but no significant building design changes foreseen.

Seven factors are listed by the National Fire Protection Association as responsible for the destruction on Aug. 12 of the General Motors Corp. automatic-transmission plant at Livonia, Mich. [ENR, Aug. 20, p. 28], reputed to be the biggest industrial fire loss on record.

Present indications are, however, that no significant changes in building design will result from the NFPA findings because of costs and production problems involved.

A final report on the $55-million disaster in the NFPA Oct., 1953, *Quarterly,* blames:

1. An undivided fire area of 1,502,500 sq ft (34.5 acres) in which absence of fire walls and roof vents denied access for fire fighting and prevented localization of heat and smoke.

2. Inadequate sprinkler protection (only 20% of the total area protected—no sprinklers where fire started).

3. Incompletely engineered processes. Fire protection for the dip tank did not protect the drip pan [under a conveyor immersing parts in oil in the dip tank]. Due to the processes, oily deposits had a tendency to accumulate and increase the fire hazard of the several heat-treating areas ; yet this condition does not appear to have received engineering attention.

4. Unprotected steel construction, in particular the thin steel deck that did not offer sufficient insulation between banking heat and the builtup roof covering to prevent asphalt from melting and dripping through joints of the heat-warped deck. Steel trusses collapsed in a matter of minutes.

5. Use of oxy-acetylene torch under unsafe conditions.

6. Lack of an effective private fire brigade.

7. Delayed fire department notification.

The transmission plant, designed by the GM Argonaut Realty Division, had been built in 1949. It was mostly one story high, with a two-story section at one end. Framing was unprotected structural steel, with columns spaced 40 and 48 ft apart. The exterior consisted of brick apron walls and large areas of glass. The flat roof was composed of light-gage steel decking covered on top with asphalt-mopped layers of "tar paper," ¾-in. thick glass fiber insulation, several more layers of asphalt-mopped "tar paper," and tar-and-gravel surfacing.

FIRE SPREAD SWIFTLY

According to the NFPA report, the fire was started by sparks from an oxy-acetylene cutting torch igniting oil in a conveyor drip pan nearly 11 ft above the floor. (The conveyor immersed metal parts in rust-inhibiting liquid in a dip tank. This liquid had a 97.7-F flash point.) Discovered by the welding crew, the fire was immediately attacked with two carbon-dioxide extinguishers from a ladder; but when the extinguishers were emptied the flames spread along the 120-ft length of the drip pan.

The drip pan warped, spilling its flaming contents on the wood-block floor. Oily condensate on steel roof members in a nearby heat-treatment area ignited. And despite the efforts of a plant fire brigade, hot tar and asphalt soon flowed through cracks between strips in the heat-warped roof deck, caught fire and dispersed the fire fighters. Three men, including the fire brigade chief, however, were trapped and killed. Meanwhile, about 4,200 other employees had evacuated the building without serious injury.

The Michigan State Fire Marshal believes there was a delay of 15 to 20 minutes before one of the plant protection men telephoned the Livonia fire department. A GM official, though, estimates the elapsed time as 6 minutes.

Upon arrival, the Livonia fire companies found the 400-ft southern end of the building in flames. Twenty hose streams were put in operation on all

Figure 3-13 Looking down into the fire-ruined Livonia plant, one can see the unprotected steel columns and the cinder-block wall that failed to stop the fire's front. *(Associated Press.)*

sides, but since the building was 866 ft wide and hose streams could penetrate only 50 to 75 ft, manual fire fighting had little effect, the NFPA report says. The fire could not be extinguished and finally burned itself out the following day.

OTHER FIRES SIMILAR

The NFPA report calls attention also to the similarity of this disaster to other large-loss industrial fires reported in 1952. Excessive areas without fire division walls were noted as contributing factors in 66% of those fires. In 32%, flammable liquids contributed to the spread of fire, and in 70% of the plants automatic protection was lacking. Lack of employee training resulted in delayed alarms being sent to the fire department in 21% of the cases.

Questioning of architect-engineer firms which have designed many plants for the automotive industry indicates that no significant changes may be expected in plant design as a consequence of the fire. Some engineers say they will give more consideration to insulating-type roof decks, such as concrete or gypsum plank. But they do not believe installation of fire walls in an assembly plant is feasible, because of the conveyors needed.

FORD EXPERIENCE

The GM fire has done little to alter thinking at the Ford Motor Co. In 1952, Ford had suffered a serious fire at its Livonia tank plant, which caused a revision then in plans for future construction. No further revision now seems necessary.

Immediately after its Livonia fire, Ford converted from a self-insured basis to purchased insurance. That step offered the benefit of inspections by an outside agency. In addition, Ford established a fire controller's office, which works closely with insurance company inspectors.

Nevertheless, Ford and the insurance companies disagree on some fire-protective measures. The insurance companies prefer that all plants be equipped completely with sprinklers. Because of the cost, Ford is not convinced that full sprinkler coverage is warranted.

Ford engineers do not look favorably on fire walls either. But they are considering fire curtains, hung as far down from the roof as possible without interfering with manufacturing operations.

Industrial architects were remarkably slow in applying the lessons learned at Livonia. They argued that modern plants need large, unobstructed spaces,

Figure 3-14 The McCormick Place fire, which occurred in 1967, 15 years after the Livonia fire. Here, too, note the unprotected framing. *(United Press International.)*

precluding the use of fire walls inside. Protection of all interior spaces with sprinklers would be too expensive, they contended.

Slowly, however, many modifications have been made to plant design, to reduce the rate at which fire can spread. Most important, design codes restricted the use of combustible tar in built-up roofs. Gypsum board, concrete, Styrofoam panels, and other materials took its place. Automatic fire doors have become common, although for reasons of plant efficiency, large areas often remain open, rather than being subdivided by fire walls, or even fire curtains. Extra-hazardous operations, such as paint spraying, are often relegated to separate buildings or to carefully segregated areas within a large plant.

Sprinklers have become more common, too. Nevertheless, it is rare that an entire plant floor will be protected by sprinklers, even in the newest plants.

Some jurisdictions also still allow unprotected steel framing—especially since one favorite method of insulating framing against fire, the use of sprayed-on asbestos-cement, has been banned due to health problems.

The chief line of defense against fires, therefore, is often good plant housekeeping to prevent the buildup of inflammable materials, combined with good employee safety-training programs.

Our Lady of the Angels School, 1958

The fire fighters arrived at the school less than 3 minutes after the alarm was sounded. The fire was officially "struck out" an hour later. In that short time, ninety children and three nuns were fatally injured by flames and dense smoke. Partitions, ceilings, and part of the timber-supported roof had collapsed almost immediately, trapping pupils in their classrooms. Dense smoke quickly spread from the basement up stairwells unprotected by fire doors. The smoke then jumped into classrooms, spreading quickly along interior corridors.

Adding to the pain, the building had been inspected only 2 months prior to the fire, and had been given a passing grade by Chicago fire officials. ENR reported the story on December 11, 1958:

Chicago Fire Stirs Safety Plans

Accumulated rubbish. Fire. A stairwell acting as a flue. Wooden stairs. Open corridor. No sprinklers. And 92 dead.

That's the story of the fire at Chicago's Our Lady of the Angels School last week in which 89 children and three nuns perished. [Another person later died of burns suffered in the blaze.]

Figure 3-15 Our Lady of the Angels School. The fire started in the basement below a stairwell, and shot up to the second floor. *(United Press International.)*

A stairwell apparently acted as a flue for a fire that started in the basement—cause unknown. Best guess is it originated in an accumulation of paper and rubbish under the stairs leading to the first and second floors.

The flames climbed up the wooden stairs to the first floor, where they were blocked by a pair of steel doors to the first floor corridor. Then they shot up to the second floor to find an open archway to the corridor.

The fire may hold special meaning for the construction industry. In cities throughout the country officials are now re-examining their own schools, asking themselves: "Could it happen here?" . . .

The building is U-shaped. The stairs that burned were in the rear, at the outside of one bend in the U. There is a fire escape outside the bottom of the U.

The other side of the U—the south wing—was relatively undamaged.

Each of the two wings has three stairwells, two at the front and one at the rear, and none is protected by so-called fire doors.

The stairways are of ordinary timber frame construction. Partitions are timber framed with lath and plastering and the roof is ordinary tar paper and gravel on timber rafters and purlins.

Exterior walls are load-bearing with brick construction chiefly, although there appears to be some concrete construction. The building is not protected by a sprinkler system.

About 1,200 pupils were in the school on December 1 when the fire broke out.

One of the mysteries is that the smoke that poured up the ill-starred northeast stairwell so quickly was "oil type" dense and black. Burning linoleum could have been the cause.

There was no explosion when the fire started. Some evidence indicates the fire may have been smoldering for some time before being noticed.

Another point hard to understand is how the smoke and fire spread so rapidly upward, along the corridors and into the classrooms on the second floor. The fire's speed apparently panicked many children into immobility. Many fatalities were caused by suffocation or inhalation of the super-heated fumes.

Each wing is about 60 ft wide and 120 ft long and contains eight classrooms on each floor. The classrooms are high-ceilinged and have considerable wood trim. Most of the fire damage, or at least the worst of the damage is in the northeast corner of the north wing, where the fire started, and along the north side of this wing. The stairs in the north wing stairwells are burned and badly charred.

The structure was built in 1910 and remodeled in 1951. It passed a regular inspection by city officials in October.

This stairwell, about 15 ft wide and 25 ft long, has six flights of stairs.

Within a month, Illinois had tightened its fire code for schools. The state required the following items to be installed in every school building by the end of 1959:

- A standard fire-alarm system
- Completely enclosed stairwells, sealed off with material able to resist fires for 1 hour
- Noncombustible acoustical materials (outlawing wood fiberboard)
- Walls and partitions able to withstand fire for 1 hour, minimum
- Adequate exit signs, fire escape signs, and directional signals, with lighting operating from electrical circuits separated from other circuits in the building
- Noncombustible, 2-hour fire-resistant floors over basements; first-floor ceilings of mineral acoustical tile backed by noncombustible materials if ceilings are suspended; flooring on upper stories with a minimum 1-hour fire rating
- Furnace rooms separated from other rooms by fire doors and equipped with fire-resistant walls and ceilings
- Self-closing exit doors, opening outward

The state also required installation of automatic sprinkler systems in schools where the "type of construction or occupancy" makes them necessary in the opinion of local fire marshalls. State officials estimated that only 1 percent of all schools would be sprinklered under that provision.

Chicago officials were active as well; three fire-safety ordinances were passed in the first month after the disaster.

It often happens after a fire causes great loss of life or property that public attention is riveted on less serious blazes, all across the country. Fires that would not normally be national news—because they don't involve loss of life— are reported fully on the evening news. Local governments take stock in their own safety laws. Six weeks after the Chicago disaster, on January 22, 1959, ENR reported the nation's mood this way:

Why Schools Are Not Fire Safe

"It Could Happen Here."

So read the headline of the *Providence Journal* one day last month.

Five days later, it did happen. A century-old school in North Providence burned to the ground.

Fortunately it was Sunday. No one was in the building; the incident made no national headlines.

But it demonstrated graphically that the recent Chicago school fire that killed 93 persons wasn't an isolated, freak accident.

No one contends that schools can be made 100% fire safe. But in the past month, numerous communities have been finding that their own schools do not comply with even the most basic fire protection principles.

Schools with open stairwells, inadequate exits, highly inflammable interior finishes, poor alarm systems, rubbish stored in open areas—all the factors that contributed to the Chicago tragedy and more—are being discovered in towns and cities of every size and description. A few examples:

- Philadelphia officials found 96% of the schools violating the fire code or tolerating unsafe conditions.
- Detroit investigators found 57 schools that had been constructed before the 1912 building code established standards for fire-resistant construction.
- Kentucky's state fire marshal estimated that the Chicago disaster could be duplicated in 75% of Kentucky's schools.
- Milwaukee investigators charged 10 new schools with building code safety violations.
- New York City closed 36 schools after fire department inspections turned up serious fire violations. After second inspections, 28 were allowed to reopen. Nearly 3,700 violations were found in the 2,000 schools inspected. The fire department now plans semi-annual inspections.

The big questions: Why do such conditions exist? How can they be corrected?

TO BLAME: BUILDING CODES

Major blame for present school conditions can be attributed to inadequate and insufficient building codes and enforcement.

Some cities and states have adequate, up-to-date building codes, rigorously enforced. But they are exceptions to the rule.

Chicago has a building code covering schools. But it was adopted in 1949 and it's not retroactive to schools built earlier.

That is typical of many municipalities. It is the older schools that require corrective measures most urgently.

Other communities are covered by codes so antiquated that some of the building products called for are no longer being manufactured. Every structure built in such areas must, therefore, violate the code in some way.

Some areas have an adequate school code made virtually worthless because it is unenforced.

And some towns have no school building code at all.

In some states, a state agency has jurisdiction over school construction; in others, local authorities enforce the rules. In still others there's a combination of the two—and no one is quite sure who is responsible for what.

Result: Too much enforcement some of the time; not enough most of the time.

Other Factors Responsible for Existing School Problems: Apathy of local citizenry; lack of understanding on the part of educators; dearth of school funds; penny-wise, pound-foolish school boards; and architects who allow unsafe designs to be used.

Government red tape and local politics can also cause trouble. And there are indications that some manufacturers of combustible building materials lobby against revision of code requirements.

WHAT THEY'RE DOING

Most communities inspected their schools immediately after the Chicago fire. The findings are now coming in, and attempts are being made to remedy defects.

A number of old schools have been condemned and abandoned. Repairs have begun on others. Inspectors are checking carefully for housekeeping violations.

Other measures are coming. Some municipalities and townships plan to spend millions of dollars to make their schools fire-safe. Plans are afoot to revise building codes or adopt new ones. Responsibilities for school building supervision are being more carefully delineated.

MGM Grand Hotel Fire, 1980

The MGM Grand Hotel in Las Vegas reopened about a year after a November 21, 1980, fire had left 85 dead and 500 injured. Included in the $50 million reconstruction: An extra $5 million for the very latest in fire-protection devices. The MGM fire started at a short circuit in wiring behind a refrigerated pastry display case—wiring that had been improperly installed. It spread unseen in its early stages, thanks in part to poor construction work and in part to breaches in firewalls—holes made after the building went into service, to accommodate new ductwork and wiring.

The public's memory of the tragedy lingers on, however, not so much because of the MGM fire itself as because there was a cluster of hotel fires all at about the same time. The MGM blaze was followed by arson at the Las Vegas Hilton nearby and by an explosive fire at the Stauffer's Inn in Westchester County, just north of New York City.

As a result, fire codes and inspection procedures are being changed all

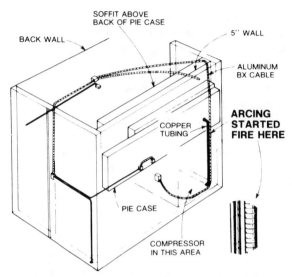

Figure 3-16   The MGM Grand Hotel fire started in wiring behind a refrigerated pastry case. *(ENR.)*

across the country. Still to be settled are a staggering $1 billion in death and injury claims at MGM.

Here's how *Engineering News-Record* began covering the story, on November 27, 1980:

MGM Grand Hotel Victim of Old Code

Clark County fire officials blame the 84 deaths [another victim died later] and 500 injuries in last week's disastrous MGM Grand Hotel fire on three main things; the lack of sprinklers in the hotel's casino, the failure of the manual alarm system and smoke that billowed up the hotel's stairwells and elevator shafts and entered the building's air handling system.

In the opinion of some fire researchers, the Las Vegas fire also underscored the need for emergency systems to control smoke, the major cause of death at the MGM Grand.

The seven-year-old hotel had no sprinkler system to douse the casino fire, which consumed the 200,000-sq-ft gambling area in 10 minutes. Nevada fire marshal's regulations did not require sprinkler systems in high-rises until July, 1979. "The theory was that in an area where people were present 24 hours a day, no fire would go unnoticed," says Stuart J. Mason, president of the Las Vegas-based Taylor Construction Co., which built the MGM Grand.

The hotel did have sprinkler systems in convention areas and in the two showrooms in the main floor, however, and these sprinklers did retard the spread of the fire, according to a fire department spokesman.

The hotel had manually operated alarm boxes on each floor, but no alarm sounded to warn guests of the early morning fire. Clark County Fire Chief Roy E. Parrish speculates that the casino fire may have burnt out the wiring in the alarm system's amplifier in the basement.

MGM Hotels Board Chairman Fred Benninger says the lack of working fire alarms at the hotel "may have been a blessing in disguise" because it kept hotel guests from entering the smoke-filled hallways.

CHOKING SMOKE

Smoke from the casino fire billowed up the central elevator and stairwell shafts and entered the hotel's air handling system, asphyxiating as many as 70 of the 84 known dead. Three of the hotel's elevators were found below the casino level, where the fire started and spread, although the casino-level elevator doors were open, Parrish says.

Fire officials believe the smoke rushed up the central elevator shafts and the auxiliary stairwells alongside them. Smoke quickly filled the stairwells and spread into some floors when guests, fearing that they would be trapped in the stairs, propped open self-locking fire doors.

Figure 3-17   The massive gaming floor of the MGM Grand Hotel, before the fire. *(MGM.)*

Figure 3-18 The gaming floor of the MGM Grand Hotel, after the fire. Note the melted slot machines. *(United Press International.)*

Fire officials believe that the hotel's central air handling equipment also spread the smoke throughout the hotel.

Although the hotel did have three "smokeless stairways"—exterior stairwells perforated to allow natural ventilation—few guests used them, according to chief county fire investigator Michael Patterson. "We took people down those stairways, but no one went of his own accord," Patterson says. Most guests apparently tried to escape down the central stairs next to the main elevator bank.

BUILT BEFORE CODE CHANGES

The hotel had no smoke alarms. Changes in the Clark County Uniform Building Code in 1973 and 1976 that require smoke detectors in all hotel rooms and a public address system audible in every room did not apply to the MGM Grand, which was built on an 18-month "fast track" construction schedule in 1972 and 1973. "Smoke alarms and a sprinkler system would have made all the difference," Parrish says.

But Robert Taylor, president of the Smoke Control Association and chairman of an ASHRAE committee on the control of fire and smoke, says that a smoke control system would have been much more effective than sprinklers in preventing the many deaths at the MGM Grand. The systems, which have been extensively used in Cleveland, Denver and Atlanta, are technically proven and inexpensive, Taylor says. According to Taylor, the U.S. is behind the rest of the world in recognizing smoke control systems, which are mandated by law in Australia, Canada and Great Britain.

The systems involve fans that exhaust air from the fire floor and pressurize all other floors to prevent smoke from spreading to them. They can be set off by smoke detectors, sprinkler surge detectors or other means, Taylor says.

Fire officials say the MGM Grand is a Class One building under National Fire Protection Association guidelines, and thus has concrete floors and concrete walls separating meeting areas. "When the building was built, it was built to code," Patterson says, "the same code that applies to 80% of the hotels in this city."

Fire Chief Parrish points out that several hotels built under the former code, including the Flamingo, the Silver Slipper and the Desert Inn, have voluntarily installed smoke detectors and sprinklers during recent renovations. He adds, however, that the MGM Grand underwent a fire inspection six months ago and "it was clean."

STARTED ABOVE DELI

Las Vegas fire officials believe an electrical fire above a delicatessen restaurant touched off the three-hour blaze. Patterson says the fire started in an electrical "gutter box" and smoldered for two to three hours before spreading into a false-ceilinged catwalk directly above the hotel's 200,000-sq-ft casino. Patterson says smoke and hot gases may have built up for several more hours in the 8-ft-high "eye in the sky" catwalk, used to monitor gambling operations, before exploding downward.

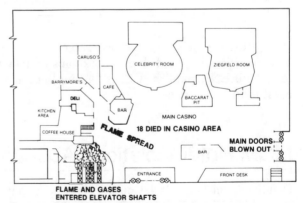

Figure 3-19 Within 6 minutes of discovery of the MGM Grand Hotel fire, it had spread through the casino and into the elevator shafts. *(ENR.)*

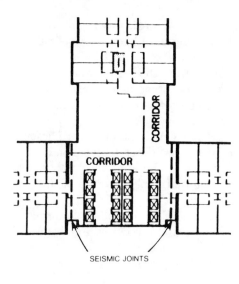

CORRIDOR

CORRIDOR

SEISMIC JOINTS

61 DIED FROM 16TH FLOOR UP

Figure 3-20 Joints designed to isolate the elevator shafts of the MGM Grand Hotel from earthquake motion were 12 inches wide; they acted as ducts for the smoke. *(ENR.)*

Construction officials at the scene estimated that the fire, which was contained on the first floor, caused $5 million to $10 million in damage to the $120-million, T-shaped, structural steel hotel. Serious fire damage was mostly limited to the casino, office and entrance areas on the main floor, and to the basement.

Patterson says he saw one I-beam that appeared to have been bent by the heat, which reached 3,000 F in some parts of the casino. Structural damage is still an open question, however.

Nonetheless, MGM's Benninger told a press conference Sunday that the hotel would be rebuilt, redecorated and reopened by July 1.

Sifting through the wreckage, safety officials soon uncovered evidence of how code violations and sloppy workmanship had allowed the fire to start and to spread. ENR published the following report on January 8, 1981, about 2 months after the tragedy:

MGM Hotel Violations Abound

Building officials in Clark County, Nev., have found building code violations in the MGM Grand Hotel in Las Vegas that they say endangered the hotel's guests.

"Code violations exist throughout the complex and hundreds contributed adversely to the life safety of the occupants," according to a memo from Building and Zoning Department Director Robert D. Weber to Clark County Manager Bruce Spaulding. The memo lists the code violations only briefly, but a more detailed report is in preparation. The Clark County Fire Department is also preparing a report based on its investigation of the hotel, in which 84 persons died in a Nov. 21 fire.

"Extensive smoke paths from casino to high-rise hotel allowed smoke to penetrate essentially all floor levels," the memo says. Among the code violations that allowed the smoke to spread were:

- Penetrations in air shafts which should have had at least a two-hour fire rating.
- Fire protection of only thin rib metal in the corridor.
- "Numerous holes" in corridor fire walls. Openings around pipes and ducts were as large as 12 sq ft, the memo says. The Uniform Building Code requires fire dampers for air ducts that penetrate through fire walls.
- Plastic pipe, the remains of which were found melted, passing through fire walls.

In addition, the memo reports, "Exiting systems were totally inadequate for code compliance." Problem areas included:

- Inadequate exit width in some areas.
- Inadequate exit signs and emergency lighting.
- Improperly fire-rated stairways and corridors.
- A south wing interior stairway in which equipment access openings were not protected by a fire door and steel flooring was not fully fire protected.

ENR followed up with a June 11, 1981, report based on the final Clark County investigation, just as the hotel was getting ready for reopening:

MGM Fire: Short Circuit to Disaster

A short circuit in a delicatessen's serving station started the fire that killed 85 guests and employees of the MGM Grand Hotel last November, according to fire department investigators. Vibrations and heat from a condenser and the chemical reaction of two dissimilar metals helped create the conditions that allowed the Las Vegas hotel fire to take hold.

In a 186-page final report, the Clark County Fire Department describes in copious and precise detail how the fire was touched off, how it spread into the 84,000-sq-ft casino and, most significantly, how its deadly smoke was able to pass so freely into the 26-story tower.

The department's investigators avoid scolding the hotel's owners about how the fire could have been prevented, however, and they assign no blame.

The hotel's 2,076 rooms are housed in a high-rise tower laid out in a T pattern. Under that spreads a low-rise section housing the casino, restaurants, nightclubs and convention rooms.

Shortly after 7 a.m. on Nov. 21, 1980, most of the restaurants hadn't opened for the day, but about 50 persons were eating breakfast in the coffee shop. Independently, two employees discovered signs of fire in the empty delicatessen next door. Within very short order the fire had engulfed much of the casino floor and smoke had migrated throughout the 2-million-sq-ft building.

The fire department's investigation began four and a half hours later. After months of examining char patterns, interviewing witnesses and testing samples, the department placed the fire's origin at a serving station in the delicatessen.

The semi-enclosed station, called a side stand, protruded 6 to 8 ft into the restaurant. Along its front wall was a refrigerated pastry display case.

The fire department found two ¼-in. copper tubes that carried refrigerant from the compressor unit in the base of the side stand to the pie case. They were wrapped in insulation to a point 40 in. above the floor, and were bare from there up.

BX cable ran alongside the copper tubing, in places touching it. Both the tubing and the cable had been enclosed by gypsum wallboard with a plywood soffit. It was in this length of BX cable, 45 in. from the floor, that the second most deadly hotel fire in U.S. history began.

GROUNDLESS

The aluminum sheathing, or raceway, of the BX cable was to have acted as a ground for the circuit. According to the fire department, this ground was sabotaged by loose connections, the result of "poor construction techniques."

Improper installation and the exposure to warm moisture over a period of years deteriorated the insulation on the wires within the raceway, and in time the bare copper was exposed. The system short circuited.

Because the installation of the raceway was faulty, the ground could not function as it was intended to. The copper wires heated up, and the aluminum raceway began to glow. There was arcing around the short circuit contact, and a flame appeared within minutes.

One factor that contributed to the fire was the contact between the copper refrigerant tubes and the aluminum raceway. Two metals in contact with one another in a moist environment are susceptible to galvanic action, an electric current from one metal to the other.

As the process continues, one or the other of the metals dissolves, depending on their relative chemical properties. In this case, the aluminum raceway gradually corroded. In addition, vibration from the compressor was rubbing the aluminum and copper together. Eventually, a hole appeared in the raceway.

The wires inside it were exposed to the warm, moist air coming from the compressor, and this is what deteriorated their insulation and caused the short.

In addition, the hot air from the condenser kept the materials within the soffit of the side stand warm, making them easier to ignite. Once they had caught, the fire spread upward and outward.

PASSED TO PLENUM

The fire consumed wood and plastic trim first, passing on to hollow false beams in the ceiling. It consumed gypsum wallboard and cellulose fiber acoustical tile. Heat from the ceiling ignited plastic-covered furniture. Eventually the fire broke into the plenum that passed not only over the deli but the entire length and width of the building.

With nearly all of the deli consumed, the flames passed into a coffee shop next door through a small bar. Once there, it got caught for a minute in the bottleneck of a narrow foyer, then erupted full-force into the casino.

The fire spread horizontally and vertically into the casino, giving off volumes of black smoke. As heat and gases built up in the room, flashover occurred. Within six minutes after the fire was discovered, the entire casino was on fire.

Pressure of the hot gases blew out the main doors of the casino, and the fire quickly consumed the carport area outside. It destroyed a protective plywood covering at the bottom level of a stairwell, and smoke shot up the stairs. Heat, smoke and flame also passed into elevator shafts through unsealed doors.

The fire spread down a hallway, but sprinklers in the hall stopped it.

Some flames passed through a deteriorated opening in the ceiling of the casino, and two guest rooms on the floor above caught fire. Fortunately, by this time firemen were dousing the fire on the main floor and clouds of steam from their hoses put out the fires up above.

"If extinguishment had not occurred as promptly as it did," the fire department speculates, "a high-rise fire would surely have ensued."

SMOKE SPREAD

Even before the first flame was noticeable, smoke was passing into the plenum and rising at every opportunity. It passed through the 12-in.-wide seismic joints running from the casino-level plenum to the top of the tower. It followed pipe chases and open shafts, particularly those not properly sealed. It passed up the stairwells and elevators it had infiltrated.

Adding to the problem were HVAC smoke dampers that were "bolted in such a manner as to make them inoperable," the fire department says.

It was this rising smoke that proved most fatal at the MGM Grand. Only 18 of the fire's 85 victims died on the casino floor. Sixty-one others died on the 16th through 26th floors. Six other victims died on unknown floors.

The owners of the MGM Grand have attempted to make the best of the disaster, moving quickly to reopen the hotel with sprinklers and other fire protection that were largely lacking previously [ENR, Mar. 19, 1981, p. 53]. Hotel President Bernard J. Rothkopf has announced that the hotel will open on July 30.

4

Dam
Failures
and
Slides

Europe's tortured rock formations are still not entirely understood by the dam builders. But failure of the rock around two thin-arch concrete dams—the French Malpasset Dam in 1959 and the Italian Vaiont Dam in 1963—helped show the way. What's more, the memory of the wave that swept over Vaiont after the abutting mountainside slid into the reservoir behind the dam led engineers in Los Angeles to order the evacuation of a section of the city just before the Baldwin Hills Reservoir failed in 1963. Thus, the tragedy of Vaiont, in which more than 2000 Italians died, helped save hundreds of American lives just a few months later.

The tragedy at Malpasset had its origin in a decade of glorious dam building that had started after World War II, and in the evolution of a design approach that had started in the 1930s. Famed dam designer André Coyne had slowly been raising the acceptable stresses in concrete dams from 355 pounds per square inch. With each new project, confidence grew. Malpasset was the thinnest-arch dam of its size in the world when it was completed in the midfifties—4.9 feet thick at its crest, 22.9 feet thick at its base, almost 200 feet high, and about 700 feet long at the top. The engineering firm of Coyne & Bellier had designed it to withstand a mean compressive strength of 680 psi.

In December 1959, after 5 days of heavy rain, Malpasset collapsed without warning, releasing 40,000 acre-feet of water into the narrow Reyran Valley and down to the Mediterranean. The water destroyed everything in its path for more than 3 miles, including road and railroad bridges. In Frejus, a town of 13,000 population, more than 4 miles downstream, over 300 people died.

It was not, however, the fragile-looking dam itself that failed. Instead, engineers later determined, failure started in clay seams only 1 or 2 inches wide, in the rock near the dam's left abutment. André Coyne had often spoken about the need for careful foundation work, however, because of the tremendous forces built up in the weight of water behind his tall and graceful structures. How could he have missed this? Coyne himself was not around to answer; he died only 6 months after the disaster, at the age of 69. The French government offered little help, either. It prosecuted one engineer on the project, and then four more; all were ultimately acquitted. The effort that went into the court cases could have been more profitably spent on careful engineering studies.

Figure 4-1 The failure of St. Francis Dam in 1928 started California thinking about the nation's first dam safety laws. The dotted lines enclose the section of the dam that remained standing after the catastrophe. *(ENR.)*

Figure 4-2 St. Francis Dam after the failure. *(ENR.)*

Figure 4-3 Only a low barrier formed by the sheared-off base of Malpasset Dam in France remained to block the scarred canyon after the failure. *(ENR.)*

The French prosecutors had tried to prove that the dam simply slipped on the clay seam—a seam that should have been taken into account while the dam was being designed, the prosecutor alleged. To this day, many engineers think of the tragedy in those simple terms. In a letter to the editor of *Engineering News-Record,* published November 2, 1967, P. Londe of Coyne & Bellier explained that the problem wasn't so simple:

It is true that the geological formation of the Malpasset foundation rock did contain such a seam. In point of fact, it was a shear fault, similar to the faults encountered in most dam foundations.

Several years of exhaustive rock mechanics studies and research have now made it possible to understand what really happened at Malpasset.

The failure, which was of an explosive nature, was due to the pressure of the water percolating through the rock abutment. Three conditions, which occurred together, caused the water pressure in the left bank to reach catastrophic proportions:

1. The upstream geological discontinuities.
2. The downstream shear fault.
3. The watertightness of the rock *under compression.*

The last-mentioned phenomenon was particularly intense at Malpasset and is now thought to be a fundamental property of rock considered as a discontinuous and anisotropic medium.

The Malpasset Dam did not merely slip on a clay seam. In a sense, this is fortunate because many arch dams are founded on rock masses containing clay seams of all descriptions. In the case in point, the seam was perfectly safe under the thrust of the dam alone, had not unprecedented water pressures developed within the rock itself.

Before Londe's letter was published, however, the Vaiont Dam tragedy would serve to direct the focus of study onto the geology of dam reservoirs, and away from the courtroom.

Vaiont and Other Double-Arch Dams, 1959 and 1963

The Vaiont Dam was reaching completion just about the time Malpasset failed. In fact, in 1960—the year Vaiont was finished—a small dam in northern Spain near the Bay of Biscay failed as landslides dumped mud and sand into the reservoir behind it. At least twenty persons were killed in the village of Reocin, downstream.

At the Vaiont site, too, engineers from ENEL, the Italian government's electric power monopoly, had been nervous about slides. Before the 1963 disaster they had driven a tunnel 15 feet in diameter from a point just above the dam on the reservoir's floor, back more than a mile upstream. The idea was to

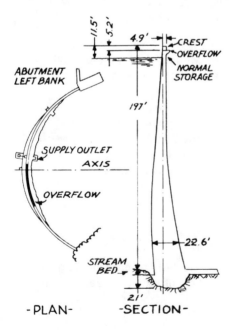

Figure 4-4 Malpasset's plan and vertical section. *(ENR.)*

Figure 4-5 A model of the Vaiont Dam in Italy being studied during construction planning, September 1958. *(An ENR photograph by G. Chiolini.)*

keep water flowing to the dam to generate electricity even if a slide partially blocked the reservoir itself.

ENEL and the original builders of the dam itself (Società Adriatica di Elettricità, or SADE, a private power company) could not have imagined the size of the slide that actually occurred, however.

The Vaiont Dam was only one unit in a complex of dams, reservoirs, and hydroelectric powerhouses connected by tunnels and pipelines. The system lies in the Piave River Valley, high in the Italian Alps. On October 9, 1963, a mountainside slid into the Vaiont Reservoir during a driving rain. Here's how ENR reported the disaster, in the October 17, 1963, issue:

Vaiont Dam Survives Immense Overtopping

Loss of life running into the thousands in an Alpine valley of northern Italy last week overshadowed a remarkable exhibition of stoutness by the world's second highest dam.

Figure 4-6 This view from slightly downstream of Vaiont Dam shows the giant slide, to the left. The tidal wave of water that washed over the dam barely damaged the top, near the left abutment. *(ENR.)*

Except for crumbling along a section of its crest near the left abutment, Vaiont Dam, an 858-ft-high concrete arch, appeared intact after a landslide sloshed enough water over the top in a matter of minutes, or perhaps only seconds, to demolish a town of 4,600 and several villages.

Early reports said the dam had collapsed, and the destructiveness of the wave that swept down the narrow Vaiont and Piave valleys lent plausibility to the reports. The surge almost completely destroyed the town of Longarone and several small villages. And it knocked out all normal access routes and communications, thereby isolating the area from outside assistance for many hours. . . .

The fatal slide is reported to have been observed moving down Mount Toc at about 16 in. a day about 10 days before the plunge. A spokesman for ENEL, the Italian national electric monopoly, said ENEL experts had been expecting a slide [of about 25 million cubic yards]. They say it was impossible to foresee, with the technical knowledge they had, that the slide would be so big.

Reservoir drawdown began about six days before the disaster in anticipation of a smaller slide. When the big one hit, water level was about 75 ft below the crest of the dam. Unconfirmed reports say heavy rains first hampered the drawdown operation by filling the reservoir, then precipitated the disastrous slide.

A U.S. Army helicopter pilot who flew over the area reported that the reservoir no longer exists. He said the entire tops of mountains on both sides of the lake slid into it and completely filled it. . . .

The only damage to the dam evident so far is the crumbling near the left abutment, about 5 ft deep and 30 ft long. . . .

The disaster has become a center of political controversy, particularly between the Communist Party and the young Christian Democrats, which has made it difficult to appraise some of the effects. It is reported that SADE (Societa Adriatica di Elettricita), the former private electric utility that built Vaiont Dam and now operates it while being taken over by the government hired a company several weeks ago to "bolster" parts of Mount Toc, but the workers struck because the job was too dangerous.

The engineer in charge of the dam is reported to have telephoned SADE's Venice headquarters several days before the disaster asking permission to evacuate the whole area because of the earth movements on the mountain. He is reported to have been told "to stay calm and sleep with his eyes open."

The Italian government appears determined to get at the facts. It has announced the establishment of a four-man committee of inquiry that is to decide by December 15:

· Whether hydrogeological examination of entire dam area was given "due weight" in planning and construction of dam and whether later landslides were regarded with sufficient seriousness.

· Whether "testing" stage of dam, which started on Mar. 25, 1960, was still continuing and what controversies there were among members of the testing commission.

· How full the lake was in the 10 days before the disaster and whether its level was in line with safety requirements.

· Whether landslides in the days before the disaster, which led to an evacuation order for the village of Erto, on the reservoir shore, were serious enough to warrant similar orders for towns downstream from the dam and whether officials showed "due diligence and initiative" in reporting events to authorities and whether authorities acted adequately.

Vaiont has attracted wide attention among engineers ever since it reached design stage. It is the highest arch dam in the world. The only dam of any kind that tops it is Grand Dixence, a concrete gravity dam 932 ft high in the Swiss Alps. The Soviet Union is reported to be building two dams higher than Grand Dixence: Ingurskaya, a 988-ft arch; and Nurek, a 978-ft-high earthfill.

The dam is only 625 ft long around the arc at the crest, and the chord length is only 555 ft, less than two-thirds of the dam height. The arch is the double-curved type, also known as the dome or cupola type, with upstream

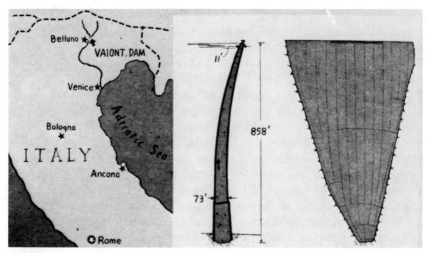

Figure 4-7 The front view and vertical section show Vaiont's graceful proportions. Notice that the dam is higher than it is wide. *(ENR.)*

face convex in both profile and plan at any section. It is 11 ft thick at the crest and 73 ft thick at the base.

The dam was designed and built under the supervision of the late Carlo Semenza, manager of the hydroelectric department of SADE. The designers used the trial-load method and other analytical methods and model studies. Two models on 1:35 scale were studied at the Instituto Sperimentale Modelli Strutture laboratory at Bergamo. The second was made after site work began and more accurately reflected actual foundation conditions. The model tests indicated maximum stresses amounting to 927 psi. Analysis showed slightly lower stresses.

Giuseppe Torno & Co., of Milan built the dam.

Far more than 25 million cubic yards came down that night, however. Final estimates placed the total at more than 300 million cubic yards—a volume slightly larger than the original working volume of the Vaiont Reservoir itself. The amount of earth and rock that slid into the reservoir was more than twice the volume of the largest earth dam ever built (Fort Peck on the Missouri River in Montana). Moving this mass out of the reservoir would have been a monumental task, especially since there was no convenient place to put it in the narrow valleys around Vaiont. As a result, the slide was never cleared from behind the dam; it remains there today, making the dam useless for the generation of hydroelectric power.

Four months after the disaster, Italian officials released their report. It caused a sensation because it blamed bureaucratic inefficiency, muddled withholding of alarming information, and buck-passing among top officials. Immediately after the report was issued, in January 1964, Italian Premier Aldo Moro ordered the suspension of the chiefs of Belluno and Udine, the provinces controlling the washed-away town of Longarone. Also suspended were the president of the higher council of the Public Works Ministry, the inspector general of the government's Civil Engineering Council, and the chief civil engineers of Belluno and Udine.

The slide's immediate cause was attributed to erosion from water in the reservoir. The force on the dam was calculated to have been 4 million tons.

Almost 4 years after the collapse, in December 1967, the public prosecutor of Belluno charged eleven men with responsibility for the disaster. By that time, two had already died. A third, Mario Pancini, an engineer who was site director during the dam's construction, committed suicide the day before the trial was to begin in November 1968. The prosecutor's charges were discussed in the ENR issue of December 7, 1967:

Vaiont Dam Engineers Are Blamed

Responsibility for the 1963 Vaiont Dam disaster, which killed over 2,000 persons, has been charged to 11 Italian engineers by the public prosecutor of Belluno, Italy. Nine of them may face trial.

Figure 4-8 During construction, care was taken to secure Vaiont Dam's right abutment into solid rock. Note the fractured rock. *(ENR.)*

Two others have died during the investigation that began shortly after an estimated 300 million cu yd of earth slid down a mountain into Vaiont's reservoir. The resulting wave overtopped the 858-ft-high concrete arch dam, which suffered little damage, and destroyed several villages [ENR, Oct. 17, 1963, p. 22].

Manslaughter is among the charges in the 496-page statement made by prosecutor Arcangelo Mandarino. After studying the report and defense briefs filed by lawyers for the nine engineers, an investigating judge will decide whether or not the men should be tried.

The prosecutor accuses Alberico Biadene, 67, and Mario Pancini, 55, of responsibility for the slide. Biadene was director of hydraulic construction for SADE, the power company in charge of the Vaiont project before it was nationalized, and vice president of ENEL-SADE, the national power authority. Pancini was head engineer at the dam site.

According to the prosecutor, both men were aware of a slide of over 1 million cu yd that took place in 1960 during a test filling of the reservoir to El. 2,133. That movement was more than was expected, but, the prosecutor says, the two continued test fillings, and conducted the final test filling too rapidly for the soil conditions. He asserts that filling, to El. 2,329, precipitated the rapid, nighttime slide.

Biadene and Pancini are also charged with ignoring consultants' cautions, and with failing to make studies to ascertain the nature of earth movements in the slide area.

Five more men, including the two who have died, are charged with

Figure 4-9 This view from upstream after the slide shows the battering Vaiont's concrete shell took from the slide and wave. *(ENR.)*

cooperating with, or being accomplices to, Biadene and Pancini. The prosecutor further charges them with manslaughter, asserting that each of them could have controlled the situation and prevented the disaster. He also accuses them of "flooding with devastation" the communities of Longarone, Castellavazzo, and Erto-Casso, as well as two bridges, and holds them responsible for damages.

The five are Pietro Frosini, 71, former president of the fourth section of the Superior Council of Public Works and a member of the Vaiont test commission; Francesco Sensidoni, 66, inspector general of civil engineers for the council, and a member of the test commission; Curzio Batini, 65, who succeeded Frosini; and the two dead men, Luigi Greco and Francesco Penta.

The prosecutor says the five knew of the 1960 slide and that they knew higher water levels in the reservoir would increase the instability of the mountainside to the left of the dam. They allegedly knew, too, that various safety measures had not been completed or checked, but took no action.

Almo Violin, 50, is accused of negligence that caused death and damages in the disaster area. The prosecutor says Violin, who was head of civil engineers at Belluno, was informed of the danger of slides in the area nearly two months before the overtopping, but failed to adopt required emergency steps at the first sign of the slide (earth reportedly crept down the mountain at increasing speeds during several days of heavy rains before it collapsed into the reservoir).

Dino Tonini, 62, a SADE hydraulics consultant, is charged with cooperating with the others, for having pressed for test fillings despite evidence of danger.

The prosecutor also blames Augusto Ghetti, a 53-year-old professor of hydraulics at the University of Padua who prepared the geologic model for the site, and Roberto Marin, 73, director-general of ENEL-SADE, for the disaster. Ghetti, he says, refused to consider other consultants' geologic and seismic studies, and guaranteed the stability of the site "even in the most catastrophic foreseeable event of landslide." The prosecutor says Marin, as supervisor of Biadene and Pancini, ignored advice contrary to theirs and failed to keep himself aware of the situation.

Sentences for manslaughter in Italy usually range from 6 months to 12 years, depending on circumstances.

[ENR reported last week (p. 13) that homicide was among the charges against some of the accused. "Homicide" is one English translation of the Italian *omicidio* (oh-mee-CHEE-d'yo), but the word can be interpreted as "manslaughter," especially if used with the modifier *colposo,* which means "unpremeditated." The Italian word that more accurately describes the U.S. concept of homicide or premeditated murder of persons, is *assassinio.* In both Italy and the U.S., manslaughter is unpremeditated or accidental killing.]

Experts who reportedly watched earth creep down the mountainside

Figure 4-10 The rugged, beautiful mountains near Vaiont and the narrow gorges between them became a death trap for 2000. *(ENR.)*

before the disaster are said to have expected a much smaller slide, being unable to predict its size with technical data at hand.

The slide choked the reservoir so completely that the dam is a useless towering monument, if nothing else, to the stability of concrete arch dams.

After listening to sixty lawyers and 2500 witnesses during a trial that lasted more than a year, the courts acquitted five engineers and found three others guilty: Alberico Biadene, director of hydraulic construction for SADE; Curzio Batini, president of the fourth section of the Superior Council of the Ministry of Public Works and head of the commission that tested Vaiont; and Almo Violin, head of civil engineering at Belluno where the dam was located. The verdict: multiple manslaughter. The term: 6 years in prison, with parole likely after 2 years. An appeals court later also convicted Francesco Sensidoni but reversed Violin's conviction for lack of evidence. Biadene, who by that time was 70, received a suspended sentence.

The chief lesson had already been learned from Vaiont 7 years earlier, however. This is the way an ENR editorial described it in the issue of October 24, 1963:

Lessons from Vaiont

The only worth of a structural failure, as we have remarked on this page more than once in the past, is the opportunity it offers for learning. This general idea ought to apply as well to the Vaiont Dam disaster, which was a disaster without structural failure [ENR, Oct. 17, p. 22].

At Vaiont, the main lesson appears to be a trite one: Get out of the way if a landslide threatens a reservoir. It's risky to jump too fast to conclusions before all the facts are in, but we can't help wondering whether it can be excusable not to evacuate people below a reservoir threatened by a slide.

Presumably those responsible for the operation of the dam felt confident that a slide of the proportions expected (it turned out to be much larger) would not cause a dangerous flood downstream. But could they have justifiably felt confidence about the ability of the dam to hold? It is true that theoretical analysis, model analysis and the intuition of the most renowned arch-dam designers all indicate that arch dams have a great deal of reserve strength.

And Vaiont proved this true. But it was a big gamble not to evacuate the towns when a slide was actually on the move that could hardly help subjecting the dam to some unusual forces of unknown magnitude. The Italian government is asking some penetrating and possibly very embarrassing questions to uncover the facts on this aspect of the disaster.

There may be other lessons at Vaiont concerning the engineering of reservoirs in such terrain. Despite the dam's remarkable performance, the project is in a sense and to an extent not yet determined a failure because the reservoir is greatly damaged if not effectively destroyed. Reservoirs have silted up; reservoirs have leaked. But here for the first time in recent history we may learn lessons from a reservoir virtually filled by massive landslides.

Baldwin Hills, 1963

Fortunately for the residents of Los Angeles who lived near the Baldwin Dam, the lesson of Vaiont had been quickly learned. The Baldwin Hills Dam in southwest Los Angeles was built in 1948 and 1949 to serve as a balancing reservoir—a giant surge tank—between the Franklin Reservoir in the mountains beyond Beverly Hills and nearby residents. About 2 million cubic yards of fill was scooped out of the hills to provide the reservoir's basin and to be used as the fill in the 650-foot-long, 155-foot-high dam itself. Construction cost: a mere $4.5 million.

A series of minor, interconnected faults was found and plotted during construction. They were not deemed serious enough, however, to force a relocation of the dam site. A geologist and two engineers appointed by the Los Angeles Department of Water and Power approved the site at that time, reporting that appreciable movement would be unlikely. The designers did, however, relocate the gate tower because of the faulting, and provided an inspection gallery through the adjacent fault zone.

By 1951, however, those "minor" faults had moved enough to rupture the reservoir's asphalt membrane floor, permitting drainage into the soil below. This breakage was not discovered when the reservoir was drained for cleaning

Figure 4-11   This photo showing construction of Baldwin Hills Dam was originally published in the August 26, 1948, issue of ENR. More than half the 2 million cubic yards of fill has been removed to provide a basin for the reservoir, as well as the material for the dam. *(Los Angeles Department of Water and Power.)*

and routine maintenance in 1957. By then, the slow seepage of water had begun to honeycomb the soil below the reservoir and dam.

In December 1963, a fault movement, probably caused by subsidence (no earthquake was reported during that period, according to the California Institute of Technology), enlarged the cracks in the lining to dangerous proportions, adding to the water flow and putting more pressure on the dam's tile and gravel drains.

On the morning of December 14, the dam gave way, sending 300 million gallons of water cascading down a residential hillside and washing away $50 million worth of property. Only five people lost their lives, however, thanks to quick action on the part of Department of Water Resources (DWR) engineers. Details of what happened were reported in an ENR editorial on January 16, 1964:

Medals for Many

A calamity but not a tragedy can be the characterization of the failure of the Baldwin Hills Dam in Los Angeles last month (ENR, Dec. 19, 1963, p. 50) thanks to the right decisions and devotion to duty of the engineers of the city's Department of Water and Power and their assistants. No group ever deserved more credit for living up to that great engineering credo: Always practice your profession in a spirit of public service.

Lest the details of the activities that preceded the failure be forgotten, here is the chronology of events, briefed from testimony given in a legislative committee hearing by Max K. Socha, chief engineer of waterworks of the Department:

Shortly after 11 A.M., on his regular rounds, Revere Wells, reservoir caretaker, noting an increase in the sound of running water in the drain system, drove to the base of the dam, entered an inspection tunnel under the reservoir, found water coming into it.

11:35 A.M.   Wells rushed out, telephoned Patrick Doherty, operations field superintendent.

12:05 P.M.   Doherty arrived, phoned Gerard Wyss, assistant operating division head; then went into tunnel and found water continuing to rise.

12:15 P.M.   Wyss arrived. He and Doherty decided to start draining reservoir. Radio requests were made for crews and also for traffic police.

12:45 P.M.   Richard Hemborg, operating head, arrived, telephoned Mr. Socha and John Cowan, assistant chief engineer of waterworks. Cowan telephoned Samuel B. Nelson, general manager and chief engineer of the Department of Water and Power.

1:00 P.M.   Wet area observed on the face of the dam near the east abutment reported to Wyss and Hemborg.

1:15 P.M.   Wyss, at east abutment, observed silt being carried by water as it came through dam. Notified Hemborg, and they concluded that area below the dam should be evacuated.

1:20 P.M.   Hemborg phoned Nelson who concurred.

1:30 P.M.   Hemborg informed police of the emergency and requested evacuation.

1:35 P.M.   Socha arrived at reservoir and informed police there might be as much as two hours to evacuate the area before the downstream boil-out on the slope of the dam eroded upward and eventually breached the dam. He also informed the police of the area where devastation from the flowing water would probably occur and the limits beyond which damage would result only from inundation.

1:40 P.M.   Socha phoned Nelson a detailed assessment of situation. Nelson said he would remain at phone to maintain communication with other authorities, while Socha should direct activities at the reservoir.

2:30 P.M.   All possible measures to drain the reservoir having been in effect since 1 P.M., men were sent to clear out any debris in catch basins so that the discharged water could freely enter city storm drain system.

2:45 P.M.   Men were lowered on ropes in an attempt to place sandbags in

Figure 4-12 Progressive failure at Baldwin Hills. First swirling waters tunnel through the dam.

The tunnel then grows, eroding the embankment.

the crack, which was visible on upstream face of dam. As Mr. Socha described the final minutes before the dam was breached, "I asked Mr. Cowan, my chief assistant, to station himself where he could observe both me and the men engaged in sandbagging. Then I went along the east embankment where I could observe the rate of erosion. When I concluded that the final breach was imminent, I called to Mr. Cowan, 'Get the men out, we have lost the race.' Only then did they leave their posts and scramble to safety."

3:38 P.M. The massive breach of the dam occurred.

Finally, the road at the top of the dam washes away as the tunnel becomes a cut through the dam's face. *(Los Angeles Department of Water and Power.)*

Mr. Socha concluded his testimony by saying: "Each of our employees as he arrived on the scene proceeded on his own initiative to carry out operations without error. In my careful review, their magnificent efforts, along with the same type of response from other organizations, prevented this disaster from becoming inestimably greater."

The magnificent efforts deserve medals.

The reservoir, once empty, displayed a large crack running its entire length. Within a week of the dam's failure, ENR noted that subsidence was the probable cause. This story appeared in the December 19, 1963, issue:

Subsidence Blamed in Earth Dam Failure

A crack running through the entire reservoir floor, probably due to subsidence not uncommon to the area, caused the failure last week of Los Angeles' Baldwin Hills Reservoir Dam.

John G. Cowan, assistant chief engineer for water works, Department of Water and Power, told ENR that up until the movement that caused the break in the 160-ft-high earthfill, there was no indication of piping (displacement of earth particles by seepage flow) under the 12-year-old structure. Nevertheless, such piping was prominently in evidence as the earth embankment fractured.

Figure 4-13 A flood swept the valley below Baldwin Hills. *(Los Angeles Department of Water and Power.)*

The dam had an elaborate system of drains. Leakage first began through the reservoir floor and into the drainage system. A watchman found water bleeding into an inspection gallery approximately four and one-half hours before the dam actually gave way. . . .

It is a 550-ft-long, 1.3-million-cu-yd embankment, designed by the late Ralph R. Proctor, who was for 27 years in charge of all dam construction for DWP and well known for his pioneering work in the control of soil compaction (ENR, Aug. 31, 1933, p. 245).

The 19-acre reservoir was lined with asphaltic concrete and had an asphaltic membrane, described (ENR, June 7, 1956, p. 50) as an "uncommon design necessary to guard the installation against leakage, because of certain geological conditions."

The lining consists of a membrane seal, a porous drainage course, a compacted earth blanket, and a layer of asphaltic concrete.

Mayor Samuel Yorty has appointed a three-man commission to choose an investigating committee of experts on soil mechanics and geology. The state also has launched an inquiry.

Mr. Cowan said DWP has had no previous trouble with the reservoir. It had not been relined recently because there had seemed no reason to do so. No breaks or malformations had been noted. The dam's drainage system is checked daily, and settlement and alignment are checked monthly by an engineering team.

Los Angeles consulting engineer Leroy Crandall told ENR that the area was subject to subsidence.

Less than 2 months later, the investigation board appointed by Los Angeles Mayor Samuel Yorty had also concluded that subsidence had caused the reservoir crack. This report, in turn, was backed up with a more detailed state study—reported by ENR on July 2, 1964, about 6 months after the reservoir failed:

Baldwin Hills Reservoir Area Settled 9 ft. . . . Land Subsidence Caused Failure

A state board of inquiry says land subsidence was the primary cause of earth movement that triggered the failure of Baldwin Hills Reservoir in Los Angeles last December (ENR, Dec. 19, 1963, p. 50). The board, established by California's Department of Water Resources, leaves little doubt in its report that the investigators believe this subsidence is related to, if not directly attributable to, oil and water withdrawals in the area during the past 40 years.

Records show a settlement of about 9 ft in the subsidence bowl, centered on the soil field nearby. Although it would have been difficult to recognize the movement as "potentially dangerous" 20 or 30 years ago, the "forces that ultimately led to trouble were in motion," the report said.

Specifically, the board of inquiry stated, "Geologic elements at the site would provide marginal foundation for any open facility for confinement of water. . . . This reservoir was called upon to do more than it was able."

The report minimizes the importance of natural geologic activity in the formation of the subsidence bowl.

The movements, which actually distorted the shape of the reservoir, apparently caused opening of pre-existing foundation faults. This ruptured the reservoir lining, which was designed to prevent water seepage into the foundation. The foundation was known to be highly susceptible to deterioration by the action of water, the report said.

"There is evidence that continuous leaking of water had created cavities in the foundation at the faults. In some places, it appears that the reservoir lining was able to bridge these cavities as they developed. With the earth movement on December 14, the lining collapsed into these cavities and accelerated the failure process," said the investigators. . . .

Robert B. Jansen, DWR engineer, was chairman of the board. Other members were DWR engineers Gordon W. Kukleth, Bernard B. Gordon and Clyde E. Shields and DWR geologist Laurence B. James. Consulting engineers J. Barry Cooke and Thomas M. Keps and consulting geologist Roger Rhoades assisted the board. Seismologist Pierre St. Amand was a special consultant.

A 10-man judiciary subcommittee of the California Assembly is conducting another study concerned with legislation to prevent future failures. This group probably will report its conclusions to the legislature.

Baldwin Hills also sparked a California Office of Dam Safety investigation of 934 dams under state jurisdiction. Of this total, 85—about 10 percent—were shown to be in need of "repair or further study." The state's Department of Water Resources immediately ordered repair work on 76 dams, and began legal action to force repairs on 2 others.

Ominously, the department found that about a third of the dams under its jurisdiction have records of surface settlement or movement and that half the dams "may be considered as sufficient potential hazards to life and property to warrant immediate development of evacuation plans and other emergency procedures in preparation for possible failure."

California's lawmakers recognized the problem by tightening existing dam safety laws. This report appeared in the ENR issue of February 25, 1965:

California Will Beef Up Dam Safety Laws

California is about to tighten up a dam safety code that is already one of the toughest in the country. Before adjourning this June, the legislature is expected to amend the law covering the more than 1,000 dams under state supervision.

The proposed amendments result directly from the 1963 failure of Los Angeles' Baldwin Hills Reservoir (ENR, Dec. 19, 1963, p. 50). California's existing laws were enacted in 1929 soon after the disastrous failure of St. Francis Dam, which killed several hundred persons and caused extensive property damage (ENR, Mar. 12, 1928, p. 456).

The state assembly will begin hearings late next month on a bill sponsored by Assemblyman George A. Willson, who was chairman of the Baldwin Hills disaster subcommittee. The Willson bill embodies the recommendations of California's Department of Water Resources submitted to Gov. Edmund G. Brown last month.

The proposed amendments would:

· Put more dams and reservoirs under state jurisdiction.

· Require more effective safety practices by owners of dams and reservoirs.

· Create an emergency "work fund" so the state can perform emergency work on dams under its jurisdiction. (The law now authorizes the state to perform such work but provides no funds.)

The bill would put more dams under state jurisdiction by redefining the word "dam" as it is used in the old laws to mean: all barriers and containers, within specified heights and capacities, that do or may impound or divert water, whether or not they are situated across a stream channel, water course, or natural drainage area, except levees.

Existing law defines a dam as an "artificial barrier across a watercourse." Baldwin Hills Reservoir, built in a natural basin in a hilly area of Los Angeles, did not fit this definition, although jurisdiction had been assumed by the state at the request of the owner, the City of Los Angeles.

The new law would make it clear that reservoirs such as Baldwin Hills are also under state jurisdiction. Federally owned dams still will not come under state jurisdiction.

Under the proposed law, owners of dams and reservoirs would have to meet the following requirements: acquire a certificate of approval for each project, which would be renewable every three years; make geologic investigations and submit geologic reports on the project area—not just the immediate site—including subsoil tests of the area; provide suitable staffs for the safe operation of dams and make engineering and geologic investigations of these operations; and report promptly and completely any sudden or unprecedented flood or any other unusual or alarming circumstances or occurrences affecting dams.

The state would be further authorized, when deciding whether a dam or proposed dam may endanger life or property, to consider the possibility that seepage, slides or other conditions might endanger the structure. If such conditions exist, the state could order the owner to eliminate them or cease using the dam.

The emergency work fund in the amount of $200,000 would provide the state with funds to perform emergency repairs on any such endangered structures. Licensing fees would replenish this fund, avoiding a drain on state funds. . . .

In his report to the governor, [DWR Director William E.] Warne reviewed the state's experience in the 35 years since enactment of the present dam supervision laws. In 1929, 453 dams were subject to the law compared with over 1,000 now. Since that time, Mr. Warne reported, "There have been 15 failures of dams which resulted in release of water below spill way crest. In addition, there have been more than 140 partial failures of dams. In many instances, complete failures were prevented by prompt action by the state."

Mr. Warne said that in the 35 years the state's population had tripled and it is estimated that "the exposure of life and property to injury from the failure of dams has increased over six times."

"As good dam and reservoir sites have become more scarce in California," he said, "it has become necessary to build on marginal sites. . . . One of these was Baldwin Hills Reservoir."

At about the same time, Los Angeles ordered the installation of electronic sensors to warn of leakage from five of its dams in heavily populated areas. The Los Angeles County Flood Control District also installed seismic sensors on all fourteen dams in the system "to aid in evaluating any earthquake damage" that might cause a dam to fail.

Teton Dam, 1976

By 1972, California had the nation's best dam safety program. Its technical staff of fifty inspected more than 1000 dams a year. At any one time, about two dozen dams were undergoing repair. Some other western states had followed California's lead. Arizona, for instance, had passed a law very similar to California's. Among states in the west, only Montana did not have an inspection law. Rural residents had compaigned against a 1972 legislative proposal for one, calling it an intrusion on local prerogatives.

The Buffalo Creek disaster of 1972 spurred at least the semblance of federal action, however. The dam that failed was not an "engineered" structure at all—merely a pile of tailings from a coal mine in West Virginia. When it collapsed after heavy rains, at least 125 people had been swept away.

Stung by a public perception of inaction—a perception fueled by continuing lawsuits over Buffalo Creek and other failures—the Senate Interior Committee began work on a federal dam inspection bill. That rankled the Public Works Committees in both houses of Congress—the traditional watchdogs over federal pork-barrel funding for water projects. The Public Works Committees rewrote and passed a dam safety bill of their own in only 4 days, with no hearings.

By then, a 20-foot-high earth fill had failed near Rapid City, South Dakota, and tropical storm Agnes dumped rain in the east causing the failure of the Barcroft Dam near Washington, D.C.

The new law called for the Army Corps of Engineers to inventory and to inspect all nonfederal dams. If any were found to be dangerous, the Corps was to notify the states, which would then correct deficiencies. The vaguely worded law also called upon the Corps to monitor the states, letting Congress know if any problems were not corrected. The law left the definition of an "unsafe" dam up to the Corps. What's more, there was no mechanism for authorizing expenditure of federal funds to repair or replace dams found to be unsafe.

All those problems were to remain academic for the next 4 years, however, because Congress had neglected one little detail: It had never appropriated any money for the Corps to inspect even a single dam. The Corps had estimated that it would cost $150 million to inspect something less than 30,000 dams. (When the inventory was actually completed, in 1980, more than 50,000 dams were catalogued.)

By 1976, only twenty-nine states had some kind of dam safety program. Fewer than half the states bothered to inspect dams at all—and those that did inspect were mainly in the west. In Tennessee, for instance, developers intent on creating lakefront property by impounding little streams had managed to have their state's inspection funding reduced to zero.

The inaction became all too apparent in 1976. If the late fifties and early sixties had been unkind years for concrete arch dams, 1976 was a bad year for earth fills. On February 22, part of a 200-foot-long, 50-foot-high earth fill near Asheville, North Carolina, failed in heavy rains. Water from a 3-acre lake behind the dam rushed into the valley 1200 feet below, killing four people and causing about $500,000 in damage.

In June, the 1500-foot-long Vestre Gausdal Dam, only 30 feet high, failed as it was being completed on the River Roppa in Norway. Engineers suspected leakage in the morainic material—glacial deposits of earth and stones—at the dam's base.

By September, Pakistan's 442-foot-high, 1650-foot-long Bolan Dam had been swept away by torrential rains. The dam lacked a spillway to relieve the rising level in the reservoir behind it; eventually, water simply swept over the top, destroying the dam and washing away twenty-six villages. Pakistan also experienced continuing problems at Tarbela.

The failure that caught most of the public attention, however, was closer to home: After 76 years of dam building, the Bureau of Reclamation (BuRec) lost one on June 5, 1976. The failure did more than remind people that the earlier inspection law had not been implemented. It also called into serious question the nation's entire dam-building program. The failure was described in the June 10, 1976, issue of ENR:

Grout Curtain Failure May Have Triggered Teton Dam Collapse

A tranquil, rural section of eastern Idaho was declared a major disaster area after the recently topped-out Teton Dam failed last Saturday as its reservoir filled for the first time. The failure dumped nearly 300,000 acre-ft of water into the flatlands downstream. The death toll had reached six by early this week with at least 80 injured and 135 missing. Madison County officials said the rampaging water caused more than $550 million worth of damage.

The 10-million-cu-yd earth and rock embankment gave way to the Teton River, a Snake River tributary, as the contractor, a joint venture of Morrison-Knudsen Co., Inc., Boise, Idaho, and Peter Kiewit Sons' Co., Omaha, was completing finishing touches under its $39.5-million prime contract.

The 305-ft-high dam failed at or near the right abutment, loosing an estimated 4 million cu yd of earth and rock. The largest rock size used in the embankment was 1 cu yd.

Figure 4-14 Teton Dam in Idaho, looking upstream about 6½ hours after the failure. *(A Bureau of Reclamation photograph by Glade Walker.)*

The dam is founded on a basalt formation containing rhyolite, a porous rock with considerable fractures and voids. Because of this, Bureau of Reclamation geologists and designers specified an extensive grouting program for the dam's foundation.

The 3,050-ft-long embankment's grout curtain extends as deep as 300 ft into bedrock and 1,000 ft beyond the abutment. Keyways, 70 ft deep and 30 ft wide at the bottom, were excavated into relatively stable rock in both abutments. A core trench across the canyon floor links the keyways.

The grout curtain was injected through three rows of holes, upstream and downstream along the core trench on 20-ft centers, and through a central concrete grout cap on 10-ft centers. On the canyon bottom, directly under the former riverbed, all grout holes were 10 ft-c-c. The core trench in this area was excavated 100 ft to sound rock.

At the time this work was under way, BuRec project construction engineer Robert R. Robison told ENR he expected total grout take to run about 250,000 cu ft [ENR, Apr. 12, 1973, p. 76]. To hold the curtain as nearly as possible on the dam's centerline, a 3.5% calcium chloride solution was added to the cement grout to accelerate the rate at which it set.

Commissioner Gilbert Stamm said in Washington, D.C., before leaving for Idaho, that water had either found its way around the grout curtain or gone right through it.

The first sign of trouble came on Tuesday, June 3, when minor seepage was detected on the right bank downstream from the spillway. . . . This seepage of only about 20 gpm went unchanged until Saturday morning at 9, when it increased markedly to 50 to 60 cfs.

At 9:30 seepage estimated at 70 cfs began in the embankment and BuRec notified news media and the sheriff's office of the problem and evacuation was ordered at the small towns of Newdale and Teton, as well as the larger town of Rexburg. . . .

But the situation worsened rapidly. At 10:30 seepage through the embankment had reached 1,000 cfs and a whirlpool in the reservoir indicated the worst was at hand. Between 11:30 and noon the embankment failed and released a wall of water 15 ft high, which roared out of the valley into the farmland and small towns.

The Teton empties into the Snake River above Idaho Falls and despite a shutdown of all releases at Palisades Dam on the Snake, the city braced for high water and evacuated low-lying areas. When the crest hit Idaho Falls, it flooded only these areas.

Assistant Secretary of Interior for land and water resources Jack O. Horton told ENR in Boise that a special blue-ribbon board of outside

Figure 4-15 Seepage at Teton first became evident at this point. *(ENR.)*

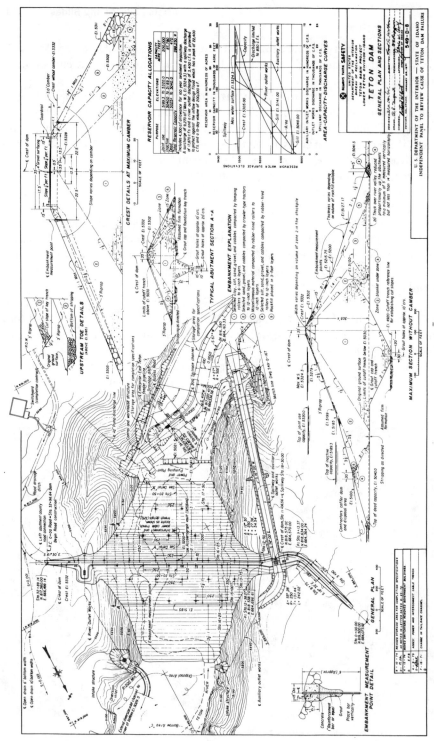

Figure 4-16 General plan and sections for Teton Dam. *(Bureau of Reclamation.)*

152

consultants as well as an in-house group to be named this week will investigate.

The final death toll was placed at 11, with $1 billion in property damage. More than 2000 people were injured in the flood that followed the Teton's collapse. More than 7000 homes and businesses were damaged or destroyed. This failure, as massive as it was, did not claim as many lives as another collapse 18 months later: Georgia's Toccoa collapse, which killed thirty-eight. In fact, while the public's mind focused on Teton, it was the Georgia failure—in President Jimmy Carter's home state—that finally forced high-priority funding into the Corps dam inspection program.

No doubt the attention paid to Teton was due in part to the controversy that had surrounded the project in the first place. Environmentalists had unsuccessfully sued to cancel Teton because it inundated 17 miles of one of the best trout-fishing areas around. There was suspicion that the Bureau of Reclamation had skimped on the dam's design since initial bids had come in over budget. In 1969, in fact, the dam had appeared on a "hit list" of water projects that either were not cost-effective or were planned for difficult sites. The state's biggest newspaper, the *Idaho Statesman,* had attacked plans for the dam as early as 1971.

Continuing coverage by ENR had focused on the grout system. A story in the issue of April 12, 1973, noted that the 250,000 cubic feet of cement grout would be needed to seal a basalt formation "with considerable fractures and voids" upon which the dam would rest. Although the winning bid for the dam's construction had come in 10 percent above estimates, the joint venture of Morrison-Knudsen and Peter Kiewit Sons' had estimated the cost of the grouting to be well above the estimates of the second bidder. Morrison-Knudsen Co., Inc., and Peter Kiewit Sons' Co. (M-K–Kiewit) won the bid by making up for the expensive grouting with more efficient movement of fill from the borrow pits to the dam site.

In the wake of the disaster, the House Subcommittee on Conservation, Energy and Natural Resources discovered that the final report of the U.S. Geological Survey (USGS) to BuRec on the site warned of seismic activity and fractured rock. USGS warned that Teton should not be built on the site. BuRec said it never received the USGS warning.

Within days of the Teton disaster, an independent investigation panel was named. It was headed by Los Angeles consultant Wallace L. Chadwick. The perception among many members of the public was that Chadwick—who was 80 years old at the time—and a handful of prominent professionals making up the committee would issue a polite report on their fellow professionals' work at Teton. Instead, the 585-page document, finished in only 6 months, was unexpectedly harsh. As ENR reported the story on January 13, 1977:

Teton Dam Failure Is Blamed on BuRec Design Deficiencies

The final report of the independent panel reviewing failure of Teton Dam in Idaho last June blames inadequate design and field monitoring by the Bureau of Reclamation for the breach, resulting in flooding that covered 300 sq miles. . . .

The 10-member panel says it is apparent that piping eroded the base of the embankment's impermeable core material in the keyway that was cut into the right abutment, and indicates that water then burst through the dam's downstream face because it was inadequately drained. The piping could be due to numerous open joints in the abutment and imperfect grouting of the highly fractured rock below the grout cap, hydraulic cracking of the key trench fill or possibly both. But because the washout carried away the failed section, the report says, the specific cause probably will never be known. The basic conclusion agrees with preliminary findings by the Interior Department's internal review group, whose report is due by early spring [ENR, Nov. 4, 1976, p. 11].

While the independent panel criticized virtually every aspect of BuRec's design, and says the dam was not sufficiently instrumented to warn of trouble, it completely exonerates the prime contractor, a joint venture of Morrison-Knudsen Co., Inc., Boise, and Peter Kiewit Sons' Co., Omaha. They were completing some minor finishing work under a $40-million contract when about 40% of the 10 million cu yd of fill washed out. Total cost of the project, a 305-ft-high earth embankment stretching 3,050 ft across the Teton River, was $96 million.

"There is no way to fault the contractor or the construction engineer for the failure," said Wallace Chadwick, the Los Angeles consultant who heads the panel. The design of the dam was "not adapted to this very difficult site," he added after a press conference last week in Idaho Falls, 40 miles southwest of the damsite, where the results of the $10-million study were released.

BuRec's director of design and construction Harold Arthur concurs: "The contractor's operations were under the control of bureau inspectors." Before completing the review of the 400-page report, Arthur said, "It really doesn't contain any surprises. It had been our conclusion that the deficiency was probably in design." BuRec has taken steps to prevent other such failures. . . .

The panel says that the site selection process and geological studies were appropriate and extensive, supporting BuRec's contention that the site was the best available. But the report says that the BuRec's design proceeded "without sufficient consideration of the effects of differing and unusually difficult geological conditions at the Teton damsite." It noted a number of deficiencies that could have led to collapse, but finds that neither differential settlement nor seismic activity contributed.

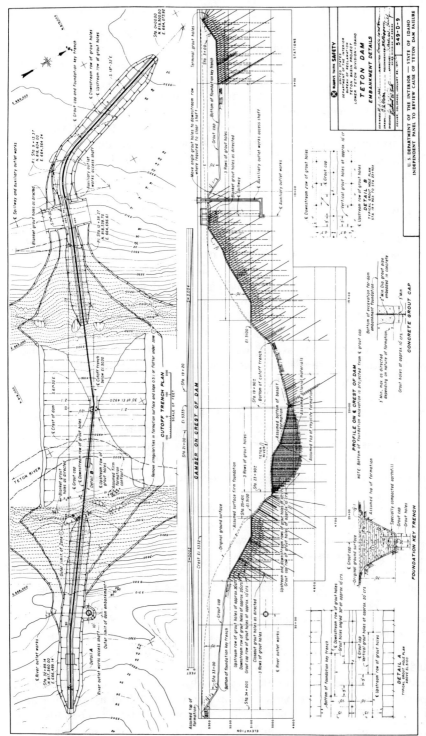

Figure 4-17 Details of grout curtains and cutoff walls at Teton Dam. (*Bureau of Reclamation.*)

155

While the panel found inadequately grouted open joints in the upstream and downstream faces of the right abutment and a trench along with evidence of some pockets of inadequately compacted core fill at the bottom of the trench, it says construction activities conformed to the original design "in all significant aspects except scheduling."

Delay in completing outlet works forced faster filling of the reservoir during last spring's runoffs than was originally planned. The report says a slower rate would have delayed the breach, but "a similar failure would have occurred at some later date."

CRITICAL RANGE

Investigators found that specific measures were not taken to insure sealing of the upper part of the rock under the grout cap. Water was able to move through the highly jointed volcanic rock "with almost equal ease in all directions, except locally where the joints had been effectively grouted." And they found large fissures elsewhere. One far back in the right abutment extends about 1,000 ft both up and downstream.

The panel also says that the steep sides of the 70-ft-deep keyways that run down the abutments and across the canyon promoted erosion of the fill as piping water struck irregularities in the rock, and favored the development of cracks "that would open channels." And it criticized the selection of "wind-deposited nonplastic to slightly plastic clayey silts" for the core and key trench fill (zone 1) because it is highly erodible.

The report also notes that while the zone 2 fill, flanking zone 1, is intended to act as a drainage blanket and chimney drain, permeability tests raised doubt about the suitability of the material for that purpose, suggesting that "much of the zone 2 material may have been nearly as impervious as the zone 1 material."

The dam's much touted "triple" grout curtain going as deep as 300 ft also came under fire. The panel says the spacing of the outer two rows indicates that full closure along them was not attempted or attained, so they do not constitute curtains at all: "The outer rows were intended to be only semi-pervious grout barriers against which the center row of grout holes could reasonably be fully and successfully grouted." It should be termed a single-row curtain, says the group.

The report says designers emphasized keeping water from seeping through the dam rather than taking measures to "render harmless whatever water did pass." Summing up, the panel says, "Thus, the final design depended for seepage through it was the drainage zone, impervious core, the key trench backfill and on the grout curtain. Although the upstream face of the impervious core in the embankment proper was protected by a transition zone, the only downstream defense against cracking in the impervious fill or against concentrated seepage through it was the drainage zone, and this did

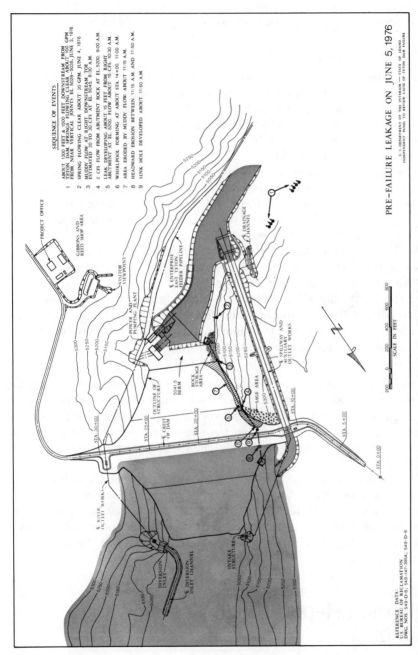

SEQUENCE OF EVENTS

1 ABOUT 1300 FEET & 1500 FEET DOWNSTREAM FROM TETON DAM SPRINGS FLOWING CLEAR ABOUT 100 GPM FROM NEAR VERTICAL JOINTS EL 5028-5035, JUNE 3, 1976
2 SPRING FLOWING CLEAR ABOUT 20 GPM, JUNE 4, 1976
3 MUDDY FLOW AT RIGHT DOWNSTREAM TOE ESTIMATED 20 TO 30 CFS AT 5045, 8:30 A.M.
4 2 CFS FLOW FROM ABUTMENT ROCK AT EL 5200, 9:00 A.M.
5 LEAK DEVELOPING ABOUT 15 FEET FROM RIGHT ABUTMENT AT EL 5200. FLOW ABOUT 15 CFS. 10:30 A.M.
6 WHIRLPOOL FORMING AT ABOUT STA. 14+00, 11:00 A.M.
7 AREA ERODED BY MUDDY FLOW ABOUT 11:15 A.M.
8 HEADWARD EROSION BETWEEN 11:15 A.M. AND 11:50 A.M.
9 SINK HOLE DEVELOPED ABOUT 11:50 A.M.

PRE-FAILURE LEAKAGE ON JUNE 5, 1976

U. S. DEPARTMENT OF THE INTERIOR — STATE OF IDAHO
INDEPENDENT PANEL TO REVIEW CAUSE OF TETON DAM FAILURE

REFERENCE DATA:
U.S. BUREAU OF RECLAMATION
DWG. NOS. 549-D-8, 549-47-395A1, 549-D-6

Figure 4-18   A description of prefailure leakage the day before Teton failed, up to the time of the washout. *(Taken from the report of the Independent Panel, Bureau of Reclamation.)*

not extend into the key trenches. In fact, there is reason to question whether there was an effective downstream drainage zone anywhere since zone 2 material does not appear to have been adequately permeable."

RESURRECTION?

Despite the design problems, Chadwick said last week that Teton could be rebuilt, but "it might cost more than you are willing to pay." His group was not charged with evaluating the cost or feasibility of reconstruction.

A recent poll taken primarily in Rexburg and Sugar City, which were heavily flooded—showed 55% in favor of rebuilding. However, 68% of those want the dam at a different site.

Willis Walker, a director of the Idaho Water Users Assocation, which favors rebuilding Teton on the same site, says, "We need it more than we ever did; now the flooded soil is sandier and will need more water for a few years until the soil's rebuilt." But Walker says the new dam should be broader based and perhaps built and tested in stages.

The president of an Idaho Falls real estate firm says, "I would be for building another Teton Dam. We live in an area dependent on dams; if we were afraid of dams we wouldn't live here."

But there certainly will be renewed criticism of the site and impact. And a local taxi driver may sum up the fears of many of the 2,000 injured and 30,000 made homeless when Teton unleashed its 300,000 acre-ft of water: "We sure don't want another one of those dirt dams."

In interviews after the report was issued, Chadwick continued to complain about what he saw as a casual attitude toward dam safety. Often, he said, he would be called in to inspect structures owned by sophisticated companies and government agencies, only to find that the original plans had been mislaid or destroyed. Even with operating and maintenance people on the site, there can be problems.

"Dams should be built to be safe even if they're neglected," Chadwick said. "Even with monitoring, operating people can't interpret the data."

Two years later, after burrowing through the rubble that had been Teton, the final Interior Department report claimed some minor construction errors. But the onus continued to fall on weak design. ENR looked at the final report on February 14, 1980:

Final Teton Report Faults Designer

The final report by the Interior Review Group (IRG) on the June, 1976, failure of Teton Dam in Idaho supports the findings of two previous

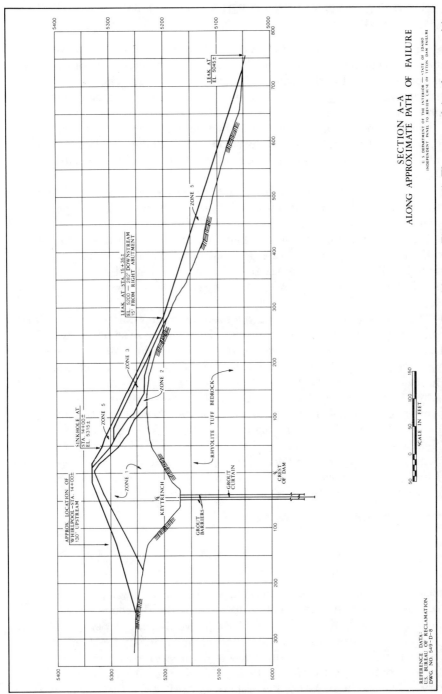

Figure 4-19 A schematic along the approximate line of failure at Teton Dam (shown in Figure 4-18). The text explains the composition of the various zones. *(Bureau of Reclamation.)*

159

BUREC IS TAKING STEPS TO PREVENT OTHER DAM COLLAPSES

The report on failure of Teton Dam calls into question the integrity of the Bureau of Reclamation's other 290 dams. But BuRec director of design and construction Harold Arthur said last week that it long ago addressed deficiencies in existing dams and now will institute greater safeguards against disaster.

BuRec Commissioner Gilbert Stamm earlier announced that it will commission independent consultants to review the design of all major new dams. Until now the bureau has sought outside advice only on specific problems, and not often.

Responding to the Teton report, Arthur says the bureau also will use more instrumentation during construction, "even where we don't expect trouble." And, he says, "We have carefully developed rules for the operation of each dam, but not for when a reservoir is filled the first time. We will develop more specific rules for controlling and monitoring initial impoundment." That includes six BuRec reservoirs that will begin filling with this spring's runoffs, although Arthur says none of them presents a hazard similar to Teton.

The bureau also is considering the need for greater outlet capacities to provide better control over reservoirs, and is reviewing seismicity, says Arthur. "The science of hydrology has developed and indicates that you can get much bigger floods than we expected. We're operating some dams under restrictions, so there's no danger."

In a 1965 survey BuRec identified 25 to 30 dams that need some improvement. None of them is a threat, a spokesman says, but the Interior Department is considering bringing in the National Academy of Engineering to review their safety.

And, Interior Secretary Thomas Kleppe called for an internal report on BuRec's management, due within a few weeks. Also, Interior will call for proposals from consultants to review the bureau's design methods.

SOURCE: *Engineering News-Record,* Jan. 13, 1977.

investigations—that the cause of the catastrophic collapse was poor embankment design and inadequate inspection by the Bureau of Reclamation, recently renamed the Water & Power Resources Service.

The report released last week discounts claims made by the dam's former chief design engineer, Jack W. Hilf, that the failure was caused by construction defects [ENR, Nov. 8, 1979, p. 17]. Rather, it reasserts the primary conclusion of an earlier IRG report, in April, 1977, that the failure

Figure 4-20 In grouting the cutoff wall at Teton Dam, care was taken to keep trenches free of contaminating material. Nevertheless, not all were prepared to receive proper fill. *(ENR File.)*

resulted from inadequate protection of zone 1 embankment material from erosive seepage [ENR, May 12, 1977, p. 14].

"If a defensive design had been provided to protect zone 1 material with appropriate embankment filtration and drainage, and adequate foundation surface treatment, a safe dam could have been constructed at the site using design concepts known at the time," the report says.

A CLOSER LOOK

The updated IRG analysis results from field investigations undertaken in 1977 and '78 to more closely determine the mode of failure. More than 882,000 cu yd of fill from the left embankment remnant were excavated to assess the effectiveness of the foundation treatment program, measurement of foundation rebound during excavation and measurement of embankment stresses in the vicinity of the left key trench prior to its excavation.

Observations made during the field studies support physical modes of failure involving seepage in the fill-rock contact at the bottom of the key trench; seepage through the top of the grout curtain; and seepage through a low-density, high-permeability lens in the core within or next to the right key trench.

Although reservoir-induced hydraulic fracturing and embankment cracking caused by differential settlement are still considered possible modes of failure, no evidence of prefailure cracking was found within the left embankment.

Among the unexpected features that were found, however, was a thin, 500-ft-long seam of saturated fill near the bottom of the zone 1 fill. In addition, the discovery of water that may have melted from ice in a core sample led to the postulation of "ice lenses" in the embankment.

These two new findings were the substance of Hilf's claims during a meeting of the International Commission on Large Dams in New Delhi last year that the failure resulted from construction defects by prime contractor Morrison-Knudsen Co. Inc., Boise.

At that time, Hilf told ENR that "frozen ground or frozen borrow soil was present virtually throughout the core and nearly coincident with the

Figure 4-21 The fractured nature of the rock underlying Teton Dam is all too evident in this construction photo, taken near where the failure was to begin. (An ENR photograph by E. Allen Soast.)

winter shut-down surface of 1974–1975. When this layer melted an avenue of easy access of reservoir water through the core resulted."

The final IRG report states that neither of these findings altered its conclusions on the causes of the failure. Wet seams were found in fill placed in late 1974, in early spring, 1975 (when construction resumed after the winter shut-down), and in late spring, 1975. In all cases, the wet seams could be correlated with the occurrence of precipitation a few days after placement of low-density, high-permeability layers of fill. The review group could find no evidence that the contractor failed to remove wet or frozen fill material before resuming work in 1975.

Further, the investigations of the postulated ice lenses found the "melt" water that was presumed to have come from a frozen layer of fill actually resulted from the core sample being dropped in the snow. Temperatures within the embankment fill were too warm to support the continued existence of ice, according to the report.

CONSTRUCTION DEFECTS

However, while the first IRG study concluded that the dam was built as specified, the updated version cited instances where that was not the case. Infractions of specifications were found in the construction of the sidewalls of the key trench and the grout curtain. In addition, inspection procedures for control of placement of zone 1 material were not always adequate.

Among the construction faults found were:

- Overhangs and ledges of rock on slopes within the key trench were not prepared adequately to receive fill.
- The grouting program did not provide for an impervious barrier.
- Dry, low-density fill was placed in zone 1 and accepted as suitable because of the incomplete procedures used for evaluation of density data from construction control tests.

Despite these findings, a technical analysis accompanying the report states: "If a defensive design had been provided for protection of the core of the dam, the consequences of these deviations would probably not have been serious enough to contribute to a failure. Because of inadequate design, these construction deviations may in some way have contributed to one or more of the possible modes of failure."

By the time the book closed on Teton, the Corps of Engineers' inspection program was well under way—and finding far more problems than had been envisioned.

ENR explained the situation on May 8, 1980:

Dam Safety: No National Answer

On-site inspections of more than half of the 9,000 nonfederal dams that represent a high hazard to life and property if they fail have brought the historical problem of unbridled dambuilding in this country into clearer focus. And the picture isn't too bright.

Of the 4,906 inspections done through March [1980] under the Corps of Engineers' National Dam Inspection Program, 32%, or 1,563 high-hazard dams were found to be unsafe. Of those, more than 70 require emergency action and the others require some remedial work to assure their stability. Moreover, the proportion of unsafe dams is growing as the inspection program matures. At the end of 1978, 20% of the inspected dams were found to be unsafe. That figure grew to 29% at the end of 1979 and is higher now.

"That's a very alarming situation," says Homer B. Willis, a consultant to the Corps on its inspection program and formerly chief of engineering for the agency. "It looks like we've got a real national problem on our hands," he says.

HIGHLY HAZARDOUS

Projections made by the Federal Emergency Management Agency (FEMA) using the Corps' inspection data indicate that when all inspections are

Figure 4-22 The canyon wall was scoured clean by the force of water escaping from Teton after the break. *(Bureau of Reclamation.)*

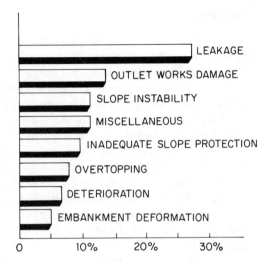

LEAKAGE

OUTLET WORKS DAMAGE

SLOPE INSTABILITY

MISCELLANEOUS

INADEQUATE SLOPE PROTECTION

OVERTOPPING

DETERIORATION

EMBANKMENT DEFORMATION

0   10%   20%   30%

Figure 4-23 Leakage causes about a third of the dam failures in the United States; this chart shows causes of accidents as a percentage of total accidents at dams built since 1930 in the United States. *(ENR.)*

completed in fiscal year 1981, about 2,600 high-hazard dams may be found unsafe. Similarly, for the total U.S. inventory of 50,000 nonfederal dams, an estimated 14,500 may be unsafe, about 5% of those would require immediate action—usually drawing down the reservoir or controlled breaching—to avoid failure, and in some cases disaster.

"We're just now learning about our oversight and we're paying for that every year and will continue to pay," says Bruce A. Tschantz, chief of federal dam safety in FEMA's Office of Mitigation and Research. A vocal critic of government inattention to the issue of dam safety while a civil engineering professor at the University of Tennessee, Tschantz was appointed to his FEMA post after the 1977 failure of Toccoa Dam killed 39 persons at a Bible college in Georgia.

The cost of making improvements to all unsafe dams could run into the billions of dollars. Calculations contained in a draft of a FEMA issue paper recently sent out for comment put the cost at between $1.5 billion and $7.5 billion to repair the projected 14,500 unsafe dams. Using a $5-billion figure, 6% discount rate and 50-year amortization period, the paper's authors figured annual costs would be more than $300 million. And this excludes social costs from lost services during repairs and assumes that few new unsafe dams are discovered.

According to a state-by-state inventory derived from the Corps' inspections by New York City consultant Tippetts-Abbett-McCarthy-Stratton (TAMS), the cost burden would not be shared equally among states. The majority of dams inspected so far in five states have been found to be unsafe. . . . West Virginia leads the nation—74% of the dams inspected were declared unsafe. South Carolina is next, followed by Tennessee, Georgia and Missouri.

WHO PAYS?

Whether the federal or state governments will provide repair funds or can force public or private owners to upgrade unsafe dams remains the key issue. The Corps' $90-million, four-year inspection program will provide only preliminary classification of the 9,000 dams it had already determined as high-hazard structures, where failure could cause significant loss of life.

The next step, performing more detailed studies to determine what needs to be done and then doing it will be the responsibility of state enforcement agencies and owners of the dams, says Tschantz. Unfortunately though, most states have continued to put dam safety near the bottom of their priority list.

According to the Corps' most recent summary of its inspection program, to be issued this week, among 53 states and U.S. commonwealths, five have no legislation authorizing dam safety activities. In 16 the legislation is inadequate and in 13 the enforcement agencies are understaffed and underfunded.

In addition, says Willis, less than 5% of the unsafe dams identified have been repaired or taken out of service. And detailed studies or remedial actions have been started on less than 30%. "The states really haven't knuckled down and provided the money or manpower needed for safe dams," he says.

A major problem facing state agencies is that half of the dams found to be unsafe nationwide serve functions needed by their public or quasi-public owners, such as city or county water authorities, churches, Boy Scouts, public cooperatives or other groups. "While the national inspection program is helping us to begin to define problems . . . it does not add to our basic problem with dam safety," said David C. Callaghan, director of West Virginia's Department of Natural Resources. Known hazardous dams in the state serve varied public purposes and are "highly beneficial," he says.

BALANCING BENEFITS

"The expense [to the state] incurred by removing such structures is usually comparable to the [owner's] cost of upgrading or repairing them and, unfortunately, funding is not available to dam owners or state governments to do either," says Callaghan. "Consequently, potentially hazardous structures do and will continue to exist."

Balancing the public benefit derived from impounding water supplies behind unsafe dams against the risk of catastrophic failure is an issue that has not been addressed except on a case-by-case basis where failure is imminent. A major problem is that no one can be sure if and when a failure will occur until, in most cases, it's too late. Besides, the fact is that not many dams have failed.

"Considering the number of dams, the number of failures and the number of people killed, what really is the magnitude of the problem?" asks George A. Gibson, a project manager for the Corps' inspection program.

A United States Committee on Large Dams study of 4,918 federal and nonfederal dams higher than 45 ft noted 349 incidents (7%) of unsatisfactory or unsafe performance, including 74 failures (1.5%). About 16% of the dams built between 1850 and 1930 performed unsatisfactorily, while 4% of the dams built after 1930 had problems.

Eugene O'Brien, a TAMS partner, put the failure rate in perspective at a recent safety seminar in New York. He noted there have been 180 dam incidents in the last 100 years involving public safety. Forty of those were major failures where the dam was abandoned and 40 others resulted in severe damage but were repaired. The 100 other dams were saved by remedial action or lowering the level of the reservoir.

Rapid advances made in understanding soil mechanics during the 1930's have resulted in the number of failures being cut by 75% for dams built since 1940. About 3,000 of the 5,000 dams in this country over 45 ft tall have been built since that time, says O'Brien.

The other side of the coin is that when dams fail, the potential for catastrophe can be great. More than 2,200 persons died in the Johnstown, Pa., flood of 1889. Some 2,000 of the fatalities were due to the failure of the South Fork Dam, a well-built earthfill that withstood overtopping for more than three hours before being washed away. Eleven died when Teton Dam in Idaho failed in 1976. Without the six hours of warning between initial signs of failure and flooding of populated areas, many more could have been killed.

NEAR MISS

Erik H. Vanmarcke, a civil engineering professor at Massachusetts Institute of Technology who is working on a National Science Foundation study of dam failure risk assessment, also points out a significant near miss. The Lower Van Norman earthfill dam near heavily populated San Fernando, Calif., almost failed in 1971 during a severe earthquake. "Only luck prevented a major disaster," he says, noting that 40,000 persons were evacuated from below the dam after the quake.

Figure 4-24 Where unsafe dams are located: Unsafe dams as a percentage of the total inspected by contractors for the U.S. Army Corps of Engineers in each state, as of February 29, 1980. The 0 for California signifies only that the Corps program was not operated there; state officials ran their own program. (*Tippetts-Abbett-McCarthy-Stratton.*)

"Dams located above population centers have a catastrophic potential that can't be ignored," says Vanmarcke. He also points out, however, that nearly half of the failures of large dams occur during the first filling of the reservoir, "So bad apples are weeded out early."

Considerations differ, however, between large dams built in the future, and the thousands of small earthfill and concrete dams built, in some cases, by someone with a bulldozer in the middle of the night. Indeed, whether states and the federal government can put together a program to improve the safety of existing nonfederal dams remains a big question. The National Dam Safety Act of 1972 was passed as a result of 125 lives lost when the Buffalo Creek coal tailings dam failed. Funding for the Corps' inspections, mandated by Congress in 1972, was delayed until 1977, after 39 Bible students and teachers died in the dam failure at Toccoa, Ga.

Unfortunately, says Tschantz, "Our dam safety constituents are dead people. Others forget very quickly."

Unfortunately, too, the billions of dollars necessary to rebuild all the dams the Corps has found to be in trouble have not been made available. Nor has the funding been provided to map out evacuation plans in high-hazard areas below dams—although large sums are being spent on evacuation plans for populations around nuclear powerplants. As events of the past decade have made clear, of course, a dam is far more likely to fail than is a nuclear reactor.

New dams, at least, now have to be designed for the "maximum probable flood," under guidelines issued early in 1980. Perhaps a few more old dams have to fail before the rest of the country follows California's lead.

5   **Bridges**

To most members of the public, a bridge is an immovable object—solid as a granite mountainside. As the engineering community is well aware, however, bridges are unlike any other structures. They expand and contract greatly in heat or cold; they shiver with the wind; they are subject to abuse in the form of road salt, corrosion, and overloading. Most engineers never get to see the really bad deterioration, though, simply because engineers are rarely called in to inspect a bridge, or to maintain one before disaster strikes.

As of December 31, 1981, according to an unpublished report by the federal Department of Transportation, 45 percent of the nation's bridges were either inadequate for today's loads, or "structurally deficient." The report counted 557,516 bridges all together, and put more than a fifth of them—126,655—into the structurally deficient category (either closed to traffic or restricted to light loads while awaiting repair).

It is some tribute to American engineering that 37 percent of the bridges surveyed are more than 40 years old but still standing. The bridges' longevity, in turn, is due in large part to the lessons of the past—lessons which helped engineers to think of bridges almost as living objects.

One of the earliest major engineering disasters befell the Tay Bridge in 1879. It was the longest and highest bridge of its age—over 5000 feet from end to end, in eighty-five through-lattice-truss spans of malleable iron supported 88 feet above the water. One January evening, a train with seventy-five people aboard started across the bridge in the teeth of a howling gale. The train never reached the other side; it and thirteen spans fell into the Firth of Tay. The failure was described vividly by David A. Watt of St. Petersburg, Florida, in this letter to the editor, published in ENR on September 7, 1944:

The bridge, completed in 1877, crossed an inlet of the North Sea on the east coast of Scotland known as the Firth of Tay, a bottle-shaped estuary about 20 miles long and opening easterly.... [The bridge was located] in the neck of the inlet, and the contours of the land were such as to compress there the full force of northeasterly gales.

Figure 5-1 A school bus stops to let children cross a shaky rural Indiana bridge on foot; only the driver will be aboard when the bus itself crosses. (*Indianapolis News Photo from* The Road Information Program.)

Figure 5-2 Twelve cars of a 76-car Seaboard Coastline train litter the Coosa River near Childersburg, Alabama, on July 5, 1976. The bridge collapsed under their weight. (*United Press International.*)

A lad in England at the time, I was vastly interested in the matter, and though I never saw the Board of Trade findings, I followed the testimony reported in the newspapers day by day. Just what actually happened on the bridge was never known. It had weathered the storm without harm until the night passenger train attempted to cross, as proved by the shore watchmen's exchange of telegraph signals, but when the day broke it was seen that nearly a third of the bridge had gone.

The storm, by the testimony of old-timers, was the wildest within memory, and the strength of the wind must have been far more terrible out in the neck of the estuary, where the bridge stood high above the water, than it was on shore. One theory was that the wind against the side of the train had buckled the track bracing, causing a sideways failure of the spans. Another was that the sway bracing of the high cast iron towers carrying the bridge had failed under the extra wind load, and that towers and trusses had gone over together. An examination of the few pieces of wreckage within reach showed that some of the cast iron lugs for attaching this bracing had been broken off. A third theory was that the train had been blown bodily off the rails, fouling the trusses and causing a general collapse of all adjacent trusses and towers. Perhaps all these causes were in action.

Of all the testimony which I now recall, that of one of the watchmen was the most detailed and graphic. He was on duty at the southern end of the bridge that night, and just before the passenger train was due from the south he had telegraphed the watchman at the north end and had received the "all clear" signal. The storm by then was at its height. When the train drew in and stopped to receive the signal, the engine driver got down and talked with the watchman about the safety of going on. He finally decided to risk it. The watchman saw the red tail-lights of the guard's van growing gradually fainter until they vanished in the murk. Half an hour went by, but no signal had come through that the train had cleared the bridge. The watchman then tried to contact the north end, but could get no reply.

As the minutes slowly passed he began to wonder if the train had been derailed on the bridge, and finally decided it was his duty to go out and see. It must have been a journey to try the soul. He started crawling on his hands and knees, but as he cleared the shore he met the full fury of the storm, and so terrible was the wind that he had to flatten himself between the rails and ceep forward inch by inch.

He worked his way some distance out, but was becoming exhausted and had decided to turn back when he noticed that the screaming of the wind in the trusses seemed to be growing less. So he crawled on as far as the next pier and then stopped abruptly, for he found the track sheared across, and before him and beneath him were only black emptiness and the roaring wind.

When he got back he telegraphed his chief that the train was in the Firth. And there it has remained to this day, for the tides run strong and the water is deep. Where the train and its passengers found their last resting place no man knows.

A new bridge was completed in 1887, located about 60 feet upstream from the old one.

The British Board of Trade, charged with making the investigation into what went wrong, uncovered grievous lapses in quality control. Designer Thomas Bouch, who died in disgrace less than a year after the bridge fell, had a financial interest in the firm that built the bridge. Cast-iron columns that should have been rejected contained blowholes filled with beeswax and iron filings so they would not be seen. Foundation design had been based on incomplete, badly interpreted borings.

The Board focused more on what it considered inadequate design than on the structural faults, claiming that the assumed wind load of 10 pounds per square foot was far too low. This was a clear overreaction, according to Sir Owen Williams, the London-based chief of the consulting firm that bears his name. Here is his letter, from the March 21, 1957, issue of ENR:

As a result of the findings of the inquiry based on this erroneous idea of wind pressure, the law for wind pressure in Great Britain became then 56 psf and was a considerable hindrance and expense in the design of structures for many years. At the beginning World War I, there were attempts to design hangars in that country for wind pressures of this order. It could not be understood how the Germans were managing with lighter constructions, until it was found that they were designing them for about 9 psf. After that there was a more enlightened angle on wind pressures, which have now been considerably scaled down as result of wind-tunnel experiments.

It is of interest that all double-deck buses in Great Britain would blow over at 15 psf wind pressure. Fortunately, they rarely do this.

The most likely thing on the Tay Bridge is that a light railway carriage under a wind pressure of 10 psf or so, lurched and broke on the cast-iron joints of the bridge, thus causing its collapse. The engineer [Bouch] was not responsible for the running of the train onto the bridge, and to that extent, should not be held responsible.

I think that the findings of the commission . . . are a typical case of there being too many causes of disaster brought up—meaning that the commission never really found the one true cause. . . .

I came to the conclusion that the commission's findings were totally wrong and that in the search for a scapegoat, they suggested every possible error, but did not pinpoint the real cause. Surely that is the lesson to learn.

By the time the Tay Bridge fell, a more carefully constructed bridge was nearing completion in the United States. It was put into service in 1883, and it still stands, connecting Brooklyn with lower Manhattan. Part of the Brooklyn Bridge's charm is its lacework of diagonal cable stays—all of which could be chopped away without affecting the bridge's ability to withstand the strongest gale.

Wind loading remained a point of some argument until well after World War II, thanks to some spectacular failures like Tacoma Narrows (discussed at length later in this chapter) and the Chester Bridge, described in the August 10, 1944, issue of ENR:

CONTEMPLATED EAST RIVER BRIDGE.

Figure 5-3   Concern about wind sway led the Roeblings to add bracing cables to the Brooklyn Bridge, shown here in an 1869 rendering. Engineers who have inspected the structure say it should stand for another 100 years. But the redundant stays occasionally break loose; one killed a passerby in 1981. *(Cooper-Hewitt Museum.)*

Chester Bridge Designed for 30-Lb. Wind Load

The Mississippi River bridge at Chester, Ill., that lost its two main spans in a violent wind storm on July 29 [*ENR*, Aug., 3, 1944, p. 125]was designed for a wind pressure of 30 lb. per sq. ft., according to John I. Parcel of Sverdrup & Parcel, the designing engineers.

In providing for wind on the unloaded structure (that is, dead load plus maximum wind effect), a pressure of 30 lb. per sq. ft. was assumed on the vertical projection of two trusses, two handrails and the floor. This was treated as a moving load. Members governed by this loading were proportioned for *normal* unit stresses. This, according to Mr. Parcel, is

Figure 5-4   The two continuous 670-foot spans of the Chester Bridge in Illinois were literally lifted off their piers in high winds July 29, 1944. The discussions and investigations that followed led to more sophisticated calculations of wind forces and to use of better anchoring mechanisms. But many bridges built before that time still could float free in a gale. *(ENR.)*

equivalent to 40 lb. per sq. ft. when applied to 1½ the "silhouette area" of the structure, as is standard practice for short spans.

Using the widely known formula

$$p = 0.032 \ V^2$$

the specifications will provide for a wind velocity of 97 mph. at normal stresses, with a large margin of safety.

In the matter of overturning, Mr. Parcel states that their computations indicate that a pressure of 83 lb. per sq. ft. over the entire length would have been required, if applied as indicated in the specifications. If only 1½ of the area seen in elevation is taken as effective, 110 lb. per sq. ft. would have been required. Using the above elevation, 83 lb. per sq. ft. corresponds to a wind velocity of 161 mph., and 110 lb. to 185 mph.

EYE-WITNESS ACCOUNTS

The storm that wrecked the bridge originated in St. Louis and Jefferson counties, where it uprooted trees and did minor damage to roofs, and gained in intensity as it moved down the river toward the bridge. Several people were on the bluff overlooking the river at Chester. Two, who have been through tornadoes before, state that they observed the typical funnel-shaped cloud characteristic of a tornado.

No damage typical of a tornado was done in Chester itself, but three towboats moored down at the river in front of Chester were sunk and a 45 ft. pusher boat was torn from its mooring.

A truck loaded with furniture crossed the bridge from the Missouri to the Illinois side just before it collapsed, and the driver of the truck told the toll collector that the wind was so high that he lost half of his load.

SPANS LIFTED FROM PIERS

Three independent witnesses have been found who claim to have seen the bridge collapse. All agree that apparently the Missouri end of the continuous span was lifted clear off its suppports, after which it fell to the river, taking the Illinois span with it. Nothing inconsistent with this behavior has been found in the condition of the pier tops, except that the teeth of the expansion joint at the Missouri end are uninjured, which would indicate that there must have been a longitudinal movement of the span at the time it was lifted. This would have been necessary to disengage the teeth without injury.

The main channel span was a 1,340-ft. through truss, continuous over two 670-ft. openings. On both sides of the main span were two 250-ft. openings spanned by continuous deck trusses, which were left absolutely intact.

The main trusses were spaced 28 ft. 6 in. on centers, height 60 ft. at hip, 100 ft. at center, and 70 ft. for the greater part of each span length. The total weight, including floor and bracing, was about 6,205,000 lb., or 4,640 lb. per lin. ft. The floor was a 4½ in. filled grating welded to the stringers.

In considering the question of uplift, Mr. Parcel states that the average weight of the bridge was 155 lb. per sq. ft. of floor area; in the outer half of the spans this was somewhat less, approximately 154 lb.

The great John Parcel was taken to task for not doing wind-tunnel testing of the bridge's design. In a letter appearing in the September 7, 1944, issue of ENR, S. P. Wing of Denver complained:

There has been no excuse for many years for any engineer to justify his wind load assumptions on the grounds that they provide for a uniform pressure of $0.0032\ V^2$ per sq. ft. acting on 1½ of the sectional area in elevation, with a wind velocity of 100 mph. Not only has it been known that the coefficient of this formula varies 100 percent or more from this value, dependent on the direction of the wind, the make-up of the individual members, the type of floor system, and upon the spacing of the trusses, but likewise data have been available showing that wind velocities may greatly exceed 100 mph. and are not constant in magnitude, direction, or frequency.

In the writer's opinion, more fruitful than model wind-tunnel tests in contributing to structural security, except for special cases such as the Tacoma bridge, will be special studies of the resistance of a structure to wind loads, varying the loading in magnitude and direction in accord with present knowledge, and evaluating loading probabilities so as to achieve a balanced design and risk.

The one and sole merit of present wind specifications, but one which is apt to be overlooked under the impact of a spectacular failure, is that, by and large, they have provided security against wind load failures, except in a very small number of cases. Public interest is best served not by having structures designed under specification such that a few failures cause less economic loss than would be the excess cost of providing absolute security for all. And the exceptional risk can be covered by insurance.

This basic engineering approach needs to be remembered not only in the field of bridge and building design, but in other fields. In recent years under the impact of active imaginations and technology, engineers have been apt to talk of providing for the absolute maximum flood or of providing absolute assurance against all risk. Life itself is filled with hazards and to attempt to make every structure stand on its own feet by prescribing extremely heavy loadings often defeats its own ends by eliminating the structure as a possibility. If an engineer, in presenting his cost estimates to his client, will frankly state that the exceptional is not provided for, and indicate the risk involved, then no one is fooled, and appropriate action can be taken.

New fabrication techniques and unfamiliar designs have also cost lives. In June 1970, a cantilevered, welded-steel box girder failed while under construction at the Milford Haven Bridge in southwest Wales. Four workmen were killed after a diaphragm plate buckled. That same month, a top flange plate on the trapezoidal box girder of the Bryte Bend Bridge, which crosses California's Sacramento River, cracked while workers were placing the concrete deck.

The preceeding autumn, a twin orthotropic box girder buckled on the Fourth Danube Bridge in Vienna. A temperature change caused uneven web plate expansion on the span. Another Austrian box girder project—a concrete span under construction near the Yugoslavian border—collapsed at about the same time; a crane had broken some of the temporary stays used to support the span as it was being laid. Three workers were killed and five seriously injured.

Those failures caused little widespread concern in the construction industry and among the public until an Australian box girder span collapsed while being built in Melbourne. At least thirty-five died and fifteen were injured. Freeman, Fox and Partners, which had designed the bridge, had also designed the Milford Haven project. A three-man Australian Royal Commission placed primary blame for the failure of Melbourne's bridge on the firm. "We are compelled to conclude that Freeman, Fox and Partners bear heavy responsibility for failure of the bridge," the report said. The commission also blamed the con-

Figure 5-5 Collapse of a 367-foot side span forced redesign of the West Gate Bridge in Melbourne, Australia. *(United Press International.)*

tractors, who were rushing to make up time after a strike had delayed construction.

Public comment at the time generally focused on the safety factor built into the design—1.31 for erection—saying it was too low. The British standard then called for a normal safety factor of 1.70 for bridges, with a 30 percent increase in allowable stresses for "stresses due to all causes at the time of erection." Application of that factor would give 1.70/1.30 = 1.31 for erection. Was the safety factor required by British standard too low, not leaving enough margin for errors in calculation of the span's dead load during erection, or of wind forces, temperature-induced stresses, and other factors? Or was the calculation of those factors simply botched by the designer? Evidence cited by the commission points to design errors. But either way, contractors upped the margin for erection forces after the disaster.

It was well they did, for 2 years later another box girder bridge failed, at Koblenz, West Germany, killing thirteen. Authorities first reported the cause as inadequate stiffening across a transverse weld seam in the lower flange. True enough, but the stiffening turned out to be inadequate because the method used to calculate the stresses involved was flawed conceptually. As noted in the ENR issue of November 23, 1972:

The collapse inquiry determined that the theory fails when it is applied to sections that are extremely wide in comparison to their longitudinal dimension and are subjected to stresses across the width. That was the case at Koblenz where 18-in. gaps were left in the T stiffeners on the bottom flange to permit automatic seam welding. After seam welding, T splices of the same size were welded on to join the stiffener ends. But the splices overlapped the top of adjacent sections, leaving a small gap below where . . . [it was reported] tremendous compression built up in the flange. Below the splice, on each side of the weld, were 9 in. $\times$ 18 ft unstiffened strips of the 0.43-in.-thick plates running transversely on each side of a center rib beam. "With such a wide section, the linear theory . . . is from 6 to 8% inaccurate," the report says.

The theory is widely used in the U.S. and elsewhere, but not when there is a possibility of buckling, according to one U.S. bridge designer who declines to be quoted without reviewing the report. Under such conditions, particularly when welds might cause cusps in the plate, a more complex nonlinear buckling theory is generally used, he says.

The designer and superstructure erector of the Koblenz bridge. Maschinenfabrik Augsburg-Nuernberg, of Gustavsburg, believed that the effects of any distortions in the plate would be overcome by applying a safety factor of 1.69 on the small unstiffened sections, well above the 1.35 then specified by national standards. While the unstiffened plate was designed to

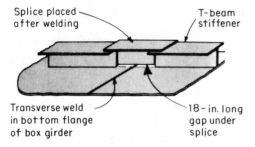

Splice placed
after welding

T-beam
stiffener

Transverse weld
in bottom flange
of box girder

18-in. long
gap under
splice

Figure 5-6 The gap left below splices of stiffening members (to allow automatic welding of the bottom flange of the box girder at Koblenz, West Germany) let compression forces build. *(ENR.)*

withstand distortions of up to 0.037 in., the investigators measured distortions as great as 0.078 in.

After the disaster, West Germany's government prohibited the type of stiffener used at Koblenz and insisted that nonlinear theory be used to calculate the forces on the plate.

Designers and builders also had troubles with electroslag-welded steel I-beam girders in bridge supports. U.S. officials embraced the process until a passing tugboat captain noticed a 2-inch-wide crack in an 11-foot-deep beam on an Interstate 79 span over the Ohio River near Pittsburgh. Hundreds of bridges were eventually repaired, starting in 1977, by bolting plates across the areas where the welds had been made. Fortunately, no collapses were attributed to the offending welds.

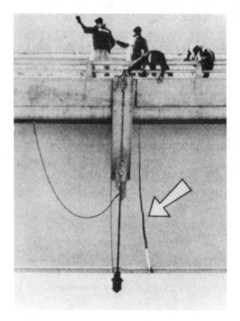

Figure 5-7 This crack in an 11-foot-deep girder on an Interstate 79 bridge near Pittsburgh began in an electroslag weld; it was discovered by a passing tugboat captain. *(ENR.)*

HOW AN ELECTROSLAG WELD IS MADE

Russian engineers developed electroslag welding in the early 1950s for splicing heavy steel girders in a single pass, cutting manpower costs significantly. Though U.S. industry glimpsed its first machine for this type of weld in 1959, the process didn't catch on until [the early sixties].

Electroslag welding is done, usually in a shop, with the steel plates held vertically and with their faces separated. Water-cooled copper shoes placed on the sides of the joint contain the weld material as the splice is, in effect, cast.

Welding begins in a sump beneath the joint as one or more electrodes are fed continuously into the area through guide tubes, which may or may not be consumed during the process. Electric arcs from the electrodes initially heat the slag until molten; then the arc is extinguished by being submerged in the slag. The conductive slag is maintained in a molten condition by its resistance to current passing between electrodes and plates. Melted electrode and plate metal collect in a weld pool beneath the slag pool and slowly solidify to form the weld. The weld solidifies from the bottom upward, always with a molten metal covering the solidifying weld metal.

Welding parameters are critical. If amperage and voltage aren't carefully controlled, centerline cracking can occur.

Electroslag welds can be made from 0 to 20 in. thick with nonconsumable guide tubes and to an unlimited thickness with consumable guides, according to the American Welding Society. For larger weldments the electroslag process in a single pass can join plates that might require 150 passes with conventional submerged arc methods, producing cost savings on the order of 10:1

SOURCE: *Engineering News-Record,* Nov. 23, 1972.

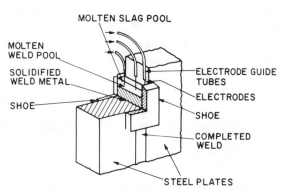

Figure 5-8 In electroslag welding, electrode wires become molten along with the ends of the members being joined. They solidify to weld the sections together. *(ENR.)*

Despite these problems with materials, however, most of the bridge disasters of the last century have been due to design methods that were not sophisticated enough to account for subtle effects—wind-induced reasonance at Tacoma Narrows, for example—or due to poor maintenance. This chapter discusses three doomed spans that illustrate the lessons learned by bridge designers over the past half century.

The Bridge as a Machine: Hackensack River Bascule, 1928

Dynamic as well as static forces must be taken into account in the design of a moving bridge. That seems obvious now, but it was not obvious before the bascule bridge carrying Lincoln Highway over the Hackensack River near Newark, New Jersey, failed on Saturday night, December 15, 1928. In a bascule, a heavy counterweight balances the weight of the bridge span itself, so the span can be swung upward for ships to pass. When the bridge is in its "closed" position, allowing cars to cross the span, the counterweight (in this case, one for each half span of the bridge) is suspended above the roadway.

Although the Hackensack's bascule counterweight weighed 770 tons, it was easily supported by thin latticework towers—or so the designers thought. As the editors of ENR noted 3 weeks after the failure, "This member apparently had only light service to perform; it was subject to small static stresses. But its actual service as a member of a moving machine was more severe. . . . The accident was a machine failure, resulting from stresses, distortions and oscillations arising under operation against the forces of friction and inertia. As such, it is one of the most important structural accidents of recent times."

The discussion which followed over the next year turned *Engineering News-Record* into an unusual forum in which the distinguished investigators of the disaster did not shrink from blaming the bridge's distinguished designer. The designer then replied that poor construction and maintenance was at fault—only to be brilliantly rebutted by the investigators. The affair also served to cement the profession's confidence in a brilliant consultant, D. B. Steinman.

The story begun unfolding in the issue of December 20, 1928:

Lincoln Highway Bascule Drops into River

East half of two-leaf drawspan over Hackensack River between Jersey City and Newark, N.J., fails while being lowered—Cause of failure as yet undetermined.

A remarkable bascule bridge failure occurred on Saturday night, Dec. 15, about 10 o'clock, at the crossing of the Lincoln Highway over the Hackensack River between Newark and Jersey City, N.J. The east leaf of the double-leaf bascule fell into the river channel as it was being lowered from open position. The west leaf, which had not yet started down, was undamaged. The bridge, which carries heavy vehicular traffic and also the main streetcar connection between Jersey City and Newark, was built less than two years ago, being placed in operation in November, 1927. It replaced a swing span in the same location which was wrecked by a steamer in 1922.

As soon as the wreckage of the east leaf is cleared away a timber pile trestle will be constructed to connect with the west leaf at the center of the river channel, thus providing a temporary crossing.

The failure is being investigated by a special committee appointed by W. G. Sloan, state highway engineer. The members of this committee are O. E. Hovey, assistant chief engineer of the American Bridge Company; Prof. George E. Beggs, of Princeton University; and D. B. Steinman, consulting engineer.

The bascule consists of two leaves 98 ft. long from trunnion to outer end and is about 48 ft. wide between trusses. It was designed by the Strauss Bascule Bridge Company, of Chicago, and is of its movable-counterweight type. It was fabricated by the American Bridge Company and erected under supervision of the New Jersey State Highway Department, which now maintains it, by the Stillman-Delehanty-Ferris Company, contractors, of Jersey City.

The counterweight system is in the form of a balanced and articulated parallelogram over the tail section of the leaf. The rear member of this parallelogram consists of a pair of heavy posts (each consisting of two built-up channels made of two angles and three plates and joined by angle lacing, one at each truss carrying its load down to pins in the ends of the tail sections of the trusses). The front member is a pair of fixed posts, one erected over the trunnion support of each truss and just back of the trunnion bearing: from a pin in the top of this fixed post a link extends to the top of the counterweight block, this link being parallel to the line connecting the trunnion pin with the tail pin. The fixed post and the upper link, which under ideal conditions carry no load stresses but serve only as a wind frame, were light members, the post being made of two 12-in. channels spread about 3 ft. at the base and connected by single angle diagonals.

The counterweight consisted of a block of concrete 20 ft. high, 11½ ft. wide and 48 ft. 10 in. long, weighing approximately 750 tons. In its down position (when the leaf was open) the counterweight cleared the roadway about 7 ft. As the leaf was lowered and the parallelogram assumed a more nearly rectangular shape, the counterweight block rose until in its highest position the bottom of the concrete block was 29 ft. above the roadway. It was in some intermediate position between low and high, and was rising, when the failure occurred, the bridge operator estimating that the leaf was between one-quarter and one-half down when he saw the north end of the counterweight move forward from its usual position followed by the crash of the structure.

A view of the wreckage [Figure 5-9] shows both the north and south trunnion pedestals in place. The north trunnion bearing, pin and curved rack all fell into the river, only the back end of the rack being visible above the water. The operating pinion is still in place on the pier and undamaged. The complete counterweight structure over this pedestal is also under water, the front channel of the fixed post breaking off at the top of the pedestal and the rear channel leaving a projection of about 18 in. above the top. The break of the front channel showed bright metal and indicated a clean tension break. The break of the rear channel, on the other hand, showed three different conditions of metal. The north flange and about an inch of adjacent web were covered with old rust, indicating a crack of some age. Next to this rust there was a section of web about 8 in. long upon which the break showed bright and coarse texture, while the remainder of the web and the south flange exhibited a somewhat duller color but a more silky texture. The break occurred through the rivet holes holding the lacing and almost straight across. The rivet hole on the north side was lined with old rust, while that on the south side was of the dull silky finish. In front of the trunnion pedestal the live-load support, a low

Figure 5-9 The wrecked east leaf of the Hackensack River bascule on the Lincoln Highway in New Jersey. In the left foreground the undamaged west leaf is shown in the closed position. At left (the north side of the wrecked leaf), the tailpiece and operating rack protrude from the waters of the Hackensack River. *(ENR.)*

Figure 5-10 The Hackensack River bascule wreckage, looking south. Trunnion pedestals are in place. The north live-load support is smashed, and the counterweight post base can be seen upside down, hanging from the pin on the tailpiece in the foreground. *(ENR.)*

built-steel post on the pier, was distorted by a blow which appeared to have glanced off of the cap plate into the river [Figure 5-10].

The south trunnion pin and bearing did not fall into the river, but the whole assembly was pulled forward off of the trunnion pedestal [Figure 5-10], one of the bearings dropping off and landing on the bridge deck. Examination of the bronze bearing surface showed some evidence of wear. A portion of the top chord and the fist web vertical are still hanging to the south wreckage. The top chord of two built-up webs laced top and bottom and with batten plates on top at the panel points was broken off squarely about 8 ft. from the end. The first vertical was buckled nearly 180 deg. upon itself. The top chord was covered with concrete dust and was badly crushed directly over the buckled web member, as shown in [Figure 5-14]. The batten plate at this point was smashed by a blow that slid off of it toward the inside or north. A large group of rivets which connected the top chord gussets to the pin plates were clearly sheared and the north gusset of this member was cracked for nearly its full length. The fixed post of the parallelogram was bent sharply forward from its connection to the south trunnion pedestal, the angle lacing being buckled upon itself. The front channel of this member was badly buckled and was broken off about 4 ft. from the pedestal. The back channel was draped over the trunnion pin and extended nearly to the water, where it also was broken off. All of the wreckage on the south of the bridge was covered with dust from the counterweight and in position was inclined toward the north. The only wreckage protruding above the water on the south side is the end of a floor beam, evidently the one at the buckled first web vertical. The floor beams were fastened by kneebrace gussets extending practically the full height of the web verticals and all of the rivet holes through which this plate kneebrace of the visible floor beam was connected to the angles on the truss were torn free, apparently by a downward and northward pull. Neither the counterweight nor its two posts are visible.

Levels taken on the piers after the accident showed them to have been unaffected by previous dredging in the channel. According to engineers of the highway department, it is extremely unlikely that any of the pins bound because of lack of lubricant, since maintenance of the structure had been unusually thorough. The main trunnion and the tail pin were lubricated through pressure fittings, while the link pins at the top were of the automatic graphite type. Examination of the pins on the undamaged west leaf showed them to be well lubricated.

With mechanical defects tentatively eliminated, present indications point strongly to a structural failure of some sort. Although lacking the essential facts concerning the conditions of the counterweight posts, several deductions can be made from what is known. The inclination of the south wreckage toward the north, the battered south top chord showing unmistakable evidence that a terrific blow struck it and glanced off toward the north, and the torn condition of the floorbeam visible above the water indicate that the north side of the bridge failed first. These deductions are checked by the statement of the bridge operator, and by the fact that divers have found the north end of the counterweight to be about 18 ft. from the pier, while the south end is very close to the pier. As one looks to the north pier for some evidence of weakness, the cracked back channel of the fixed post commands immediate attention. Failure of this member during operation of the bridge would permit the counterweight to fall forward where it would be ineffective in checking the downward movement of the leaf. The smashed condition of the live-load support is evidence that the leaf fell upon it with great force. This also would tend to throw the counterweight and the tailpiece and operating rack some distance into the river. As stated, divers have located this end of the counterweight about 18 ft. from the pier.

Pending the report of the special commission and the raising and examination of the counterweight posts, the facts suggest that failure of the north fixed post occurred at an early stage, allowing this end of the counterweight to swing forward and thereby cause the north truss to fall.

The special commission appointed to examine the wreckage was at the site eight or nine hours after the collapse, viewing what could be seen, taking strain-gage measurements on the undamaged leaf and making preparations to

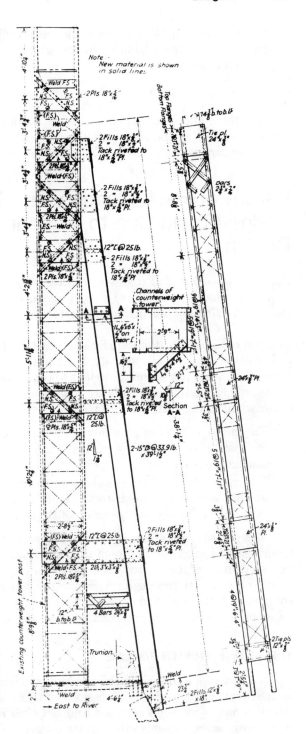

Figure 5-11 A new A-frame bracing system was added to stiffen the north and south legs of the counterweight tower of the Hackensack River bascule. *(ENR.)*

examine the submerged wreckage as soon as it could be cut into moderate-sized pieces which could be lifted by the salvaging derrick. The report of this commission is not yet available.

The three-man commission worked with admirable dispatch, rendering an initial verdict—that the design itself was at fault—only a week later. The final report was carried in the ENR issue of June 6, 1929:

Failure of Hackensack Bascule Bridge Found Due to Inadequate Design

Final report of board of engineers locates initial failure in counterweight tower and reveals existence of greatly excessive stresses in tower legs— Bearing friction not a contributing factor.

Collapse of the east leaf of the Hackensack River bascule bridge on the Lincoln Highway, near Jersey City, N.J., on Dec. 15 last, was caused by excessive stresses in the counterweight tower, according to the final report of the board of investigating engineers. The report, rendered on May 11, is summarized in two main conclusions:

1. The failure of the bridge occurred through the fracture of the north leg of the east counterweight tower, this fracture had been progressive for some time in the past.
2. The cause of the failure was the inadequacy of the design of the counterweight tower to withstand stresses readily calculable from forces known to exist during the normal operation of the bridge. . . .

The present final report is in general agreement with the preliminary report as to location and nature of the failure, but it is based on much more extended study of the actions involved, including stress measurements on the uninjured west leaf, thorough review and test of the electrical and mechanical equipment of this leaf, and analyses of the various kinds of stress that might be set up in the structure and machinery during operation.

THE BRIDGE AND ITS FAILURE

. . . The final report, declaring the breaks in the north counterweight tower to be the point of origin of the collapse, states that examination of the failed structure and of members salvaged from the river revealed no indications of failure originating elsewhere than in the counterweight tower. But it reasserts what was brought out in the preliminary report, namely, that the

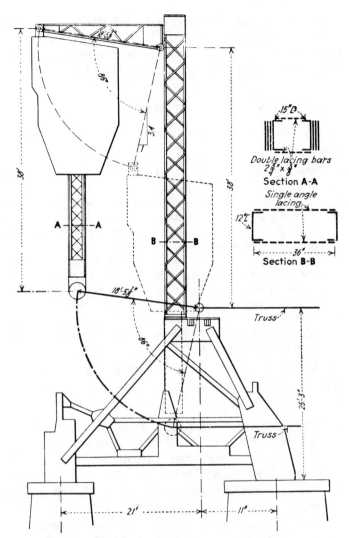

Figure 5-12 Diagram showing the counterweight system of the Hackensack River bascule. The heavy concrete block at top left was supported on slender latticework. *(ENR.)*

counterweight trunnion posts, which were heavy latticed members, were near failure through buckling of their latticing and batten plates. One batten plate of the trunnion posts of the west leaf showed a dishing of ²¹⁄₃₂ in., and the lattice bars were buckled as much as 1 in. from their original plane.

Deflections of Counterweight Tower. The board reports that while operating the west leaf of the bascule at about one-third normal operating speed, using the auxiliary gasoline engine, it observed large oscillatory deflections of the top of the tower forward and back, with a period of 4.13 sec. and a maximum amplitude of 0.48 ft., as measured by a large number of transit observations. Some 600 extensometer readings were taken on the channels of the tower near their base during the operation of the leaf, and these indicated a maximum variation of stress of 25,000 lb. per square inch, which proved to be reasonably consistent with the observed deflections.

STRESSES IN THE STRUCTURE

From study of the calculated stresses in the various parts of the bridge the board finds that:

> The critical stresses occur at the base of the counterweight tower (as designed), and these stresses are a maximum when the moving leaf is reaching its highest position at the end of the opening operation. At that position the counterweight is moving in a very nearly horizontal direction, which imposes the maximum possible inertia forces on the counterweight tower due to deceleration of the counterweight as brakes are applied. When the leaf is at or near its highest position, assumed in the design and in our computations at an angle of 86 deg. above the horizontal, any horizontal force acting on the counterweight produces a proportional horizontal component in the top link and a simultaneous vertical component amounting to 3.4 times the horizontal component, due to the obliquity of this link. The connection details are such that this vertical component acts with an eccentricity of 27 in. from the center of the counterweight tower leg.

For the just stated position of the leaf and counterweight, the board computes the separate items of stress action affecting the counterweight tower as follows:

a. The deceleration due to application of the motor brakes (service brakes) at the specified setting of 250 lb.-ft. torque at motor shaft per brake is 0.700 ft./sec.^{2} at the counterweight trunnion, causing a maximum tension of 27,000 lb. per sq.in. of net section at base of counterweight tower channels.

b. The deceleration due to application of the emergency brakes at their specified setting, which was equivalent to 350 lb.ft. at motor shaft for each of the two brakes, is 0.97 ft./sec.^{2}, causing a maximum tension of 37,600.

c. Friction in the counterweight trunnion bearings, when taken at the designer's value of 0.18, produces a tension of 9,000 lb. per sq.in., if this friction acted alone, the deceleration of the counterweight would cause an opposing stress of 5,000 lb. per sq.in., leaving a resultant stress of 4,000. The observed value of the friction, however, was only 0.13, which reduces the resultant stress to 2,900.

d. Wind on the counterweight and tower at 15 lb. per sq,ft., causes a tension of 14,000 lb. per sq.in. and 30-lb. wind a tension of 28,000.

e. Vibration of the tower as already mentioned produces a tension of 14,100 lb. per sq.in. of net section. With the higher speed of the electric motor drive much larger vibrations and hence larger stresses would probably result, but for the purpose of the report this increase was disregarded.

COMBINED STRESSES

The summation of the several items of stress is given by the board as follows:

1. Combined effect of emergency brakes, specified friction, 15-lb. wind load and measured elastic vibration,   61,700 lb. per sq.in.

2. Combined effect of motor brakes, emergency brakes and specified friction,
                                                                60,600 lb. per sq.in.

3. Combined effect of motor brakes, emergency brakes, specified friction and 15-lb. wind load,   74,600 lb. per sq.in.

4. Combined effect of motor brakes, emergency brakes, specified friction and measured elastic vibration,   74,700 lb. per sq.in.

5. Combined effect of motor brakes, emergency brakes, specified friction, measured elastic vibration and 15-lb. wind load.   88,700 lb. per sq.in.

It should be noted that any one of the foregoing combinations, all of which are possible of occurrence in actual operation, is sufficient to explain the failure as it occurred.

When the additional secondary stresses are included, the five combinations of stress-producing factors listed above will yield maximum fiber stesses at the base of the tower legs ranging from 74,500 to 109,100 lb. per sq.in. of net section, more than sufficient to account for the failure.

It should also be borne in mind that we are here dealing in large part with reversing and repeating stresses, which bring into play an endurance limit below the ultimate strength, which must be still further reduced in view of the notched section at the rivet hole through which the first fracture occurred.

The board points out that under one clause of the Canadian standard specification (1927) for movable bridges of this type, a counterweight tower must be proportioned to resist, in addition to the vertical loads, a 30-lb. wind load, or, as an alternative, a horizontal force equal to 5 per cent of the supported load applied at its center of gravity, whichever demands the greatest section. The 30-lb. wind, as already listed, would produce a stress of 28,000 lb. per square inch of net section at the base of the tower, while a horizontal force amounting to 5 per cent of the supported weight would produce a maximum tension of 64,000. The board remarks that "the requirement of the Canadian specification is not too drastic."

OTHER SUGGESTED CAUSES OF FAILURE

In order to consider all possibilities regardless of the evidence of the wreckage and the high stresses just mentioned, the committee also studied other suggested causes of failure. It finds that none of them is adequate. As to pier settlement, surveys showed the piers to be at their correct levels. As to abnormal operation of the bridge at the time, the board states that the bridge was being operated in normal manner by an experienced operator, and the electrical control devices predetermined a safe sequence of operations.

As to eccentricity of the counterweight this was calculated to be only 1½ in., and was toward the land, or in the opposite direction to the failure.

Bearing Friction.   Special study was given to the subject of bearing friction in view of a charge that the bearings had been improperly installed and may have seized. The board finds that "high trunnion friction was, at the worst, only a negligible factor in producing the failure."

The bridge had been designed on the assumption of 18 per cent bearing friction in the main and counterweight trunnion bearings, but power measurements showed that the average friction in the trunnion bearings amounted only to 13.3 per cent. It was found that wooden blocks had been left in the ends of the lubrication grooves of the main trunnions but tests showed that they did not interfere with the flow of the lubricant, and there were no such blocks in the counterweight trunnion bearings. No evidence was found that lubrication had been neglected, but to check this stress measurements in the counterweight tower legs (of the west leaf) were made first with the bearings as found and, second, after fresh lubrication of the counterweight trunnion bearings; after a few operations of the leaf with fresh lubrication, the stresses in the tower returned to substantially the same range of magnitude as before.

The material of the bushings of the counterweight trunnion bearings of the east leaf was tested physically and chemically and found satisfactory. Both the physical tests and the chemical composition (Cu 82.25, Sn 16.92, P 0.45, other elements 0.38) satisfied the specification requirements, which were the A.S.T.M. specifications for bronze bearing metals Class B.

Following the board's observation of the dangerous condition of the counterweight posts and the weakness and excessive flexibility of the counterweight tower these members of the uninjured west leaf were strengthened, according to designs prepared by the board, before the west leaf was again put into operation.

Commenting on the report, the editors discussed how such oscillations could have been set into motion. The editors warned that even stationary buildings and other types of bridges might become susceptible to resonant vibrations, and that dynamic calculations might be needed for them. Here is an editorial from the June 6, 1929, issue of ENR:

Structural Dynamics

Fully confirming early impressions of the Hackensack River bascule bridge collapse last December, the final report of the investigating board traces the collapse to the fatal weakness of an essential structural element, the counterweight tower. It also reveals the fact that this weakness was due to a startling failure to consider the bridge as a machine rather than as a merely static structure. The extraordinary stress conditions which the report discloses place such emphasis on this latter feature as to promise that the subject of structural dynamics will occupy a position of marked importance in the future development of bridge engineering. A brief discussion of the accident under the heading "Machine Stresses," in our issue of Jan. 10, [1929], p. 52, pointed out the necessity of giving consideration to the phenomena of motions in structures; the details given in the present report set off this view in sharp relief.

It is clear from the figures cited by the investigators that directly applied forces, whether of wind, motor torque or brakes, constitute only part of the actions which a bridge structure of this kind must resist, and perhaps not the most significant part. Inertia forces may be quite as great. Further, the forces developed in resonant vibrations arising from lack of rigidity may become critical. In the Hackensack bridge the stresses chargeable to oscillatory deflections were almost as large as all other stresses put together. Unless all such actions are duly provided for in the construction, claims of adequate strength are only a delusion.

It is well to keep in mind that movable bridges constitute a higher type of structure than those dealt with in the conventional engineering of fixed bridges. Even the complications arising from elastic constraint (in bridges of statically indeterminate character) are not entitled to more studious analysis than those caused by dynamic actions. But it should be remembered that dynamic effects are to be looked for not only in movable bridges, but also in various other structures which involve motion, and may also appear in building frames where height and dimensions give rise to the possibility of resonant vibration. Further, even ordinary bridges may experience dynamic stresses from their traveling loads and from the vibrations which give rise to the so-called "impact" stresses.

To what extent any or all of these dynamic actions can be accounted for through empirical allowances (as is customary in case of impact) or may be considered to be covered by the reserve strength of the material, is obviously not capable of a general answer but depends on study of the particular structure or class of structures involved. For the case of movable bridges similar to the one involved in the Hackensack accident, the expedient of an arbitrary allowance as represented in the Canadian specification requirements falls short of the needs of the case, as the figures make evident.

It is mere speculation, in a measure, to attempt to discuss the origin of the disturbances which set up and maintained the large oscillations of the tower which were noted by the investigating board. In part, however, they probably arose through irregular variations of friction at the large counterweight trunnions, for slowly moving bearings present difficulty in maintaining a continuous film of lubricant. If this is the case, there is no certainty whether greater rigidity of the tower would reduce the vibration stresses, since the development of resonant vibrations depends on the chance coincidence of period between the counterweight system and the bearing chatter. The more important, therefore, that bearing design be studied with great care.

The work of the investigating board has furnished a document that promises to hold a place of importance in the data of bridge engineering for many years. It derives its weight not only from the remarkable nature of the failure—the sudden collapse of a new and apparently strong and dependable bascule bridge—but as well from the searching tests and studies which the investigators applied to the problems set before them. The members of the board and the New Jersey Highway Department which appointed them are entitled to the thanks of the profession for the service which they have rendered the art of bridge engineering.

The report was immediately challenged by C. E. Paine, vice president of Strauss Engineering Corporation, the bridge's designer. The ENR editors did not restrain the debate to the letters-to-the-editor column; Paine's article of reply ran 4 full pages in the August 29, 1929, issue, and was followed by a rebuttal from the investigating board.

Analysis of Dynamic Stresses in Hackensack Bascule

Study of design based on spring-acting flexible counterweight tower—Results compared with high stresses found by investigators.

C. E. Paine   *Vice President,*
Strauss Engineering Corporation,
Chicago

The final report of the board of engineers appointed to investigate the cause of failure on Dec. 15, 1928, of the east bascule leaf of the Hackensack River bridge on the Lincoln Highway near Jersey City, N.J. [ENR, June 6, 1929, p. 916], places the cause of the failure in the inadequacy of the design of the counterweight tower. The board supports its finding by citing calculated unit stresses at the base of the tower caused by the deceleration of the counterweight when the moving leaf in the fully open position is stopped by application of the brakes. It also shows, combined with calculated unit stresses, a unit stress determined by field measurements of oscillatory vibrations of the tower posts of the west leaf.

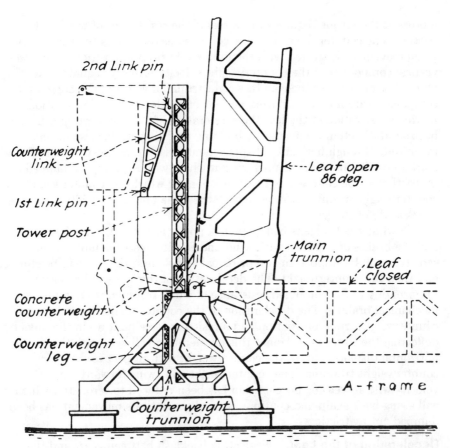

2nd Link pin

Counterweight
link

1st Link pin

Tower post

Concrete
counterweight

Counterweight
leg

Counterweight
trunnion

Leaf open
86 deg.

Main
trunnion

Leaf
closed

A-frame

Figure 5-13 As the counterweight of the Hackensack River bascule falls, the leaf rises. *(ENR.)*

The unit stresses computed by the board for various combinations of braking forces, wind and friction are of startling magnitude, and coming as they do from a board of experts, their correctness ordinarily would not be questioned except by those experienced in the design of similar elastic structures. In view of the apparent interest in such structures and in order to correct the impression that proper attention is not given to dynamic effects in the design of bascule bridges, it seems desirable to present a simple and practical solution.

ANALYSIS

Description of Action. When the bridge is operating normally, the leaf starts from rest with an acceleration approximately uniform and in a short interval of time it attains a uniform velocity corresponding to the speed of the motors at the torque required to overcome the resistances of wind and friction. The counterweight is not accelerated as quickly as the leaf except when movement is started with the link in a horizontal position. While the vertical component of the counterweight velocity is always equal to the vertical component of the counterweight trunnion velocity, the horizontal components are not equal during periods of acceleration or deceleration. During acceleration of the leaf the acceleration of the counterweight in the horizontal direction is effected by building up a link stress of sufficient magnitude through horizontal displacement of the tower post. This action will start an oscillation of the counterweight which will be promptly damped out by friction at the counterweight trunnion, after which the counterweight and counterweight trunnion will move with the same uniform velocity so long as the velocity of the leaf is uniform.

If, while the bridge is being opened, power is shut off from the motors and the brakes are applied with wind and friction resisting motion, the structure will be stopped in two principal steps—first the leaf will be stopped and then the counterweight. The deceleration of the leaf will be nearly uniform due to the combined resistance of wind, trunnion friction and mechanical braking. The deceleration of the counterweight depends upon counterweight trunnion friction and a resisting force built up in the links by deflecting the tower post. Hence this deceleration will vary with the horizontal displacement of the counterweight with respect to the counterweight trunnion. The counterweight will swing forward until its velocity with increasing deceleration has been reduced to zero, after which it will swing back again and continue to oscillate until its movement has been damped out by friction.

Deceleration of the Leaf.   Neglecting backlash between gears and the torsional displacement of shafts, it is sufficient to add to the kinetic energy of the moving leaf the kinetic energy of the counterweight, thus obtaining the total kinetic energy which must be overcome while stopping the leaf by the combined action of wind, friction and brakes. It will be seen later that the error is negligible if we include here with the leaf only that part of the kinetic energy of the counterweight which is due to the vertical component of its velocity. From these data the time of stopping the leaf may be computed. Within reasonable limits, it makes little difference what this time is, as will be shown later.

To consider a specific case: When stopping the Hackensack bascule, with the leaf moving at full speed in the fully open position (86 deg.), by instantaneous application of motor brakes and emergency brakes and with an assumed trunnion friction of 18 per cent and a 15-lb. wind opposing the motion, it will be seen from [Figure 5-14] that the direction of motion of the counterweight and counterweight trunnion is normal to the link. The velocity is 0.326 ft. per second, the horizontal component of the velocity is 0.313 ft.

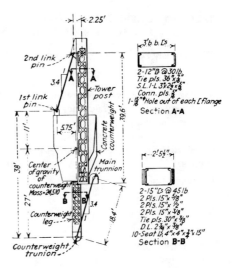

Figure 5-14 Arrangement of the counterweight system at Hackensack. As shown in this diagram, the leaf is open to an angle of 86 degrees above the horizontal and the counterweight is in its lowest position. (*ENR.*)

per second and the vertical component is 0.092 ft. per second. That part of the kinetic energy due to the vertical component of the velocity is 104, which, added to 10,674 (the kinetic energy of the other moving parts), gives a total of 10,778. The combined effect of wind, friction and brakes is equal to 5,685,000 ft.-lb. [see data in Table 5-1] applied at the main trunnion. The angular displacement of the leaf during deceleration = 10,778 ÷ 5,685,000 = 0.0019 radians. Initial velocity = 0.169 × 2π ÷ 60 = 0.0177 radians per second. Hence, time of deceleration of counterweight trunnion = 0.215 second. Deceleration of counterweight trunnion = 0.326 ÷ 0.215 × 1.515 ft. per second per second.

Wind and Friction. Wind on the leaf tends to oppose its movement, whereas wind on the counterweight reacts to aid its movement. The net result can be expressed as a retarding moment about the main trunnion which increases the deceleration of the leaf. The wind has no effect on the deceleration of the counterweight except indirectly as it affects the deceleration of the leaf.

Friction at the main trunnion and counterweight trunnion opposes the movement of the leaf and thus affects its deceleration. At the time deceleration starts the portion of the link stress due to trunnion friction has a moment about the counterweight trunnion equal and opposite to the friction moment. Hence, if we retain this portion of the link stress constant throughout the deceleration of the counterweight, no further consideration need be given to counterweight trunnion friction in so far as deceleration is concerned. It should be noted, however, that when the counterweight reaches the end of its swing and motion reverses, friction will also reverse and damp the vibration.

TABLE 5-1 Basic Data for Hackensack Bascule Design (All Figures Are Given for One-Half of One Leaf)

Kinetic energy of moving parts, motor at 840 RPM

	RPM	Kinetic Energy, Foot-pounds
Moving leaf (exclusive of counterweight)	0.169	4,700
Machinery (including emergency brake)		1,774
Motor rotor, pinion, and brake drum	840	4,200

Counterweight velocity = 0.326 feet per second. Kinetic energy = 1300 foot-pounds.

Friction torques:

	Diameter, Feet	12 Percent Friction, Foot-pounds,	18 Percent Friction, Foot-pounds,
Main trunnion	1.375	93,300	140,000
Counterweight trunnion	2.25	106,700	160,000

Motor brake torque, 250 foot-pounds at 840 rpm, allowing 10 percent for machinery losses, is equivalent to 1,370,000 foot-pounds applied at main trunnion.

Emergency brake torque, 2000 foot-pounds at 146.5 rpm, allowing 10 percent for machinery losses, is equivalent to 1,906,000 foot-pounds applied at main trunnion.

Wind on leaf and counterweight (angle of opening 86°): 15-pound wind.

Net moment about trunnion = 2,109,000 foot-pounds

Wind on counterweight = 7320 pounds at 27 feet above counterweight trunnion

Elastic relations:

Bridge open 86°

Bridge closed: 1000 pounds applied . . . will cause a horizontal displacement of the counterweight equal to 0.0159 feet, a link stress having a horizontal component of 1077 pounds and horizontal and vertical displacements of the second link pin equal to 0.0218 and 0.00183, respectively.

A compressive link stress having a horizontal component of 1000 pounds will cause tensile unit stresses at the base of the tower post equal to 2369 pounds per square inch for an 86° opening; 2187 pounds per square inch for a 79° opening; and 1639 pounds per square inch for bridge closed.

SOURCE: *Engineering News-Record,* Aug. 29, 1929.

Therefore, in the calculations wind and friction should be included in determining the deceleration of the moving leaf but need not be further considered in calculating stresses due to deceleration of the counterweight. Stresses in the tower post due to wind and friction should be algebraically added to the stress caused by deceleration of the counterweight.

Deceleration of Counterweight. The forces causing deceleration of the counterweight with reference to its trunnion may be found either by direct computation for successive time intervals or by solution of differential equations.

At the beginning of deceleration of the counterweight trunnion, it is moving with the same velocity as the counterweight. During the first small interval of time succeeding application of the brakes, the trunnion is decelerated, but the counterweight moves with the same velocity as before, because the tower post has not been displaced and no decelerating force has been induced in the link.

At the end of this first interval the counterweight is displaced with reference to the trunnion and there is a deflection of the tower post which induces a force in the link and a corresponding deceleration of the counterweight; this induced force can be computed from the data given in [Figure 5-15].

During the next interval the trunnion moves with a velocity reduced by its deceleration during the first interval, and the counterweight moves with its initial velocity reduced by the decelerating effect of the stress in the link.

In succeeding intervals the counterweight gains further on the trunnion, and the displacement of the tower, the stress in the link and the deceleration of the counterweight are all successively increased. After the trunnion comes to rest, the counterweight gains further on the trunnion with increasing link stress and deceleration. Finally the decelerating force becomes so great that the counterweight stops. This is the instant of maximum deflection and hence of greatest unit stress in the tower post.

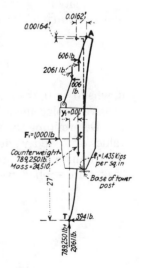

Figure 5-15 Diagram shows the elastic relations of the Hackensack counterweight system with the leaf opened 86 degrees. The figures include the secondary effect due to displacement of the counterweight with respect to the counterweight trunnion. *(ENR.)*

Differential Equation of Deceleration.   The relation between decelerating force and deceleration is expressed mathematically as $F = -Ma$, in which F is the horizontal component of the resultant of that portion of the link stress and trunnion reaction which produces deceleration a of the counterweight, the mass of which is M.

All displacements y and velocities V are measured horizontally with reference to a line through the countertrunnion parallel to the line connecting trunnion and center of mass of counterweight before brakes are applied [Figure 5-15].

After brakes are applied the trunnion has, until it stops, an acceleration a_t, which we shall assume as constant. Then

$$a = \frac{d^2y}{dt^2} - a_t$$

$$F = y\frac{F}{y} = -M\left(\frac{d^2y}{dt^2} - a_t\right)$$

$$y = -M\frac{y}{F}\left(\frac{d^2y}{dt^2} - a_t\right)$$

Since the physical properties of the structure determine a constant relation between force and deflection, let $M\,y_1/F_1 = b$, where y_1 and F_1 are as given in [Figure 5-15].

Then $y = b(d^2y/dt^2 - a_t)$, which is satisfied by

$$y = a_t b\left(1 - \cos\sqrt{\frac{1}{b}}\,t\right) \tag{1}$$

since velocity and displacement are both zero at the beginning.

Equation 1 governs until the trunnion comes to rest, after which $a_t = 0$, and $y = b(d^2y/dt^2)$ which is satisfied by

$$y = y' \cos\sqrt{\frac{1}{b}}\,t + V'\sqrt{b}\,\sin\sqrt{\frac{1}{b}}\,t \tag{2}$$

if, when $t = 0$, the relative velocity of the counterweight is V', and the relative displacement is y'.

Determining the maximum value of y from equation 2 and substituting values of V' and y', determined from equation 1 for $t = t_0$ (the time when the trunnion stops), and for a_t the value V_0/t_0 where V_0 is the velocity before brakes are applied, we obtain

$$y_{max,} = V_0 b\sqrt{2}\,\frac{\sqrt{1 - \cos\sqrt{\frac{1}{b}}\,t_0}}{t_0}$$

This expression gives maximum possible displacements due to deceleration for different times of stopping the leaf up to $t_0 = \pi\sqrt{b}$, after which the maximum is determined from equation 1 and varies inversely as t_0. The time interval between maxima, or natural period of vibration, is

$$2\pi\sqrt{b} = 3.12 \text{ seconds}$$

The maximum possible value of y occurs when the leaf is stopped instantly, and is obtained from equation 2 for $y' = 0$ and $V' = V_0$, as absolute maximum $y = V_0\sqrt{b} = 0.155$ ft.

Whence absolute maximum unit stress at base of tower post due to deceleration $= 0.155 \times 1,435 \div 0.01 = 22,200$ lb. per square inch. The same value may be obtained by equating the loss of energy to the work done when the trunnion is stopped instantly.

The coefficient

$$\frac{\sqrt{1 - \cos\sqrt{\frac{1}{b}}\, t_0}}{t_0}$$

is almost constant within the operating range as t_0 varies.

Hence the maximum stress in the tower post due to deceleration is nearly independent of the time of stopping the trunnion and the rate of deceleration of the leaf. These stresses can be accurately and easily determined by applying elementary principles of mechanics with or without the aid of calculus.

Discussion of Analysis.   The curve in [Figure 5-16] shows the maximum unit stress in the tower post resulting from stopping the leaf in different periods of time. It is noticeable that it makes very little difference whether the motor brakes only are used or whether both motor brakes and emergency brakes are applied simultaneously; the rate of stopping the trunnion is not the important factor in this problem. The determining factors are: the mass and initial velocity of the counterweight, the stiffness of the tower post and the geometric relations of the various elements of the structure at the time deceleration starts.

MAXIMUM STRESS CONDITIONS

Operating Conditions.   The Hackensack bridge was designed to be operated against a wind pressure of 7½ lb. per square foot. It could not be operated against a wind pressure of 15 lb. per square foot, and in order to get a combination of the decelerating force with a 15-lb. wind it would be necessary to assume that the wind suddenly increased to that pressure simultaneously with the application of the brakes.

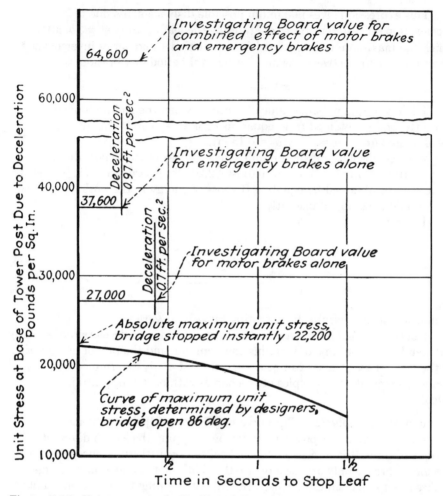

Figure 5-16   Unit stresses in the Hackensack River bascule counterweight tower post due to deceleration of the counterweight. *(ENR.)*

Protecting Devices.   The bridge is equipped with limit switches which automatically cut off power from the motors and apply the motor brakes when the leaf in opening reaches an angle of opening of 79 deg. Power to open the leaf beyond this point can be obtained only by repressing a bypass switch which will permit the application of a limited amount of power to complete the movement after passing the 79 deg. position. With a 7½-lb. wind opposing movement it would be impossible to get the bridge up to anywhere near its full speed and probably not more than half speed after passing the 79 deg. position.

Combining Calculated Stresses. The following combinations of stresses at the base of the counterweight post obtained under conditions assumed by the board are as follows:

	Correct Values	Board's Values
Due to deceleration	+22,200	+69,600
Due to 15-lb. wind	+14,000	+14,000
Due to 18 per cent friction	−8,500	−9,000
Total with wind	+27,700	+74,600
Total without wind	+13,700	+60,600

Mention was made in the report of vibratory stresses which were measured in the field. The procedure of measuring stresses in the field and adding these measured stresses to the computed stresses is unusual and questionable.

Effect of High Fluctuating Friction. Any acceleration or deceleration of the counterweight will be accompanied by a deflection of the tower post, thus imitating an oscillatory movement. Under circumstances within the range of normal operating conditions the oscillatory movement of the tower post and counterweight will be damped out quickly by trunnion friction. In a properly lubricated trunnion bearing, friction during motion should remain at a fairly steady value of 12 per cent with less than 3 per cent fluctuation. When the bearing is operated extensively without lubrication, not only does friction mount to a high figure but the movement becomes intermittent and jerky. Under such conditions friction fluctuates between an abnormally high value and an abnormally low value. It is evident that if maintenance of the structure is neglected to that extremity and operation is permitted under such circumstances vibrations of high amplitude might result. The counterweight trunnion bearing of the Hackensack bridge recovered from the river gives unmistakable evidence that it had been operated dry and with high fluctuating friction. Furthermore, the counterweight trunnions of the west leaf (which did not fail and on which the board's measurements were made) were operating in just such an abnormal manner. The effort to correct the condition by attempting to force grease into the grooves could hardly be expected to give good results, since no doubt the grease grooves needed to be thoroughly cleaned out in order to get new lubricant in and properly distributed over the surface of the trunnion.

Basis of Design. As a *normal* condition for operation the wind pressure is assumed to be 2½ lb. per square foot (about a 30-mile wind). The *extreme* operating condition is taken with pressure at 7½ lb. per square foot.

In all cases trunnion friction is taken at 18 per cent for starting and 12 per cent for moving. The investigating board reported an average trunnion friction of 13.3 per cent as determined by power measurements. The dependability of values found by such measurements is doubtful, because there are many other losses involved for which correction factors must be determined. At the best this gives only approximate *average* values which are no indication whatever of the value for any particular bearing nor of the maximum value where there is a great fluctuation due to improper lubrication.

The tower post is designed for a decelerating force due to stopping the bridge by the motor brakes at an angle of opening of 86 deg. with friction at 12 per cent and with a wind pressure of 2½ lb. per square foot opposing the motion. For the bridge stationary, in the closed position, the tower post is designed to withstand a wind pressure of 20 lb. per square foot on the counterweight and tower. The unit stresses at the base of the tower post for the above cases are as follows:

1. Stopping bridge in the fully open position while opening at full speed against a wind pressure of 2½ lb. per square foot and 12 per cent trunnion friction:

Deceleration of counterweight	$+20,600$ lb. per sq.in.
Wind	$+ 2,300$ lb. per sq.in
Trunnion friction	$- 5,700$ lb. per sq.in.
Total	$+17,200$ lb. per sq.in.

2. Bridge closed: Wind pressure of 20 lb. per square foot on counterweight and tower.

Wind	$+18,700$ lb. per sq.in.
Friction at 12 per cent	$-6,700^*$ lb. per sq.in.
Total	$+12,000$ lb. per sq.in.

*Owing to its elasticity the tower post will deflect and rotation will take place at the counterweight trunnion.

It is apparent that a certain degree of flexibility in the tower is desirable in order to absorb the inertia of the counterweight mass during periods of its acceleration or deceleration. The stress in the link and link pins is largely dependent upon the stiffness of the tower, and it follows that if the tower is made stiffer, the stresses in these parts will be increased accordingly.

CONCLUSIONS

The following conclusions are indicated:

1. The rate at which the leaf is stopped (deceleration of counterweight trunnion) has little effect on the maximum stresses in the tower post from deceleration.
2. The maximum stress computed by the board from deceleration is the greatest single factor in its amazing totals and is about three times the correct maximum value.
3. Maximum stresses for normal operation if computed by correct principles of mechanics are moderate.
4. Prolonged vibration during uniform movement indicates abnormal conditions in the bearings due to poor bushings and lack of lubrication.
5. The fact that the failure took place from fractures occurring at three different times indicates that it was due to the cracked flange rather than to general overstress. The original fracture at the rivet hole, in all probability, occurred during fabrication.

Investigating Board's Discussion of Counterweight Tower Action

Proofs of the above article were submitted to the members of the official investigating board whose conclusions are traversed by Mr. Paine. Their reply follows.—Editor

In connection with the collapse of the Hackensack River trunnion bascule bridge, it is significant that the designer's stress sheet does not show the stresses in the counterweight tower. It also is noteworthy that the accompanying specifications do not mention wind pressure, inertia forces or frictional resistance, although existing specifications of other authorship cover such subjects. That these forces are of vital importance in the design of the structure which supports the counterweight, which acts as an inverted pendulum, will be evident from the corrections to Mr. Paine's analysis made in the following paragraphs.

UNIT STRESSES

In order to indicate that the design of the tower does not conform to good practice, one needs only to discover stresses greater than allowable by any good specification. The specification under which this bridge was designed allows tensile unit stress on net section of 16,000 lb. per sq.in. and compressive stresses on gross section of $16,000 - 70\ l/r$. In order to explain failure one must account for stresses greater than yield point of structural steel, say about 36,000 lb. per sq. in., at which value the counterweight tower channel will begin to stretch rapidly without further increase in stress until the counterweight tips forward and destroys the tower. It is important to note, therefore, that the yield point and not the ultimate strength of the steel governs; also that the major part of the stresses in the tower channel are completely reversible as load conditions reverse in direction, thus bringing into consideration compressive stresses and the endurance limit. If the errors in the application of the theory in Mr. Paine's article be corrected, the calculated stresses in the channel will become considerably greater than the yield point of the material.

SIGNIFICANCE OF ERROR IN PERIOD OF OSCILLATION

Mr. Paine predicts an oscillatory period of 3.12 seconds as compared to an observed period at the bridge of 4.13 seconds. From his equation that the natural period of oscillation equals $2\pi \sqrt{b}$ it appears that the true value of $\sqrt{b}$ must be 4.13/3.12, or 1.32 times his estimated value. Furthermore, from his equation that maximum deflection, $y = V_0\sqrt{b}$ and from the fact that deflection and stress are proportional, it follows that his estimated deceleration stress must be changed to 1.32 times 22,200, or 29,300 lb. per sq.in. One reason for this error is the assumption that the counterweight tower is fixed at its base. This clearly is incorrect, because the stresses in the A-frame caused by a load at the top of the counterweight tower cause movement of the top of the A-frame due to the elasticity of the members of the A-frame. This action was observed on the bridge.

Another reason for this error in estimated period is that the mass of the counterweight was considered concentrated at its center of gravity instead of at the center of percussion. Attention is also called to the neglect of the effect of the weight of the counterweight tower and half of the weight of the links and their bracing in modifying the oscillatory period, and the corresponding stresses and deflections.

WIND STRESSES AND FRICTION

We agree with Mr. Paine's estimate of 14,000 lb. unit stress due to a wind pressure of 15 lb. per square foot.

The most reliable measurement of friction in the counterweight trunnion bearings depends upon the measured change in stress in the channel of the counterweight tower as caused by the reversal of trunnion friction as the leaf is closed slowly and then slowly opened when there is no wind. This change of stress we charged to counterweight trunnion friction, and from these observations we compute a maximum coefficient of friction of 13.3 per cent. Our observations indicated that after a thoroughly fresh greasing of the counterweight trunnion bearing a coefficient of friction not exceeding 8 per cent was developed for a few movements of the leaf. Inasmuch as friction in a counterweight trunnion bearing reduces stress caused by other effects, this reduction should be estimated at the minimum observed value of 8 per cent and not at 18 per cent as estimated by Mr. Paine. This yields a correct deduction from unit stress on account of friction of 8/18(−8,500), or −3,800 lb. per sq.in.

OSCILLATION

Mr. Paine states in his article that the starting oscillation of the counterweight will be promptly damped out by friction at the counterweight trunnion. Contrary to this assumption, we have the remarkable phenomenon that an oscillating pendulum cannot be retarded by friction of the supporting shaft if the angular velocity of this shaft be greater than the maximum

TABLE 5-2 Net Unit Stresses in Channel at Base of Tower Post, Hackensack River Bascule Bridge*

Cause of Stress	Values by Paine	Value by Paine's Analysis as Corrected by the Board
Deceleration	+22,200	+29,300
Oscillation	Not given	+14,650
15-pound wind	+14,000	+14,000
Friction	− 8,500	− 3,800
	at 18%	at observed 8%
Total primary stress with wind	+27,700	+54,150
(Total primary unit stress without wind)	(+13,700)	(+40,150)
Secondary stress	Not included	+12,450
		(23% of primary)
Maximum unit stress	+27,700	+66,600
Yield point (unit stress corresponding to failure)	Not given	+36,000
Unit stress as allowable by design specifications	Not given	Tension on net section + 16,000
		Compression on gross section 16,000—70 l/r or 12,465 lb per sq in of channel section

*The maximum stresses in this table were calculated on the theory that they would follow the same law above the yield point of the material which they are known to follow below the yield point. The calculated stresses above the yield point, therefore, are less than the probable stresses.

SOURCE: *Engineering News-Record*, Aug. 29, 1929.

angular velocity of oscillation. This condition existed at the Hackensack bridge. On account of this phenomenon, which has been checked by laboratory experiments and other tests, the starting oscillation of the counterweight persists during the entire movement of the leaf as though the trunnion friction were zero, and furthermore this starting oscillation was observed to increase to double its initial value and to persist at its maximum value until the counterweight trunnion was stopped. If the brakes are applied at a time when the counterweight has its maximum oscillatory velocity, and in the same direction as the movement of the counterweight trunnion, the horizontal components of the two velocities should be added, thus increasing the value of V' which is used in calculating maximum displacement and the resulting stress.

The oscillatory effect adds considerably to other calculable stresses, and from our observations we find that a 50 per cent addition for oscillatory stress is a minimum permissible amount to add to the deceleration stress of 29,300 above.

OTHER STRESSES

There are other possible causes of stress which are not calculable. The tower post is essentially a vertical truss with inclined diagonal members which do not intersect at the panel points. An estimate of the secondary stress caused by such eccentric details gave values about 23 per cent greater than the primary stress in the region where the failure occurred. Another possible cause of stress is eccentricity of the center of gravity of the counterweight due to its construction.

SUMMARY

From the tabulated stresses it is apparent that a combination of braking stress, 29,300, oscillatory stress 14,650, and a stress of 7,000 lb. per sq.in. due to a wind pressure of 7½ lb. per square foot, less a 3,800-lb. unit stress due to 8 per cent trunnion friction, gives a total of 47,150 lb. per sq.in. This is far above the yield point of structural steel and is adequate to account for unlimited deflection of the tower which would mean failure.

Prolonged oscillation of the counterweight and tower during uniform movement of the counterweight trunnion does not indicate poor bushings or lack of lubrication, because this oscillation is independent of friction, as explained above. The chemical analysis of the bushings showed good material and there is little evidence that lubrication was neglected.

Poor lubrication should not wreck a movable bridge.

The fact that the fracture in the tower channel was progressive and occurred at three different times, as clearly shown by the appearance of the fracture, demonstrates that the failure was caused by recurring conditions of overstress.

The members of the board agree that in their opinion a tower which is depended upon to prevent the overturning of a heavy mass in unstable equilibrium should be designed and built to secure such rigidity that any perceptible oscillation cannot occur.

O. E. Hovey, George E. Beggs, and D. B. Steinman   *New York City*

In those days, of course, calculations were carried out by hand and with slide rule. Simplifying assumptions—absolutely necessary to allow the problem to be calculated at all—were tested by model and by practice. Dozens of readers tested the bascule's design assumptions and generally found them wanting. One of the first "outside" commentaries to appear was in the ENR issue of September 12, 1929, only 2 weeks after the Paine article:

Models Verify Observed Behavior of Hackensack Bascule

Counterweight oscillations not damped by friction of trunnion shaft has greater angular velocity than the counterweight.

In order to confirm the observations made on the operating leaf of the Hackensack double-leaf trunnion bascule bridge, following the collapse of the other half into the river [ENR, Jan. 10, 1929, p. 74, and Aug. 29, 1929, p. 340], Prof. G. E. Beggs, of Princeton University, who was a member of the investigating board, made several experimental studies.

It was observed at the bridge during the motion of the operating leaf that the initial oscillation of the inverted counterweight pendulum persisted, undamped by the friction of the supporting trunnion. This phenomenon was brought to the attention of Prof. C. H. Willis, of the electrical engineering department of Princeton University, who has had considerable experience in the mathematics of harmonic analysis. The conclusion indicated by his analytical study of the phenomenon was that the oscillation of a pendulum will not be readily damped by friction of the supporting shaft if that shaft rotates at a greater angular velocity than the maximum angular velocity of the oscillating pendulum, as was the case at the Hackensack bridge.

To check this conclusion, Professor Beggs made the model shown in [Figure 5-17]. From a dry unlubricated wooden shaft, a wooden pendulum weighted with 40 lb. of iron is suspended. The shaft can be turned or held fixed at will by means of the crank. An index pointer placed so as to make contact with the swinging weight enables one to gage the rate at which the oscillation is damped. When the weight is drawn back to the index pointer and released, while the supporting shaft is held fixed, the oscillation of the pendulum is damped completely after ten swings. However, if the shaft is rotated at a moderate rate so that the slip of the shaft in the pendulum bearing is always in the same direction, the oscillation is maintained for 200 or more swings, the damping being found to be no greater than when the pendulum has a knife edge support. This phenomenon is important, for it emphasizes the necessity of taking persistent oscillations of this sort into account when designing bascule bridges.

Another observation made at the bridge indicated that the top of the A-frame supporting the counterweight tower tipped back and forth through a readily measurable angle during the operation of the bridge. To confirm this elastic action of the structure, Professor Beggs cut a celluloid model of proportionate stiffness [Figure 5-18]. This model can be deformed by H and V forces applied at the top of the counterweight tower, in a manner similar to the force acting at the upper link pin of the steel bridge. By means of the double pointer, registering against the fixed index marks *A* and *B*, the rocking of the top of the A-frame is evident as the top of the counterweight tower is bent back and forth.

Figure 5-17 This simple hand-cranked model demonstrates the inability of trunnion friction to damp out counterweight oscillations. The horizontal shaft with crank corresponds to the counterweight trunnion, and the pendulum corresponds to the counterweight and its supporting shaft. *(ENR.)*

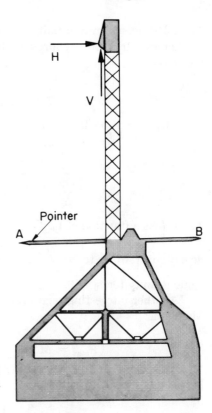

Figure 5-18 A celluloid model
of an A frame and counterweight
tower. *(ENR.)*

A second observation made from this model is that secondary bending
occurs in the two vertical members of the counterweight tower. These
members are deformed into a multiple number of reverse curves as the tower
is deflected by an H force, this action being a result of the eccentricity of the
connections of the lacing members with the vertical members of the tower.

This commentary was followed in the November 14, 1929, issue of ENR by
a large number of letters, several of which are reprinted below along with the
"last word" from the investigating board.

Calculated Stresses in
Counterweight Tower

The analysis of the forces produced by deceleration of the counterweight in
the Hackensack River bridge, as given by C. E. Paine in your issue on Aug.

29, p. 340, solves an unusually interesting and clear-cut problem in mechanics. Mr. Paine's expression for y_{max} may be somewhat simplified as follows:

$$y_{max} = V_0 b \sqrt{2} \, \frac{\sqrt{1 - \cos \sqrt{\dfrac{1}{b} t_0}}}{t_0} = V_0 \sqrt{b} \, \frac{\sin\frac{1}{2} \sqrt{\dfrac{1}{b} t_0}}{\frac{1}{2} \sqrt{\dfrac{1}{b} t_0}}$$

$$= V_0 \sqrt{b} \left[\frac{\text{chord}}{\text{arc}} \text{ of angle } \sqrt{\frac{1}{b} t_0} \right] = K V_0 \sqrt{b}$$

where K is a function of t_0. This shows by inspection why this coefficient is nearly constant up to $\sqrt{\dfrac{1}{b} t_0} = \pi$ and also that the absolute maximum value is unity for $t_0 = 0$.

Another interesting relation may be deduced from the equations given by Mr. Paine:

$$F_{max} = M \frac{y_{max}}{b} = M \frac{K V_0 \sqrt{b}}{b} \qquad F_{max} \, \alpha \, \frac{1}{\sqrt{b}}$$

If t_1 is the period of oscillation

$$t_1 = 2\pi \sqrt{b}$$

$$\frac{1}{\sqrt{b}} = \frac{2\pi}{t_1}$$

Hence F_{max} varies inversely as the period of oscillation. If the period of oscillation can be accurately determined either by computation or by measurement in the field, the absolute maximum value of the decelerating force acting on the counterweight can be directly computed from elementary principles of mechanics.

Mr. Paine computes 3.12 seconds for the period of oscillation, but the investigating board gives a measured value of 4.13 seconds. If we accept the latter value, the deceleration force in Mr. Paine's computations should be divided by $4.13/3.12 = 1.32$. The board has erred in multiplying by 1.32, for it is evident, without reference to Mr. Paine's analysis, that with the more flexible tower—longer period of oscillation—a smaller decelerating force is needed to absorb the kinetic energy of the counterweight, since the force acts through a greater distance.

The board also errs in assuming that the ratio of decelerating force to resulting stress is the same for the two periods of oscillation. The tower stress is a result both of the decelerating force and also of the eccentricity of the counterweight which accompanies deflection of the tower. If the period of oscillation is longer, this shows that the tower is more flexible; the decelerating force then is smaller, as is also the stress due to this decelerating force, but the stress due to the eccentricity of the counterweight is relatively greater. If the period is 32 per cent greater than that computed by Mr. Paine, the stress due to counterweight eccentricity for a given decelerating force will be more than twice as great as before. For small changes in the period it is found that the total stress resulting from deceleration is nearly constant.

For tower stress resulting from deceleration of the counterweight, the following different values are reported:

	Lb per Sq In
Final report of the investigating board:	
Bridge stopped by motor brakes	27,000
Bridge stopped by emergency brakes	37,600
Bridge stopped by motor brakes and emergency brakes	64,600
Bridge stopped by motor brakes, and emergency brakes and friction	69,600
C. E. Paine, for a period of oscillation computed as 3.12 seconds:	
Bridge stopped instantly	22,200
Bridge stopped as in any of above cases, from his curve, about	21,000
Board—revised value for a period of oscillation of 4.13 seconds (measured):	
(Based on its assumption that the ratio of decelerating force to tower	
stress is the same for the two periods of oscillation) $22,200 \times 1.32$	29,300
Corrected value which board should have deduced for a period of 4.13	
seconds, from the erroneous assumption just stated	
$22,200 \times \dfrac{1}{1.32}$	16,800
Value for a period of oscillation of 4.13 seconds with allowance for change	
in eccentricity of counterweight:	
Bridge stopped instantly	21,500
Bridge stopped by any combination of brakes, about	20,000

This seems an unreasonably wide variation of solutions for a definite problem in mechanics. It is hoped that the board will explain the method of computing the values for tower stresses due to deceleration as given in its final report.

Tower stiffness affects also the stresses in the links and link pins resulting from deceleration of the counterweight—the stiffer the tower the greater are these stresses. If for the stresses from this source, with the tower as designed, the values given by the board in its final report could be deduced, it is pertinent to ask what stresses exist in the links and link pins with the tower stiffened as recommended by it.

Hardy Cross   *Professor of Structural Engineering, University of Illinois, Urbana*

Behavior of a Pendulum
Suspended from a Rotating Shaft

In *Engineering News-Record*, Sept. 12, 1929, p. 426, attention is called to the fact that the trunnion friction of the Hackensack bascule could not be depended upon to damp the oscillations of the counterweight. By keeping in mind the rule that dry-surface friction is independent of speed, it is very easy to understand the behavior of the model shown. The friction exerts a constant torque on the pendulum, and the angular momentum imparted during the forward stroke is exactly neutralized by the angular momentum taken away during the back stroke. With a lubricated bearing, however, the case would be different. Since, for low speeds, the friction decreases rapidly with speed, and the relative speed being greater during the back stroke than during the forward stroke, the angular momentum imparted during the forward stroke would be more than that taken away during the back stroke. Consequently, the amplitude of the vibration would increase as long as the angular speed of the shaft is greater than the maximum angular speed of the pendulum.

To test this conclusion, a model similar to the one made by Professor Beggs was set up with a motor and worm gear drive capable of speeds from 4 to 40 revolutions per minute. The model had a ½-in. steel shaft with a well-

Figure 5-19   Another approach to calculating tower sress—a heavy pendulum swinging from the spindle of a milling machine. *(ENR.)*

fitted (but not tight) brass bearing from which hung a pendulum weighing 11 lb. and having a period giving 70 vibrations per minute. At all speeds up to 40 revolutions per minute, without an initial start except that given by friction on starting the apparatus, the vibrations built up until the maximum angular speed of the pendulum slightly exceeded that of the shaft, or, in other words, until the minimum velocity of the pendulum relative to the shaft became negative. Lubrication was freely supplied with an oil can through a hole in the top of the pendulum bearing.

The expected amplitude of the vibration can be worked out by a very simple rule: Mark on the pendulum the point at which the amplitude is to be measured. Then the expected amplitude times the vibrations per minute equals twice the distance from the marked point to the center of the shaft times the number of revolutions per minute of the shaft.

When the speed of the shaft is large and the amplitude of the pendulum is small, there is a smaller relative difference between the maximum and minimum relative speeds. This accounts for the fact that the amplitude builds up more quickly with low speeds and that it builds up with increasing rapidity as it approaches the maximum. At speeds above 40 revolutions per minute the vibrations would not start automatically but built up readily if given a start. By changing the drive to get higher speeds and by gradually speeding up the motor to keep the speed of the shaft greater than the maximum speed of the pendulum, the amplitude was built up until the pendulum went entirely over and took up the speed of the shaft.

Without lubrication, the amplitude does not build up, but remains practically constant for any start up to the maximum angular speed of the shaft. With a ball bearing (clean, dry, and new), there is a very slight tendency to build up. With cup grease lubrication, the small model would not build up, and the experiment was tried on a larger scale.

A pendulum weighing 101 lb. was hung from the spindle of a milling machine. . . . The collar bearing was 1¼ in. in diameter, and of hard steel, ground to a running fit on steel spindle ¼ in. wide, giving a bearing pressure of 322 lb. per sq.in. of projected area. With good grease lubrication, the spindle was started at 20 revolutions per minute. No initial push was given the pendulum, and the following readings were taken:

Time from Start Seconds	Amplitude of Vibration 10 In. from Center of Shaft, In.	Time from Start, Seconds	Amplitude of Vibration 10 In. from Center of Shaft, In.
1	¼		
20	½		
30	1	80	4
50	2	90	5
65	3		

The following table shows the maximum amplitudes resulting from three speeds of the spindle:

Shaft Speed, R.P.M.	Pendulum Speed, V.P.M.	Amplitude at 10 In. Expected, In.	Actual, In.
			6⅝
20	64	6¼	
27	64	8⅞₁₆	9¾
35	63	11	14

Oil lubrication gave about the same results.

At any of these speeds the vibrations would start automatically when the spindle was started, the rate of building up being slower with the high speeds, as in the small model.

The whole experiment strikingly illustrates the observations of Goodman on friction of lubricated surfaces, in his "Mechanics Applied to Engineering," 4th Ed., pp. 247–248.

P. W. Ott   *Department of Mechanics, Ohio State University, Columbus, Ohio*

Reply of Investigating Board

The board appreciates the discussion contributed by Professor Ott, confirming and strengthening previous experimental and analytical conclusions as to the persistence and augmentation of oscillations in the elastic counterweight towers of the Hackensack River bascule bridge.

Referring to the discussion by Professor Cross, the board does not care to be drawn into any secondary controversies involving juggling of formulas or mathematical quibbling. The evaluation of maximum stresses in the counterweight towers of the Hackensack River bridge is more than a "clear-cut problem in mechanics," inasmuch as even the most advanced mathematical solution is valueless if the underlying assumptions are incorrect or incomplete. The board has already shown that Mr. Paine's analysis was incorrect or incomplete in his erroneous assumption that oscillations would be damped by friction and that their effect may therefore be ignored. This important point emphasized by the board has since been independently confirmed by the investigations of Professor Ott, who shows that, with lubricated bearings, the oscillations are subject to serious augmentation. There are also other factors that would make the stresses much higher than those submitted by Mr. Paine. In fact, under the action of certain conditions that should be considered in a complete investigation of the safety of the design, the board is prepared to show resultant stresses greater than any that have thus far been reported. In view of these facts, the board reiterates its conclusion that the structure as designed was subject to excessive and dangerous stresses.

[Figure 5-20] shows the counterweight tower structure as rebuilt following the failure. The vertical member, consisting of a pair of laced 12-in. channels, in the middle of the A-frame, corresponds to the original counterweight tower. The board is pleased to report that actual stress measurements in the tower and the top link since the structure was stiffened show unit stresses due to full braking deceleration to be materially lower than those observed before stiffening the tower.

O. E. Hovey, George E. Beggs, and D. B. Steinman   *Board of Engineers*

At the time of the disaster, D. B. Steinman was a partner in the consulting firm of Robinson & Steinman, New York City. An associate engineer in the firm, C. H. Gronquist, was given the job of directing the removal of the wreckage from the Hackensack River. He described this operation with great lucidity in the pages of ENR. The successor firm of Steinman, Boynton, Gronquist & Birdsall today continues to design and inspect bridges, and to plan the repair of old ones. New York City's decayed spans have evolved into a practice all its own for the firm—a business in which the firm's advice was ignored by the city's political leaders until 1977 when money began flowing for repairs.

Hundreds of bascules were built in the 1930s and 1940s in the United States. Thanks to the lessons of the Hackensack River, most are still standing today. Unfortunately, most are deteriorating under the double burden of poor maintenance and heavy traffic. Disaster is very close. "Only luck kept a huge counterweight from crashing through the lower section of the Portland [Maine] Bridge while its bascule was opening or closing," reported ENR on November 12, 1980. "A ½-in wide vertical crack developed across the entire 4-ft depth of a steel plate girder where it meets the bascule's concrete counterweight. . . . Corrosion is believed to have caused the crack."

Maine's Department of Transportation called in Steinman, Boynton, Gronquist & Birdsall to make an in-depth inspection, prepare contracts for fixing the bridge, and supervise the actual construction work required. As for the Hackensack River bascule: It stands to this day.

Clifford E. Paine and Joseph Strauss also went on to bigger and better things: the original design for the Golden Gate Bridge and a 1954 stiffening of the Golden Gate among them. In the wake of the Tacoma Narrows Bridge failure in 1940, the twenty-two insurance companies that had written policies on Tacoma Narrows created the Narrows Bridge Loss Committee to study the disaster. Paine was hired to head the committee. He in turn selected three other bridge experts to help. Among them was Holton D. Robinson of Robinson & Steinman.

Figure 5-20 The strengthened counterweight tower on the Hackensack River bascule; the A frame was added in 1929; the original counterweight tower is the laced vertical member in the center of the A frame. *(ENR.)*

Tacoma Narrows, 1940

What happens when a bridge moves—and it shouldn't? Well, it can just shake itself apart. That's exactly what happened to the Tacoma Narrows Bridge on November 7, 1940. By that time, the failure had been expected and the whole affair was recorded for posterity by camera crews, to the delight of engineering students everywhere. Is there a class of civil engineers anywhere in the world that has not seen Tacoma Narrows come down?

What is not generally known among members of the lay public is that Tacoma Narrows was similar in design to New York City's Bronx-Whitestone Bridge, a 2300-foot main span that is used by thousands of commuters every day. The Bronx-Whitestone has also been plagued with excess vibrations—verical movements that in no way threaten the structural integrity of the bridge, but which do make many motorists queasy. A new attempt to cure the Bronx-Whitestone's galloping was made in the summer of 1982.

TABLE 5-3 Unit Prices for the Narrows Bridge, Washington

Owner: Washington State Toll Bridge Authority, Olympia; L. V. Murrow, state highway director.

Project: Construction of a suspension bridge over the Narrows near Tacoma, Wash. Total length is 5560 feet, and suspension span is [2800] feet. Job includes four piers and 11,440 tons of structural steel. Bridge is to be finished by June 5, 1940. Transportation facilities by rail, highway and water are available. Wages are as follows: skilled, $1.60 per hour; semi-skilled, $1.25 per hour; common, $1.00 per hour.

Bids: Two complete bids were received Sept. 2, 1938. The first, $5,949,730, was made by the Pacific Bridge Co., San Francisco; Columbia Construction Co., Bonneville, Oregon; General Construction Co., Seattle. The second bid was $6,038,560 by Columbia Steel Co., Seattle. Unit bids of the two contractors vary somewhat on items because bids were made on separate schedules. The bid of the Columbia Steel Co. calls for an alternate design for the two water piers.

| | | Unit Prices, | |
Item	Quantity	(1)	(2)
1. Structural excavation, class E	29,600 cu yd	6.00	
2. Structural excavation, class F	6,700 cu yd	2.50	
3. Structural excavation, class G	5,360 cu yd	8.00	
4. Structural excavation, class H	5,360 cu yd	9.00	
5. Structural excavation, class K	5,360 cu yd	10.00	
6. Structural excavation, class B	630 cu yd	15.00	
7. Class D concrete piers 4 and 5	9,900 cu yd	15.00	
8. Class D concrete pier 3	460 cu yd	20.00	40.00
9. Class B concrete piers 4 and 5	44,700 cu yd	15.00	
10. Class B concrete pier 3	735 cu yd	20.00	22.00
11. Reinforcement	5,892,100 lb	0.064	
12. Structural carbon steel	2,430,000 lb	0.10	
13. Structural silicon steel	386,000 lb	0.10	
14. Structural steel grillage	80,000 lb	0.00	
15. Untreated timber	840 M.bd.m.	110.00	
16. Creosote timber	390 M.bd.m.	200.00	
17. Pier anchorages	2 each	350,000.00	
18. Steel piling	8,910 lin ft	2.50	3.32
19. Steel piling	12 each	68.00	50.00
20. Test piles	8 each	300.00	285.00
21. Class B riprap, pier 3	360 cu yd	6.00	8.00
22. Class B riprap, piers 4 and 5	1,000 cu yd	6.00	6.00
23. Structural excavation, B, pier 3	630 cu yd		1.50
24. Structural excavation C	16,600 cu yd	0.70	0.64
25. Reinforcement	2,663,400 lb		0.0485
26. Structural excavation C	44,000 cu yd	0.70	0.60
27. Reinforcement pier 3	19,000 lb		0.07
28. Structural excavation D	2,250 cu yd	2.50	1.50
29. Steel grillage, pier 3	180,000 lb		0.10
30. Class A concrete	4,435 cu yd	28.00	30.10
31. Pier 4 complete	L.S.		1,247,500.00
32. Class B concrete	2,150 cu yd	24.00	23.50
33. Pier 4 deductions	L.S.		1,150.00
34. Class C concrete	49,000 cu yd	8.85	8.60
35. Pier 4 addition	L.S.		1,800.00

TABLE 5-3   Unit Prices for the Narrows Bridge, Washington   (*Continued*)

Item	Quantity	Unit Prices, $	
		(1)	(2)
36. Structural carbon steel	1,150,000 lb	0.09	0.061
37. Pier 5 complete	L.S.		1,294,000.00
38. Structural carbon steel	13,200,000 lb	0.0678	0.073
39. Pier 5 deduct	L.S.		1,150.00
40. Cable wire	7,635,000 lb	0.149	0.1322
41. Suspender rope	81,000 lin ft	0.50	0.5725
42. Toll house equipment	L.S.	3,500.00	3,500.00
43. Hand rope	21,000 lin ft	0.40	0.41
44. Electrical equipment	L.S.	31,000.00	26,000.00
45. Wrapping wire	240,000 lb	0.19	0.177
46. Painting field coat	L.S.	35,000.00	25,000.00
47. Cast and forged steel	400,000 lb	0.25	0.228
48. High tensile bolts	15,000 lb	0.042	0.157
49. Messenger cable	10,500 lin ft	0.017	0.24
50. Structural silicon steel	3,650,000 lb	0.0695	0.076
51. Uncl. excavation	75,000 cu yd	0.40	0.40
52. Concrete pavement	5,200 sq yd	2.50	3.25
53. Cr. stone surf.	230 cu yd	3.00	4.00
54. Integral concrete curbing	851 lin ft	0.40	0.70
55. Split concrete curb	1,070 lin ft	0.80	1.30
56. Concrete walks	830 sq yd	1.50	2.53
57. Buildings and booths	L.S.	17,500.00	18,000.00

SOURCE: *Engineering News-Record*, Nov. 24, 1938.

As for Tacoma Narrows, the original "Galloping Gertie," let's turn to the November 14, 1940, issue of ENR:

Tacoma Narrows Bridge Wrecked by Wind

Roadway and stiffening girders of 2,800-ft. central span wrenched off and torn to pieces after 42-mi. wind set up violent waving and twisting. Towers bent backward 12 ft. under pull of surviving side spans and plates buckled. Wavelike oscillation of deck gave trouble ever since construction, but was not thought dangerous.

N. A. Bowers   *Pacific Coast Editor, Engineering News-Record*

Wind wrecked the 2,800-ft. main span of the Tacoma Narrows suspension bridge shortly before noon Thursday, Nov. 7. Almost the entire suspended structure between the towers was ripped away and fell into the waters below, but the 1,100-ft. side spans remained intact. Cables and towers survived and held up the weight of the side spans, though the latter sagged about 30 ft. as the towers, which are fixed at the base by steel anchors deeply embedded in the concrete piers, were bent back sharply by the unbalanced pull of the side-span cables.

Fortunately there was no loss of life, as only a few persons were on the bridge. Traffic had been limited or shut off some time before because of the excessive and dangerous motion of the bridge. Among those on the span at the time was Prof. F. B. Farquharson, of the University of Washington (Seattle), who had been conducting extended experiments on a model of the bridge with a view to controlling its oscillation. At the time of the collapse he was on the main span taking motion pictures of the abnormal waving and twisting.

WIND CONDITIONS NOT ABNORMAL

A wind reported as 42 mph was blowing on the morning of the accident. Higher winds had been experienced previously without damage, but this wind caused a vertical wave motion that developed a lag or phase difference between opposite sides of the bridge, giving the deck a cumulative rocking or side-to-side rolling motion.

Failure appeared to begin at mid-span with buckling of the stiffening girders, although lateral bracing may have gone first. Suspenders snapped and their ends jerked high in the air above the main cables, while sections of the floor system several hundred feet in length fell out successively, breaking up the roadway toward the towers until only stubs remained.

EFFORTS TO CHECK WAVE MOTION

Tie-down cables that had been put in the side spans to damp out vertical wave motion previously observed on the bridge are credited with having prevented the violent waves in the main span from being transmitted to the side spans and perhaps doing greater damage to the towers. However, with the load removed from the main spans by the fall of the floor, the side spans sagged 30 ft. making the check reins inoperative and permitting a movement which buckled the stiffening girders and deformed the steel in the floor system.

Under the unbalanced loading the towers were bent back 12 ft. shoreward (about twice the designed maximum) until unloading of the side span began, when the tower deflection gradually decreased. Outward evidences of tower damage are buckled plates and angles, especially near the piers where plate thicknesses are ½ to ¾ in. An inspector reports that the cables show no evidence of movement in the saddles in the course of the violent bouncing. The piers are believed to be undamaged.

Tacoma Narrows Bridge, third longest suspension span in existence (Golden Gate 4,200 ft., George Washington 3,500 ft., Tacoma Narrows 2,800 ft.) was built between October, 1938, and July, 1940, and was opened to traffic in July. It was by far the most slender suspension bridge ever built, both laterally and vertically, the width of the roadway and spacing of cables being only 39 ft. (span ratio 1:72), and the depth of the stiffening girders 8 ft. (span ratio 1:350).

In general conception it followed the model set by the Whitestone Bridge (span 2,300 ft.), but was longer in span and much narrower. To suit the expected traffic it was built for only two traffic lanes against six on Whitestone and Golden Gate and an ultimate of twelve [later, fourteen] on the George Washington Bridge.

WAVE MOTION STUDIED

The destructive wave movements that wrecked the bridge were the sequel to a history of disturbing oscillation that had been under observation and study since the bridge was built. Similar but much smaller oscillation occurs on the Whitestone Bridge, but while there it amounts to only a few inches, the vertical waves in the Tacoma Bridge were very much greater, having reached as much as 50 in. amplitude.

Various means were tried to check the movement, and elaborate model experiments were conducted, those for Whitestone by Prof. E. K. Timby at

Figure 5-21 Hundreds of feet of roadway tear away from suspender cables of the Tacoma Narrows Bridge and flip over, falling to the waters of Puget Sound below. *(University of Washington Archives.)*

Figure 5-22 Damage where the south cable at Tacoma first crosses the concrete of the east abutment. The housing was smashed by the bouncing of the cable. *(University of Washington Archives.)*

Princeton University and those for Tacoma Narrows by Prof. F. B. Farquharson at the University of Washington. The Tacoma Narrows model, 54 ft. long, is a precise scale representation of the bridge in 1:100 ratio and is fitted with a series of electromagnets to apply horizontal and vertical forces simulating the effect of wind pressures. It was found that the behavior of the actual bridge could be duplicated with great accuracy, and various corrective arrangements and devices were tried out.

TIE ROPES REDUCED MOVEMENT

In the Whitestone Bridge, short inclined rope ties were placed between midpoints of the main cables and the top flanges of the stiffening girders to hold the bridge deck from moving logitudinally with respect to the cables and friction brakes were placed at the connection of bridge deck and towers to damp any longitudinal movement; these provisions reduced the vertical oscillation materially.

At Tacoma Narrows one control method applied, after proving effective on the model, was to tie down a point in each side span to the ground below. Such tie was provided on the bridge in the form of 1¾₆-in. cables extending from the deck of the side spans to 50-yd. concrete anchors on the ground below, at points 300 ft. out from the anchorages. These ropes broke three or four weeks [before the collapse] during a moderate blow. Diagonal ties from the tower tops to the stiffening girders were considered but not tried.

STREAMLINING FOUND EFFECTIVE

Recent work with the big Tacoma Narrows Bridge model and with smaller models exposed in a wind tunnel was directed to determining whether the form of the stiffening member contributed to the oscillation trouble, and to trying out the effect of various shielding or streamlining fascia arrangements along the sides of the girders. Proper streamlining almost completely suppressed the disturbing wind effects, it was found. Application of these experimental findings to the bridge had not been possible at the time of the accident.

Prior to Nov. 7 such vertical waves as had occurred never got out of step on opposite sides and no damage was done, although at times smooth uniform waves with as much as 50-in. amplitude were observed.

Ten different wave periods had been observed on a 1:100 model in the University of Washington laboratory, and on the bridge itself, observed perhaps more frequently than others, was the 12-second period, the same as the period of the towers.

In the various waves it had been noted that the midspan was subjected to the least vertical movement and, presumably, to the maximum of flexure. It was here, most witnesses say, that the first structural failure occurred.

Supporting the theory that the stiffening girders were the first to fail is a picture that shows a decided disalignment of these girders at midspan (possibly a kink or a shear rupture) at a time when the concrete roadway can be seen to be still intact. Another picture, taken soon after the first concrete fell out, shows a pair of diagonals of the lateral system broken loose and hanging below the floor system.

EYEWITNESS ACCOUNT

F. B. Farquharson, associate professor of civil engineering, University of Washington, who directed the model studies and is familiar with the traits of the bridge, was on it as the destructive wave motion built up. He reports that the deck tilted from side to side more than 45 deg., that the edges of the deck had an up-and-down movement of 28 ft., and that the acceleration in the movement of the deck at times exceeded that of gravity.

Conditions observed in the collapse support the theory, reached about a month ago, that the cause of the vertical waves was aerodynamic instability of the floor system. A 1:20 model of a section of the floor system, tested in the wind tunnel at the University of Washington, was found to have unstable characteristics that fully account for the wave movement. This test was followed by studies looking to remedial measures. These had been developed and a contract for their installation on the bridge was under negotiation when the collapse occurred.

The remedy is extremely simple, consisting of a deflector vane that changes aerodynamic characteristics in such a way as to prevent the continual reversal of vertical components of wind forces. Unchecked, these forces build up cumulative wave motion which, after a considerable weight of bridge deck is involved, accumulate destructive energy. . . .

Figure 5-23 A 2½-foot buckle of the stiffening girder on the south side of the sagging east side span of the Tacoma Narrows Bridge. Note the break in the roadway. *(University of Washington Archives.)*

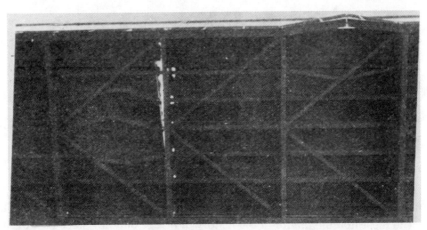

Figure 5-24 Looking up from the water level at the same buckled girder as seen in Figure 5-23 shows the remarkable buckling of stringers without any deformation of the K-brace diagonals. *(University of Washington Archives.)*

WHO BUILT THE BRIDGE

Tacoma Narrows Bridge is a state-owned structure built with federal funds by the Washington Toll Bridge Authority, an agency of the state of Washington, as a toll-refunding structure. It cost $6,400,000. A grant of $2,880,000 was made by the Public Works Administration and a loan of

$3,520,000 was provided by the Reconstruction Finance Corp. The design was prepared by the well known suspension-bridge authority, Leon S. Moisseiff, consulting engineer, New York, in cooperation with the staff of the Washington Toll Bridge Authority (L. V. Murrow, chief engineer, Clark H. Eldridge, bridge engineer, and Charles E. Andrew, principal consulting engineer). The superstructure was fabricated and built by the Bethlehem Steel Co., cable wire and suspender ropes being made by John A. Roebling Sons Co. The deep open dredging piers of the main towers were constructed by Pacific Bridge Co., San Francisco, General Construction Co., Seattle, and Columbia Constructing Co., Bonneville, Ore., as general contractors for the entire undertaking.

Once again, a distinguished investigation board was appointed. It included Othmar Ammann, designer of the George Washington Bridge in New York. And because studies of the Tacoma Narrows Bridge before it failed pointed conclusively to aerodynamic instability, aerodynamicist Theodore von Kármán also served. Within 6 months, the board presented a report, in remarkably clear language, which was summarized in the ENR issue of May 8, 1941:

Why the Tacoma Narrows Bridge Failed

Contents in Brief—Report of Federal consultants finds members of the structure showed remarkable strength; towers severely damaged; aerodynamic instability responsible for torsional motions; torsion, to which width gives important resistance, is a greater danger than is lateral deflection; greater attention to structural damping desirable.

A comprehensive report based on "a complete investigation of the design, the behavior after completion and the failure" of the Tacoma Narrows Bridge, "the most notable failure in the history of bridge building since that of the Quebec Bridge," has been prepared by O. H. Ammann, Theodore von Kármán and Glenn B. Woodruff, acting as a board appointed for this purpose by John M. Carmody, Federal Works Administrator. Findings of the board emphasize the extreme flexibility of the structure and point out that lateral deflections as the result of wind on this bridge (and on other long suspension bridges) are of much less consequence than are the torsional movements made possible by the combination of narrow width and small vertical rigidity. Widespread attention that is now being given to the stability of suspension bridges is sure to increase the sum total of knowledge, the report states, but present knowledge, expertly applied, is already sufficient to permit safe design of long, slender spans.

In the analysis made by this board, recent wind tunnel tests were considered and numerous calculations and comparisons were made. Particular attention was given to flexibility and resistance of the structure to torsional motion. The board sees little advantage in fairing, emphasizes the need for rigidity as expressed by the respective moments of inertia in both vertical and horizontal planes, and points out the advantages of weight. Resistance to dynamic forces, the report says, must be considered in terms of dynamics, which makes it necessary to take into account the structural damping in the system. The following has been taken from the report, which is a volume of 290 pages with 62 illustrations and drawings.

The report records the vertical and torsional oscillations of the bridge and the progress of the failure. By analyzing the records of the vertical oscillations the relations between their frequencies and wind velocities shown by [Figure 5-25] were developed. For each frequency there was a considerable range of velocities, the points plotted being the average of all observations for each frequency. A mathematical analysis of the natural periods of the patterns of the various modes is given. Both the periods and the patterns correspond very closely to those observed on the bridge and also on the models. It was observed that, frequently, the side and center spans were oscillating quite independently of each other.

BEHAVIOR OF THE BRIDGE

In describing the events shortly previous to and during the failure, emphasis is laid on the slipping of the north cable band at midspan and also on the large deflections of the towers. This description also develops the previously unreported fact that there were some deviations from the single noded torsional motions.

As to the condition of portions of the structure that remained: anchorages and piers show only local damage. The tower shafts have buckles

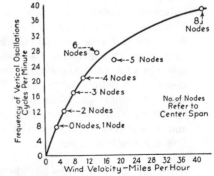

Figure 5-25 Relationship between wind velocity and frequency of vertical oscillations on the Tacoma Narrows Bridge. *(ENR.)*

in the cover plates (shoreward sides) throughout their entire height, indicating stresses beyond the yield point; some yielding in adjacent parts is also probable. The channelward sections were stressed beyond their yield point, and at least the splices yielded allowing joints to open. The top struts failed at center points. At the center of the north cable about 500 wires were cut by the chafing of the cable band to which the diagonal ties to the stiffening girders were attached. At the southwest hold-down point, at the end of the west side span, the cable was thrown off the saddle. Although not evident from surface inspection, the cables were severely overstressed, possibly to the point of incipient failure. Stiffening girders in the side spans buckled beyond repair at some points and stringers and laterals failed by buckling. [See Table 5-4.]

The damping devices installed on the bridge evidently checked longitudinal motions of the floor but had little effect in reducing the vertical oscillations. Stays at the center of main cables may be expected to be effective only for very moderate deformations of the cables. Such central stays when properly designed, exercise a limited effect on vertical oscillations but when loose they are largely ineffective and may become a source of danger when the motions of the cables become large. They were effective in preventing torsional motions, but when one center stay became ineffective (center of span, north cable) it not only rendered the structure more sensitive to torsional motions, but actually induced them by creating a torsional moment. Observations indicated that the change from the moderate parallel motions of the cable to the more violent out-of-phase motions "was almost sudden." Tie-down ropes in the side spans probably had some effect in restricting vertical movements of those spans. Since the center span motions were largely independent of the side spans, the effect of these tiedowns on oscillations of the center span was not appreciable. The effects of the hydraulic buffers installed at the towers was probably negligible.

REVIEW OF DESIGN

The behavior of the Tacoma Narrows Bridge during the hour before the final failure of its center span was a severe test of the strength of the structure as a whole, as well as of its major component parts. Under the violent dynamic motions and during the final failure, certain parts of the floor structure, the suspenders, the cables and the towers were subjected to stresses far beyond the safe limits for which these parts were designed, and at many points to stresses under which failure had to result. That under these severe stresses the main carrying members, in particular the towers, did not actually fail attests to the excellence of their design, quality of materials and workmanship and to the ample margin of safety which the structure would have had except for the severe dynamic motions.

Although its review was based on an assumed live load of 1,500 lb. per linear foot of bridge, in place of the 1,000 lb. used in the design, the board found that, considering static loads only, all stresses were within safe limits. Calculations with the live load in a position to produce the maximum torsion indicated the extreme flexibility of the bridge in this respect.

Calculations of stresses made on the basis of observed amplitudes during the torsional oscillations of the structure show that, where failure or permanent local damage occurred, stresses had reached the yield strength of the composite members. This indicates that neither faulty design nor defective material or workmanship was a factor in the failure. Under the alternating 45-deg. torsion of the floor, torsional shearing stresses in the concrete exceeded ultimate strength; this explains concrete floor breaks near the center of the span where maximum stress would be expected. Similarly, the wind truss was subjected to the most severe stresses near the center of the span, and this is where the first buckling of girders and failure of laterals was observed.

Maximum stresses in the side spans occurred when a portion of the center span dropped, allowing the side spans to sag 60 ft. at their centers, six times the maximum calculated deflection. Bending stresses in the cables at the tops of the towers together with the axial stresses were much higher than safe design stresses. It is not certain that incipient failure was not produced.

Stresses in the towers also reached their maximum when, as a result of the dropping of most of the center span, shoreward deflection at the tower tops was about 27 ft., 12 times the maximum calculated. Thus, yield strength was exceeded on both compression and tension sides of the tower shafts. Tension splices failed, probably by shearing deformations of the rivet shanks. Twisting about the vertical axes of the towers caused permanent deformation in the top struts between the two tower shafts.

COMPARISON WITH OTHER BRIDGES

The behavior and final failure of the bridge can be explained only by its responses to aerodynamic forces. A complete analysis of these forces and of the response of a suspension bridge thereto is not possible with present knowledge; further observations, experiments and mathematical analysis are required. A comparison between the Tacoma Narrows Bridge and other long span suspension bridges, in [Table 5-4], on the basis of their deflections under static load, partially explains the excessive motions of the Tacoma Narrows Bridge and also why aerodynamic forces do not cause motions of similar extent in the other bridges. Two of the other bridges, Golden Gate and Bronx-Whitestone, have relatively flexible stiffening girders, or trusses, and both have experienced to a mild degree vertical oscillations similar to those at Tacoma. At the bottom of [Table 5-4] are given the relative resistances of these five bridges to vertical and torsional motions. These are also shown by [Figures 5-26 and 5-27]. Three shorter bridges which have shown similar motions were not included in the comparison since they would not explain the "behavior of a suspension bridge 3½ times longer and 6 times heavier."

TABLE 5-4 Elastic Properties and Comparative Deflections of Five Long Suspension Bridges, as of 1941*

	Tacoma Narrows	Golden Gate	Bronx-Whitestone	San Francisco Bay	George Washington
General dimensions and weight:					
Length of center span, feet	2,800	4,200	2,300	2,310	3,500
Length of side spans, feet	1,100	1,125	735	1,160	650
Width between cables, feet	39	90	74	66	106
Average weight of center span, pounds per lineal foot	5,700	21,035	11,000	18,740	31,590†
Properties of cables:					
Number of cables	2	2	2	2	4
Cable sag, feet	232	475	200	231	319.2†
Diameter, inches	17¼	36⅜	22	28¾	36
Net section, all cables, square inches	383	1,664	594	1,050	3,195
Properties of stiffening girders:					
Number of girders and type	2 pl. girders	2 trusses	2 pl. girders	2 trusses	2 chords
Depth (c.c. chords for trusses), feet	8	25	11	30	0
Moment of inertia, all girders, in² ft²	2,567	88,000	5,860	156,000	168
Properties of lateral system:					
Horiz. wind force acting on floor and vehicles, pounds per lineal foot	560	1,130	800	1,400	1,200
Horiz. wind force acting on cables, pounds per lineal foot	60	200	120	145	300
Total wind force on floor and cables, pounds per lineal foot	620	1,330	920	1,545	1,500
Width of wind truss, feet	39	90	74	66	106
Moment of inertia, wind truss, in² ft²	95,000	1,236,000	410,000	743,000	481,100†
Properties of towers:					
Height of towers (top of pier to center of cable)	425	702	353	462.41	582
Width at top (parallel to bridge axis), feet	13	24.6	12	15	37.5
Width at bottom (parallel to bridge axis), feet	19	52.6	18	32	56
Area at top—both tower legs	1,524	7,340	3,300	3,712	5,978
Area at bottom—both tower legs	2,287	14,384	4,200	8,000	14,624

	40,500	1,500,000	60,000	290,000	3,130,000
Average moment of inertia both tower legs, in² ft²	40,500	1,500,000	60,000	290,000	3,130,000
Vertical deflections from live load at normal temperature:					
Live load, pounds per linear foot bridge	1,500	4,000	3,000	6,000	4,000
Down at ¼ point center span with load on ½ center span, tower to center	10.95	12.41	8.41	10.70	5.88
Down at center-load center span	10.50	7.34	6.50	11.85	2.92
Up at ¾ point of center span, same loading	2.74	6.72	3.30	7.50	3.54
Up at center-load side spans	5.93	2.34	2.35	8.18	0.48
Maximum change in grade, %	3.6	2.6	2.8	3.3	1.2
Maximum grade, %	6.2	5.7	6.8	6.3	3.4
Tilting from live load at ¼ point of center span, %	17.54	10.88	7.88	14.27	4.44
Lateral deflection of truss from design wind at center of center span, feet	20.03	21.5	8.93	11.42	10.7
Maximum longitudinal deflection of tower top from live load, feet	1.98	1.36	0.83 2.6†	2.53	0.34
Relative vertical rigidity at quarter point	1.0	2.3	3.0§ 4.4‡	4.0	5.0
Relative torsional rigidity	1.0	4.2	5.9§	4.9	14.1
Influence of stiffening girders on cable deformations, %	1.3	7.5	2.5	29.0	0

*Since 1941, the Golden Gate and the Bronx-Whitestone have been stiffened, and the George Washington's extra deck (added in 1953) also had a stiffening effect.

†Single deck conditions. Final condition—39,500 pounds per linear feet of bridge. Sag 325 feet.

‡Without stays.

§With stays.

SOURCE: *Engineering News-Record*, May 8, 1941.

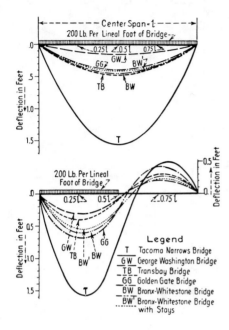

Figure   5-26 Comparative vertical rigidity of five long suspension bridges (see Table 5-4). *(ENR.)*

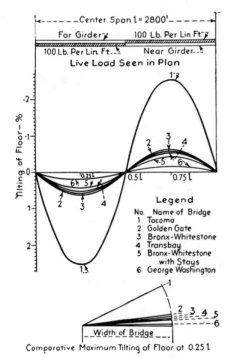

Figure 5-27 Comparative torsional rigidity of five long suspension bridges (see Table 5-4). *(ENR.)*

Experience with early suspension bridges indicated the danger of extreme flexibility, and as a result greater stiffness had become standard before the end of the last century. Then came a tendency to excessively deep and rigid stiffening trusses, ignoring the fact that weight has an important influence on rigidity. Later the value of weight and the stiffening effect of the cables were appreciated and less rigidity was provided in the stiffening trusses, the extreme in this direction being the George Washington Bridge with no stiffening trusses. Now it appears that resistance against dynamic forces must be considered to attain a well-balanced design.

The fundamental weakness of the Tacoma Narrows Bridge was its great flexibility, vertically and in torsion. The comparatively narrow width gave adequate lateral rigidity but combined with the extreme vertical flexibility, the narrowness made the structure extremely sensitive to torsional motions created by aerodynamic torsional forces.

> The principal elements which influence vertical deflections are weight, cable sag, stiffening girders, towers and side spans. Torsional deformations are influenced by the vertical deflections, hence, by all the above-mentioned elements, and by the width between the cables. Weight not needed to meet the design requirements is, however, an expensive way to supply additional rigidity. To bring its comparative vertical rigidity within the range of the Golden Gate and Whitestone Bridges would require that the Tacoma Narrows Bridge be made 2½ times heavier than it was, other proportions remaining the same.

Within the usual sag ratios of 1/9 to 1/12 any variation in cable sag has no marked effect upon the vertical rigidity. The cable sag has a material effect upon the lateral rigidity, the lateral deflection being roughly proportional to the cable sag.

Stiffening girders or trusses are the most effective and most economical means to provide rigidity as far as it is now provided by weight. The effect of the slender type of towers on the static deformation is negligible. Long side spans have a material influence upon the flexibility of the center span.

Without further aerodynamic experiments and experience on actual structures, it is not possible to set a limit to torsional flexibility. On the Tacoma Narrows Bridge, an increase in width to 53 ft., an increase in weight by 100 percent and stiffening trusses 24 ft. deep would be required for a torsional rigidity approaching that of the Golden Gate Bridge.

Wind forces are classified as static, or steady, and dynamic, the former being the force usually considered in structural design and expressed in pounds per square foot, this force varying as the square of the wind velocity. The wind tunnel tests indicate that the 30 pounds on 1½ times the exposed surface assumed for the design of the Tacoma Narrows Bridge was equivalent to the pressure produced by a wind velocity of 108 mph.

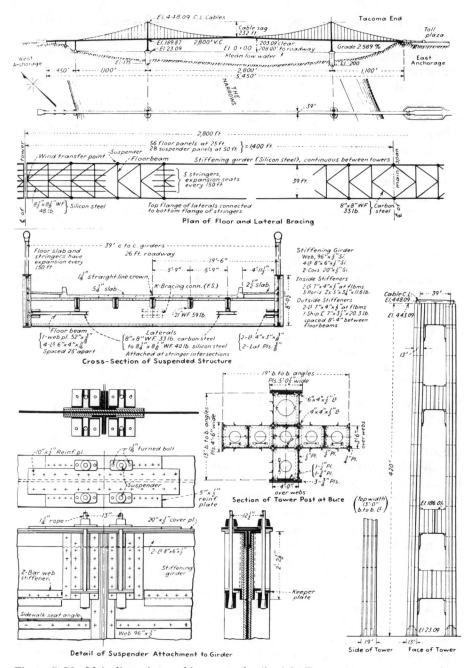

Figure 5-28 Main dimensions and important details of the Tacoma Narrows Bridge. *(ENR.)*

AERODYNAMIC FORCES

Three possible sources of dynamic action were considered; aerodynamic instability (negative damping) producing self-induced vibrations in the structure; eddy formations which might be periodic in their character; and the random effects of turbulence, in fluctuations in the velocity and direction of the wind. These sources require separate consideration in seeking the causes of the vertical and of the torsional oscillations.

VERTICAL OSCILLATIONS

The first wind tunnel tests on a model of a section of the Tacoma Narrows Bridge at the University of Washington, as reported in *Engineering News-Record,* indicated that the bridge was aerodynamically unstable—i.e., in a steady wind stream self-induced vibrations would be established. A check of these results at California Institute of Technology on a model with a larger aspect ratio (representing a longer length of the bridge so as to eliminate the end effects in the wind tunnel) failed to substantiate these results but showed instability when the depth of the girders was increased. Even with these deeper girders the negative air damping disappeared when the amplitudes on the prototype exceeded 18 in. Moreover, wind tunnel tests made on a model of the Golden Gate Bridge at Stanford University did not indicate any

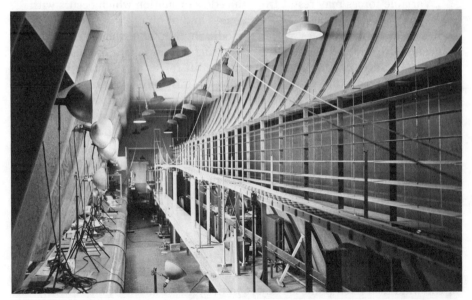

Figure 5-29 This giant 1:50 scale model, used to test designs for the new Tacoma Narrows Bridge, was built during a summer by ten mechanics and students under the direction of Prof. F. B. Farquharson. *(University of Washington Archives.)*

Figure 5-30 The Tacoma Narrows Bridge model was tested in this building, a hut 100 feet long and 34 feet wide. It was built of laminated wooden arches spaced 32 inches apart. *(University of Washington Archives.)*

aerodynamic instability and therefore this reason does not explain the vertical oscillations which have been observed on that structure. Slight aerodynamic instability may be overcome by a small amount of structural damping.

Variable forces may result from the eddy formation which occurs with the air flow around bodies with sharp edges and of blunt cross-sections. These eddies occur, in many cases, with a periodic rhythm, and when their period coincides with the natural period of the structure a resonant oscillation may develop. To develop periodically alternating lift forces on the structure it would be necessary that eddies be produced alternately at the upper and lower edges of the girders. To decide this question, velocity fluctuation measurements were conducted on a model of the roadway. The fluctuations were measured by a hot wire anemometer which permitted simultaneous recordings at the upper and lower edges of the front girder. The fluctuations were of a large order and fairly periodic but the fluctuations were more frequently in phase than otherwise. Flow pictures, taken by Beeuwkees at the Case School of Applied Science, of a model in a tank showed similar periodic eddies, but when the model does not oscillate in torsion the eddies are not alternating.

The board believes the most satisfactory explanation of the vertical oscillations is that of forced vibrations excited by the random action of turbulent wind. Because of its natural turbulence, the velocity and [direction] of the wind at a fixed point is subject to random variations. Consequently, the horizontal wind pressure and the lift forces are varying. The vertical forces vary not only in amount but also in direction and are apt to produce vertical oscillations of the roadway. These fluctuations are random, without definite periodicity. Nevertheless, these fluctuations exert an action similar to a great number of superimposed periodic fluctuations. The deflections produced by those fluctuations whose period approaches one of the natural frequencies of the structure will be amplified especially if the structure is not sufficiently damped. Higher frequencies of these fluctuations prevail in winds of higher velocity. This explains the correlation between modes of oscillation and wind velocity [Figure 5-25].

TORSIONAL OSCILLATIONS

The board conducted oscillatory tests in the wind tunnel on a number of suspension bridge models and found, for all models, negative air damping, or aerodynamic instability, above a certain wind velocity. For narrow bridges, this limiting velocity is relatively low, 25 m.p.h. in the case of the Tacoma Narrows Bridge. For similar cross-sections, this limiting velocity increases as the ratio of width to the depth of the girder is increased. This negative damping does not become critical, i.e., amplitudes will not become increasingly large, until it is sufficient to overcome the structural damping in the system. The board believes this point to have been reached in the Tacoma Bridge at about 40 mph.

The torsional motions involve distortion of the wind truss (which at Tacoma was 35 times as rigid as the suspended structure in a vertical direction) and also of the concrete floor. The towers are more resistant to torsional than to parallel motions. Consequently, greater structural damping is involved, and this explains why torsional oscillations did not occur at lower velocities and why they were not caused by the random wind effects. Once started these self-induced torsional oscillations become very violent; the amount of energy input in the prototype, estimated as the result of negative damping in Tacoma Narrows Bridge model experiments, gives a figure, for a plus or minus 45 deg. amplitude, on the order of 5,000 hp.

RESISTANCES

The resistance of a suspension bridge to vibrations from dynamic forces is furnished by its rigidity, inertia and structural damping. The Tacoma Narrows Bridge was deficient in all three respects and therefore the amplitudes were greater than have occurred on other bridges. Suspension bridges differ from others in that the potential energy in vibration is largely stored in the form of work done against gravity, that is, the bridge behaves somewhat as a pendulum. The result is that the damping in a suspension bridge is materially less than in other types of bridges. Tests by [Farquharson] indicated that the damping constant of a model of the Tacoma Bridge was only 1/30 of that of the more common bridge types. These tests showed the beneficial effects of more rigid stiffening trusses and of friction in the system. The report suggests further investigations of means to secure more structural damping, including participation of the concrete floors in the chord stresses of the stiffening truss and deliberate means of introducing friction, and states "It is at least doubtful that streamlining is the desirable solution for elimination of large oscillations or aerodynamic instability." Nevertheless, it is highly desirable to determine the influence of form on the aerodynamic characteristics of various structures.

It is also pointed out that the criteria for dynamic stability differ materially from those usually considered for static rigidity. Since, for example, the center spans may oscillate without involving motions of the side spans, it is evident that short side spans and even straight backstays have little influence in this respect.

It will never be possible to establish cut-and-dried rules or formulas for the design of long suspension spans; each will require analytical study by the experienced designer. With the emphasis that the Tacoma Narrows Bridge collapse has put on the importance of providing damping, vertical rigidity and torsional resistance (as distinct from the less important resistance to horizontal deflection under assumed, steady wind forces), there need be no fear that these factors will be overlooked in future competent designs. Long, light suspension spans can now be made safe and adequate.

SUMMARY OF CONCLUSIONS OF FWA REPORT ON TACOMA BRIDGE

As a result of the investigations which are described in detail in this report, we have reached the following conclusions:

1. The Tacoma Narrows Bridge was well designed and built to resist safely all static forces, including wind, usually considered in the design of similar structures. Its failure resulted from excessive oscillations caused by wind action.

2. The excessive vertical and torsional oscillations were made possible by the extraordinary degree of flexibility of the structure and of its relatively small capacity to absorb dynamic forces. It was not realized that the aerodynamic forces which had proven disastrous in the past to much lighter and shorter flexible suspension bridges would affect a structure of such magnitude as the Tacoma Narrows Bridge, although its flexibility was greatly in excess of any other long span suspension bridge.

3. The vertical oscillations of the Tacoma Narrows Bridge were probably induced by the turbulent character of wind action. Their amplitudes may have been influenced by the aerodynamic characteristics of the suspended structure. There is, however, no convincing evidence that the vertical oscillations were caused by so-called aerodynmic instability. At the higher wind velocities torsional oscillations, when once induced, tend to increase their amplitudes.

4. Vertical oscillations of considerable amplitudes were first observed during the erection of the suspended floor and continued, at intervals, until the day of failure. While, at times, the resulting stresses in the stiffening girders were high, there is no

evidence that any structural damage resulted. Under certain observed conditions very high stresses were caused in the ties which connected the suspended floor structure to the cables at mid-span.

5. It appears reasonably certain that the first failure was the slipping of the cable band on the north side of the bridge to which the center ties were connected. This slipping probably initiated the torsional oscillations. These torsional movements caused breaking stresses at various points of the suspended structure and further structural damage followed almost immediately. The dropping of the greater part of the suspended structure of the center span was made possible by the failure of the suspenders. This was followed by the sudden sagging of the side spans with resulting bending and overstressing of the towers and of the side spans.

6. The suspension type is the most suitable and the most economical that could have been selected for the Tacoma Narrows Bridge. No more satisfactory location could have been chosen.

7. Both the Public Works Administration and the Reconstruction Finance Corporation were entirely justified in assuming that, because of the experience and reputation of the consultants employed by the Washington Toll Bridge Authority, there could be no possible question as to the adequacy of the design. Both agencies exercised thorough and competent supervision during the construction of the bridge.

8. There can be no question that the quality of the materials in the structure, and the workmanship, were of a high order.

9. Certain parts of the towers were severely overstressed and permanently deformed during the failure. While there is no visual evidence of damage to the cables, except at the center of the north cable, it is probable that they were overstressed during the torsional oscillations and as a result of the sagging of the side spans. The main piers were not damaged, except locally, during the failure and can withstand considerably heavier tower reactions than they received from the bridge as it existed. The anchorages were not damaged and are safe for forces not greater than those imposed by the original construction.

10. The criteria usually considered for rigidity against static forces do not necessarily apply to dynamic forces.

11. The remedial installations in the bridge represented a rational effort to control the amplitudes of the oscillations. Further installations, including diagonal stay ropes from the top of the towers to the floor were being investigated when the failure occurred, and these would have increased the rigidity. It is doubtful that any measures of this nature would have been sufficient to compensate for the extreme flexibility of the structure.

12. The evidence as to whether the vertical oscillations of the bridge would have been affected by fairing (streamlining) is inconclusive. There is certain evidence that fairing would have had an unfavorable influence on the torsional stability.

13. Further experiments and analytical studies are desirable to investigate the action of aerodynamic forces on suspension bridges.

14. Pending the results of further investigations, there is no doubt that sufficient knowledge and experience exists to permit the safe design of a suspension bridge of any practicable span. The results of further research should furnish knowledge that will permit of more economical design.

15. This report has been restricted to the Tacoma Narrows Bridge, except that available information from other bridges has been considered.

SOURCE: *Engineering News-Record,* May 8, 1941.

The Tacoma Narrows Bridge was eventually to be rebuilt on the same site. Because of World War II, however, the new bridge was not begun until 1946. During the intervening 6 years, numerous studies resulting in hundreds of technical papers explored numerous refinements to suspension bridge design. Large-scale models of the old bridge and new alternatives were built and tested in giant wind tunnels. One such tunnel had a throat 100 feet long and 10 feet high. It was manned at the University of Washington by Prof. F. B. Farquharson, under the direction of Charles E. Andrews, chief engineer of the Washington Toll Bridge Authority.

As Andrews pointed out many times in articles for ENR and other publications, the public would have to be doubly reassured of the new bridge's safety before the commitment could be made to go ahead with the new design's construction. Therefore, the process was remarkably open to discussion from bridge experts from around the country. Some wanted the bridge to sport diag-

Figure 5-31 Inside the hut (see Figure 5-30) the 100-foot-long model, scaled 1:50, is mounted at the throat of a low-velocity wind tunnel. *(University of Washington Archives.)*

Figure 5-32 Modjeski and Masters staff suggested triangulated suspender cables along with shallow stiffening trusses for long suspension bridges, in an article in the October 23, 1941, issue of ENR. *(ENR.)*

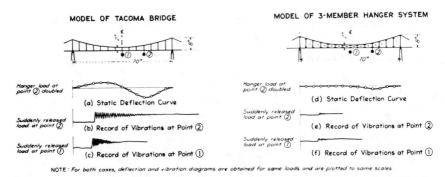

MODEL OF TACOMA BRIDGE

MODEL OF 3-MEMBER HANGER SYSTEM

Hanger load at point ② doubled

(a) Static Deflection Curve

Suddenly released load at point ②

(b) Record of Vibrations at Point ②

Suddenly released load at point ①

(c) Record of Vibrations at Point ①

Hanger load at point ② doubled

(d) Static Deflection Curve

Suddenly released load at point ②

(e) Record of Vibrations at Point ②

Suddenly released load at point ①

(f) Record of Vibrations at Point ①

NOTE: For both cases, deflection and vibration diagrams are obtained for same loads and are plotted to same scales

Figure 5-33 This cross-braced, three-hanger system was proposed by George A. Maney, chairman of the civil engineering department at what was then the Northwestern Technological Institute in Evanston, Illinois. The design was discussed in ENR on April 24, 1941. No resonant vibration is possible, but such a design is expensive to build. *(ENR.)*

onal stays, like John A. Roebling's Cincinnati bridge built in 1867 with a 1057-foot span (ENR, Oct. 23, 1941, p. 97). Still others preferred cross-braced stays (ENR, Apr. 24, 1941, p. 64). Ammann and Steinman argued over the efficacy of stiffening schemes each had employed on other bridges. Steinman complained that Ammann's stiffening of the Bronx-Whitestone was less satisfactory than the approach used by Steinman on the Thousand Islands Bridge (ENR, Febr. 27, 1941, p. 516, and May 8, 1941, p. 728).

After the smoke cleared, however, the Washington Toll Bridge Authority settled on a bridge of conventional design, with four roadway lanes instead of two, and with deep stiffening trusses for the deck—33 feet deep instead of the original bridge's 8 feet. Cable spacing is 60 feet. The bridge still stands in daily service, fully confirming that its designers had learned from the disaster.

Silver Bridge, 1967

On December 15, 1967, only seventeen states had bridge inspection programs that were considered acceptable by the federal government. A year later, every state did. That day, December 15, 1967, the eyebar suspension bridge between Gallipolis, Ohio, and Point Pleasant, West Virginia, collapsed under the strain of a Friday traffic jam. Forty-six people died and nine were injured, in the worst failure of a highway bridge in U.S. history. Only the Ashtabula Creek disaster of 1876—in which a 150-foot long cast-iron bridge gave way under the weight of the Lake Shore and Southern Michigan Railroad's Pacific Express, killing 91 and injuring 64—was worse.

Oddly enough, the Silver Bridge's unusual eyebar design had been trumpeted by ENR the same month the final investigative report on the Hackensack River bascule failure was published. Here are the editors' comments from the June 29, 1929, issue:

An Eyebar Suspension Span for the Ohio River

Stiffening Trusses on 700-Ft. Span at Point Pleasant, W. Va.,
Utilize Eyebar Chain as Top Chord for Half of Both Center
and Side Spans—Unique Anchorage on 405 Concrete Piles

By WILSON T. BALLARD
Vice-President, J. E. Greiner Company, Consulting Engineers, Baltimore, Md.

Figure 5-34   ENR headlined design and construction of the Silver Bridge in the June 20, 1929, issue. It took 40 years for poor maintenance to kill it. *(ENR.)*

Eyebars for Cables

Strong emphasis is placed on the eyebar or chain type of suspension bridge by the design and successful erection of two such structures over the Ohio River at Point Pleasant and St. Marys, W.Va. . . . As in the Florianopolis bridge in Brazil, opened in 1925, parts of the suspension system are used as top chords of the stiffening trusses. The Brazilian bridge has straight unloaded backstays, and the eyebar chain is a two-purpose member over the center half of the main span only, while the designs of these Ohio River bridges go a step farther and replace the structural top chord with the eyebar chain in the landward halves of the side spans as well as in the main span. Variable-depth stiffening trusses are also . . . integral [to these three] designs. . . .

Economy and logical design are the principal advantages claimed for this type of suspension structure by its advocates. Briefly, the design is based on the fact that the tensile stress in the cable and the compression in the top chords of the stiffening trusses can be carried by a single tension member, designed for the greater of the two stresses instead of for their sum, the compression member being eliminated. Economy, based on the often-stated principle that truss outlines closely approximating the curve of maximum bending moments provide maximum utilization of material, also dictated the use of the variable-depth stiffening trusses.

Investigation of the failure naturally turned on two issues: the Silver Bridge's unique design and the quality of inspections done on the bridge by

West Virginia's highway department. The wreckage was so tangled, however, that investigators at first thought they would have little physical evidence to go on. As reported in the ENR issue of December 21, 1967:

Collapse May Never Be Solved

A bridge that made engineering history for its design when it was built 40 years ago created history of another kind last Friday when it collapsed.

The bridge, which carried traffic of U.S. 35 over the Ohio River between Gallipolis, Ohio, and Point Pleasant, W.Va., was the first eyebar suspension bridge in the U.S. in which the eyebars formed the top chords of the stiffening trusses in both the main and anchor spans. . . .

When the bridge fell, the main span apparently flipped over, dumping the vehicles into as much as 70 ft of murky water with a current of almost 6 knots. The span then fell on the vehicles, and both towers fell atop that. The result was a tangled mass of bridge members and vehicles.

Figure 5-35   The wreckage of the Silver Bridge. A railroad trestle in the background was not affected by the collapse. *(United Press International.)*

FAILURE EVIDENCE IS SECONDARY

Primary concern at the site has been recovering the vehicles and the bodies in them, and in freeing the river channel for the heavy barge traffic it carries. Barge cranes and divers are removing some of the bridge piecemeal, cutting it as necessary to get at the submerged vehicles. Thus, it may be very difficult later to pinpoint the member, or members that failed and triggered the fall.

No one on the site was talking officially about the cause of the tragedy, or about whose responsibility it was. On the scene were investigators from the U.S. Bureau of Public Roads, and a team of engineers from Baltimore consulting engineers J. E. Greiner & Co., who designed the bridge for a private company but have had little to do with it since.

THE INVESTIGATIONS

The Corps of Engineers disclaims any interest in the cause of the collapse; its responsibility is to get the channel cleared and river traffic running again. The West Virginia Road Commission, which owns the bridge—having bought it from the Ohio-West Virginia Bridge Co. in 1941—apparently is still organizing its investigative team.

Said ENR's associate editor Ed Young on the scene, "I've never seen such a pile of junk. Every joint is broken, and every broken piece is rusted (because of rains after the collapse). It's going to be almost impossible to separate old breaks from new."

But knowledgeable authorities on bridge design pointed the finger at several possible contributing factors: age, corrosion, fatigue and overloading.

Responsibility for maintenance of the suspended spans apparently rested with West Virginia. It conducts detailed inspections of all bridges every two years, according to road commission chairman Burl A. Sawyers. The "Silver Bridge" (so-called locally because of its aluminum paint) was last inspected in detail by state bridge engineers in April, 1965, at which time nothing irregular was reported.

Sawyers also said, "All bridges are under constant surveillance by the road commission maintenance division and the district engineers."

A DESIGN "FIRST"

The bridge was unique in U.S. bridge annals in two respects: It was the first to use the eyebar "chain" for portions of the top chords of the stiffening trusses, and it was the first use of high-strength, heat-treated carbon steel eyebars. Its anchorages also are unusual.

The two-lane bridge had a total length of about 1,750 ft, including short approach spans on both sides of the river. The main, suspended span was 700 ft long. It was flanked on either side by 380-ft anchor spans. All three of these spans, and the two towers, fell.

THE MEMBERS

The eyebars, each about 2 in. thick and 12 in. wide, were in pairs of varying length, dependent on their location in the bridge, to maintain equal panel lengths in the stiffening trusses. In each side span the chains formed the top chord of the stiffening trusses for the first seven panels on the outside end; in the center span 12 panels of a total of 28 each of each truss used the eyebar chain as a top chord.

The stiffening trusses were of the Warren type with subverticals. The bottom chords and the parts of the top chords not provided by the eyebar chains comprised two 15-in. channels laced together. The diagonals were four angles laced with lattice bars. Except where the eyebar chains formed the top chords, 1½ x 6-in. eyebar hangers suspended the trusses from the chains.

The deck originally was wood planks topped with rock asphalt. This was replaced by a concrete-filled steel grid during a general renovation of the bridge in 1941.

The towers, about 131 ft high, were steel boxes made up of prefabricated sections. The towers were of the rocker type to permit movement due to moving loads and to changes in length of chains caused by variation in temperature.

Each anchorage was a reinforced concrete trough 200 ft long and 34 ft wide filled with earth and concrete, and founded on 405 sixteen-inch octagonal reinforced concrete piles.

The General Contracting Corp., of Pittsburgh, was the general contractor and built the piers, anchorages and approaches. The American Bridge Co., of Pittsburgh, furnished and erected the steel superstructure under a subcontract.

LOADING AND FATIGUE

The bridge was designed for "ASCE H-15 loading," a much lower live load than the AASHO H20-S16 live load used today in the design of bridges on the Interstate highway system.

One suspension bridge expert pointed out that on modern bridges the ratio of dead load to live load might range between 5 to 1, and 8 to 1. On the Point Pleasant bridge, the ratio may have been much less, with increases in live loads since the time it was designed. If so, the variations in stress may have been greater, a situation that could be conducive to fatigue failure in the bridge members.

Another suspension bridge built in the late 1920s at St. [Marys], W.Va., 75 miles away, to the same plans has been closed by the state road commission pending a thorough inspection.

The Point Pleasant bridge had not been posted for load limit; a state law limits vehicles to a maximum gross weight of 35 tons, except by special permit. Speed limit on the bridge was 25 mph.

HOW IT COLLAPSED

The sequence and manner in which the various elements of the bridge gave way have not been determined conclusively but ENR's Young pieced together a tentative picture from eyewitness reports and questioning officials: The suspended side span toward the Ohio (west) shore collapsed first. Its upstream (north) side dropped, then the span rolled in the upstream direction and came down on its side. The bridge then "snaked," contorting like a ribbon being twisted, and the main span fell. It rolled in the opposite direction, the downstream (south) side falling first, and landed upside down. Both towers are believed to have fallen toward the river, but divers had not located them by Monday night. The entire collapse took from a few seconds to half a minute, judging from varying reports by witnesses.

Four men in an icehouse about a half-mile downstream at the time said they began counting vehicles upon hearing a tremendous crack. They counted nine trailer trucks and 17 automobiles on the bridge before it fell.

LOTS OF POSSIBLE CAUSES

"We understand the failure was in one of the supports of the side spans, which is unusual," said Edward J. Donnelly, a partner in J. E. Greiner & Co. "You could let your imagination run wild and find a ton of things that could have gone wrong," he said. "Overloading could have been one of them. The bridge was not designed for modern traffic loads. A failure might have begun with one of the main supporting members. We won't know until the superstructure is recovered from the river and inspected piece by piece."

Greiner voluntarily sent its engineers, as a courtesy, because they have done a lot of work in both states, Donnelly said. "In the late 1930s, however, we were called in by West Virginia to have a look at it and that examination resulted in renewing the decking."

He also noted that bridge design technique has changed considerably since the completion of the span at Point Pleasant. "Back in those days, our engineers would prepare stress sheets and the steel and bridge contractors would design to meet the needs. We don't do it that way today. We design the total bridge, abutment to abutment."

OTHER STATES REACT

The West Virginia failure triggered other states into promptly investigating the safety of their older bridges.

Ohio called in Modjeski & Masters, consulting engineers of Harrisburg, Pa., to inspect two Ohio River suspension bridges built in 1896 and 1927.

Maryland's state roads commissioner says the state already has a good bridge maintenance and inspection program. But, as a result of the accident, he says he will ask the legislature to increase annual maintenance and inspection expenditures from $350,000 to $750,000.

Kentucky's Department of Highways with two suspension bridges (one built in the 1860s, the other in 1931) under its jurisdiction, met to review its bridge inspection program.

URGENCY OF CLEARING

This stretch of the Ohio is one of the busiest waterways in the world. It handles about 30,000 tons of cargo a day, more than the Panama Canal and St. Lawrence Seaway combined. Cargo is now backing up at both ends of the 43-mile stretch that is closed.

Actually barges could pass through a 270-ft-wide channel now where the wreckage is too far under water to endanger vessels. But with most of the presumed dead still in the water, no one suggested that shipping resume immediately.

The Corps of Engineers has Dravo Corp., of Pittsburgh, at the bridge with some heavy salvage equipment and personnel, including divers, from a lock construction site upstream; and Marine Contracting, Inc., Southport, Conn., with 20 divers, some in conventional gear, others with self-contained breathing apparatus.

The diving operation is dangerous, difficult and not very effective, because of almost total lack of visibility, coldness of the water (34F), fast and erratic currents and the instability of some of the underwater wreckage. The Corps slowed the current to 3 mph from 6 mph by shutting off dam gates upstream to cut down 20% (20,000 cu ft per sec) of the river flow; and by closing them at Gallipolis Dam downstream to slow the escape of water from the collapse site.

The Silver Bridge failure was unlike the Tacoma Narrows collapse or the earlier failure of the Hackensack River bascule; simply appointing a team of three expert engineers to study the failure was not enough. In these modern times, the federal government appoints an overseeing "blue-ribbon panel" to second-guess the engineers and sanitize the final report. The Silver Bridge panel was headed by Joseph J. O'Connell Jr., chairman of the National Transportation Safety Board. Other panel members included Paul Selby, dean of West Virginia University's law school; Emmett H. Karrer, professor of civil engineering at Ohio State; Vice Admiral Paul E. Trimble, assistant commendant of the U.S. Coast Guard; General Harry G. Woodbury, Jr., director of civil works for the Army Corps of Engineers; Francis C. Turner, director of the Bureau of Public Roads (now the Federal Highway Administration); A. E. Johnson, executive director of the American Association of State Highway Officials; and Louis M. Thayer, a member of the National Transportation Safety Board. Much of the actual investigation work was carried out by two Bureau of Public Roads bridge experts, Stanley Gordon and Charles F. Scheffey. West Virginia hired consulting engineers Modjeski & Masters to help with its probe, and temporarily closed a near twin of the Silver Bridge, the span at St. [Marys].

Confidence in West Virginia's inspection program was shaken only 10 days after the collapse, by an incident on Christmas Day. Two people were walking across the Washington Street Bridge in Charleston when one of them fell through the sidewalk up to his armpits. He was saved from falling into the Elk River below by his companion. The bridge had been inspected by the state's road commission only 2 days earlier, and had been pronounced safe for loads under 5000 pounds.

With Senator Jennings Randolph, a West Virginian, head of the Senate Public Works Committee—source of highway construction bills—President Johnson moved within days to start the paperwork for a new bridge on the site. The committee to do that job was headed by Price Daniel, former governor of Texas. Still another group, headed by Federal Highway Administrator Lowell K. Bridwell, was put in charge of "analyzing procedures" to make sure other bridges were safe.

Given all the public attention, combined with public inaction, numerous theories were put forth on how the bridge might have failed. Observers generally agreed that the failure began at or near one of the cable bents on the Ohio side of the river. Each eyebar of the sidespan suspension chain passed through a vertical strut on its way from the cable anchorage to the main tower. At each strut, the joints between struts and eyebars were pinned, however. Did the failure start in an eyebar, in a strut, or in a connecting pin? While the bridge's pieces were being spread out for study on a 27-acre site nearby, the public heard that "crystallization" in an eyebar had caused it to snap. Metallurgists quickly noted that the so-called "crystals" were a sign of brittle fracture, but that there is no such thing as "crystallization" in steel and that the rough features of such breaks simply expose metal grains that exist in all eyebars, even unbroken ones.

Professor Thomas Stelson, head of the civil engineering department at Carnegie-Mellon, was hired by NBC News to inspect the pieces only 3 days after the disaster. He said "the wreckage not in the river showed no structural fatigue or stress corrosion." Professor Stelson examined the questionable cable-bent strut and found only evidence of a ductile break, leading him to suspect the failure started elsewhere.

Stelson suggested that the bridge failed because it was overloaded—that it was supporting vehicles weighing up to 36 tons at the time of the collapse, but had been designed for 15 tons maximum in any one vehicle. ENR looked back at the 1927 stress analysis sheet prepared by the bridge's designers and found the margin for safety much higher than that. The bridge's stiffening trusses, cables, and towers had been designed for a live load of 1400 pounds for every linear foot of the spans, and a 42,000-pound (21-ton) load at any one point. The floor system could hold three 15-ton trucks placed side by side, or one 20-ton truck in the middle of the roadway.

Eyewitnesses also came forward to dispute initial reports of heavy traffic. Ohio-bound vehicles did fill the upstream lane, but the other lane was nearly empty. The Corps of Engineers pulled twenty-three of the twenty-four vehicles that had been on the bridge out of the Ohio River. Their weight, the Corps said, did not overload the spans.

Others pointed to the possibility of continuing punishment of structural members from occasional overloading—punishment not detected by West Virginia inspectors. That point, and complaints about the slow-moving investigation, were made in an ENR editorial on May 23, 1968:

Figure 5-36 In investigating the Silver Bridge collapse, the National Transportation Safety Board focused on these pieces—fragments of eyebar (foreground), an eyebar pin (right), and the bent strut (left rear). *(United Press International.)*

Know When to Stop

Investigations of last December's failure of the Silver Bridge at Point Pleasant, W.Va., may continue for some time.

But the most important cause of the failure already has been revealed: inadequate inspection of the 40-year-old structure. This fact came into sharp focus in recent hearings [ENR, May 16, 1968, p. 28]. A state bridge inspector admitted the incompleteness of an inspection done in 1965 and said that the last full inspection had been in 1951. Even then, some of the prescribed procedures were circumvented.

Some such revelation of the State Road Commission's carelessness seemed inevitable since the moment the tragedy occurred. The agency has been one of the weakest in the country, notorious for its low salaries, political interference and corruption. It has been unable to hire and retain enough qualified engineers to handle properly the expanded highway program that began in 1956.

Few highway departments can afford to be smug about their bridge inspection programs. Since the West Virginia accident, most have reviewed and tightened their inspection procedures and have accelerated their inspections of major structures. And the Bureau of Public Roads is developing bridge inspection procedures that it will ask the states to apply to small bridges on the federal-aid roads.

In the midst of all this activity, one note of caution seems in order: The states should make certain that the time, effort and money spent on bridge inspection do not grow out of proportion to the problem. After all, the West Virginia collapse was unique in U.S. history. There is just one other bridge like it, the one over the Ohio at St. [Marys], W.Va.; and it is under detailed study, constant surveillance, and is allowed to carry only light traffic.

Concern might also be expressed about the Silver Bridge investigation. Competent engineers now seem to know exactly where the failure began, and how. The federal investigators should narrow their studies to this section of the structure, do the necessary testing, publish a report and be done with it, avoiding whatever temptation there may be to do an aircraft-crash-style investigation of the entire structure.

The last paragraph in the above editorial referred to testimony of G. K. Gillan, senior structural associate with Modjeski & Masters, before the federal board of inquiry earlier that May. Gillan blamed "eyebar 330," the second upstream eyebar west of the tower on the Ohio side of the bridge. The companion to that eyebar had been found intact but with the edge of its eye peened over—rolled back—which suggested that before the collapse, this eyebar was carrying the total load, with no help from the bar that broke. This uneven load-

Figure 5-37   The giant eyebars—most longer than 50 feet—at Silver Bridge were hard to handle; federal investigators spent months trying to put each into its proper place in the structure. *(National Highway Transportation Safety Board.)*

Figure 5-38   The eyebar that shattered, eventually leading to the Silver Bridge collapse. *(ENR.)*

ing would have rolled the edge of the eye back as the pin twisted free of its connection. The pin itself, 13 inches long and 11½ inches in diameter, was still missing at the time Gillan testified.

The ENR issue of May 16, 1968, summarized other testimony as well:

West Virginia's State Road Commission bridge inspector, Paul McDowell, told the board that he did not follow nearly half of the bridge inspection procedures outlined in his inspection manual when he last looked at the bridge in 1965. He said the last full inspection of the bridge was in 1951 and it was done with a pair of binoculars working from the deck, although the manual requires climbing the towers to inspect the top members.

Witnesses who were on the Ohio side of the bridge said they heard loud noises immediately before the collapse. Those in the center span east of the Ohio tower said they heard nothing.

One survivor, almost in the middle of the span when it fell, said that just prior to the collapse the bridge was shaking "like a grandmother would shake a baby carriage." He told the board that the shaking stopped momentarily, then the deck turned toward the upstream side and fell into the river.

A barge officer, who had a broadside view of the bridge, said the Ohio tower began to twist, then the main span carrying traffic between the two main towers turned upside down and fell.

According to Bill Thatcher, assistant to the vice president for engineering at American Bridge, fabricator of the bridge, the company has no record of ever having tested the 50 to 55-ft eyebars used on the bridge. He said the testing equipment couldn't handle the long bars, so the fabricator tested a 40-ft eyebar instead.

In April 1971, more than 3 years after the disaster, the National Transportation Safety Board released its final report, confirming Gillan's analysis. The collapse did start with an eyebar failure, a "fracture . . . caused by the development of a critical size flaw . . . as a result of the joint action of stress corrosion and corrosion fatigue."

Three months later, about 5 pounds of explosives were used to bring down the St. Marys Bridge, to make way for another structure. A 14-month exami-

Figure 5-39 The failed eyebars were near the point shown by the arrow, at the cable bent strut on the Ohio side of the Silver Bridge. The eyebars pulled apart, tearing this strut away from the bridge. *(United Press International.)*

Figure 5-40 The Reichbruecke in Vienna, before its collapse. Here, eyebars were used as part of a more true suspension bridge, but with the deck in compression. *(ENR.)*

nation of the bridge by Steinman, Boynton, Gronquist & London and Gates Engineering had called for either replacement of the entire bridge or adding two new wire suspension cables next to the eyebars to "carry the entire load of the bridge after a break anywhere in the eyebar chains" and to share the load under normal circumstances. The new cables would have cost $1.5 million. The replacement cost $6 million, and the federal government paid the entire price.

In the summer of 1976, one of the few remaining eyebar structures in the world, the Reichsbruecke over the Danube in Vienna, collapsed. Fortunately, the failure occurred at 5 A.M. on a Sunday; only one person died. The failure was immediately compared to Silver Bridge; each had collapsed just short of its fortieth year. Investigation showed, however, that the failure started in a bridge pier originally built in the 1870s to support an earlier steel truss. The downstream side of one of the piers, enlarged in 1937 for the eyebar bridge, had sheered away.

Two weeks after the collapse, a five-member commission of Austrian engineering experts reported that concrete fill placed around the grillage of structural steel beams at the pier's base had been of inconsistent quality and had included sand and clumps of noncompacted concrete. This, the commission said, "was instrumental in permitting the entry of water and action by frost and resulted in greater than foreseen vibration movement of the unreinforced pier base."

Inconsistent load distribution and fissuring forces in the concrete fill, the commission reported, "resulted in progressive disintegration of the pier base concrete hidden behind the pier's stone facade."

One commission member, Prof. Hans Reiffenstuhl, chairman of Vienna's Institute for Reinforced Concrete and Massive Construction, said that normal visual inspection of the bridge with binoculars would not have spotted the pier's weakness, but that there were formations of calcium compounds on the facade that would have suggested to an expert the possibility of something wrong inside.

ENR editors commented in the issue of August 19, 1976, "This failure confirms that bridge inspection must not be left up to nontechnical personnel. With the forces of nature constantly acting on structures, especially the type

Figure 5-41   The new Silver Bridge developed cracks in sixteen truss welds, only 8 years after being placed into use. The welds were "conventional" submerged arc passes, not electroslag. *(An SRC photograph by Herb Clagg.)*

that is subject to the daily ravages of a river, frequent expert inspection is a must."

The Reichsbruecke normally carried 15,000 cars per hour and was crossed by two tram lines as well. The lesson for the public would have been far more severe if the bridge had failed at midday instead of on a Sunday morning.

As for the Silver Bridge's replacement, a cantilever through truss: A routine inspection in July 1977 turned up a 0.75-inch crack in a top chord weld of a steel girder in tension. The bridge was immediately closed for repairs on sixteen of the welds. "We're not taking any chances," said the chief bridge engineer, Harry Stephens.

6 Materials and Methods

The failures discussed in this chapter have one thing in common: They became more prevalent as structures grew higher, lighter, and more complex. Only now has the building "profession"—including architects, engineers, contractors, and materials suppliers—begun to pull together to keep such failures to a minimum. Contrary to popular belief, the stimulus for these improvements has come more from the private sector, especially insurance companies tired of paying off claims, than from local building inspectors or from the federal Occupational Safety and Health Administration (OSHA).

Lamellar Tearing, 1972

Sometimes a disaster can be purely financial, with no lives lost. Twin towers in Los Angeles, the 100-story Hancock Tower in Chicago, and numerous other steel-framed structures shared an ugly little secret: that welded connections, especially in heavy plates and at constrained joints, could create hidden rips in the plates themselves. On July 27, 1972, ENR associate editor Richard Kielar reported that such cracks had developed in the compression ring of a new civic center being built in El Paso, Texas. That first report stimulated consultants and builders to talk about other instances of tearing—instances that had occurred as early as the midsixties, when large plates began to be used more frequently in structures.

When large sections are welded, the heat of the welding creates expansion in the metal. When the weld cools, the metal contracts. If the joint is highly restrained—that is, if it offers little leeway for expansion and contraction—the steel may tear. The problem may occur in diaphragm stiffener plates in box girders, at floor beam connections, or when welding different-size columns to a cap plate where transitions are made. In the September 21, 1972, issue of ENR, Kielar put the facts together for the first time in any publication:

Lamellar Tearing of Steel Worries Designers

The increased incidence of lamellar tearing, or failure of steel in its through thickness dimension, is drawing the attention of large numbers of design professionals. The tearing, which usually occurs in plates over 1.5 in. thick used in complex structures, including skyscrapers, where big loads are a part of design, can take two forms. It may appear as internal microscopic cracking detectable ultrasonically, or at the surface where it is frequently visible. Either way, repair costs run high.

The twin 52-story Atlantic-Richfield towers, recently completed in Los Angeles, ran up a $400,000 repair bill attributed, in part, to lamellar tearing. In El Paso, the new civic center theater has been delayed more than four months because of cracks that developed in a compression ring: On one job, the 50-story Trans-America Tower under way in San Francisco, the owner is so concerned, that he ordered the large members of space frame structures that carry the tower uncovered until 80 to 90% of the load is on all connections checked ultrasonically.

One testing engineer says most structures containing large plates with welded connections, built in the last 10 years in New York City, have had the problem. F. Robert Preece, executive vice-president of Testing Engineers, Inc., Oakland, Calif., says cracking has occurred in San Francisco's Alcoa Bank of California, Bechtel and Security Pacific buildings, and the Embarcadero Regency Hyatt House hotel, all of which range from 19 to 46 stories. He indicates in a report presented to the International Conference on Tall Buildings, recently held at Lehigh University, that if the problem isn't corrected in a structure, the results could be disastrous in an earthquake. . . .

Generally, little is known about the stresses in steel in its through-thickness direction or z axis (if x and y are its longitudinal and transverse axes). The tearing usually occurs where steel has laminations that result from impurities, including trapped gas.

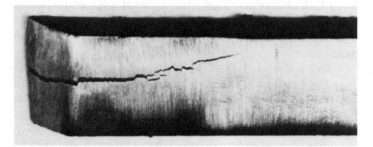

Figure 6-1   Lamellar tearing in a steel bar. *(ENR File.)*

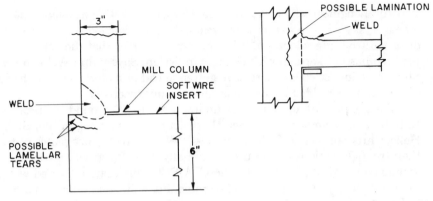

Figure 6-2 Visible tears can occur in steel in the vicinity of welded connections. Invisible tears can be detected by ultrasonic probing. *(ENR.)*

CONCERN SPREADS

The concern over lamellar tearing has spread to professional societies and institutes. The American Institute of Steel Construction (AISC) has a task committee reviewing all research on the subject and plans to issue recommendations before year's end on prevention of tearing in the shop, field and through design modifications. The American Welding Society, for the first time, will include a section on lamellar tearing in its new code. The American Society for Testing and Materials is reviewing the problem, because presently there are no methods for testing thick steel in its [z-axis].

There is also much argument as to what causes tearing, and also controversy over where the blame lies when a job is held up and who should pay for repairs. But the costs and who pays them are not usually openly discussed.

Argument is also going on as to who should assume responsibility for solving the problem. Designers say that it's a metallurgical problem, and that there should be ultimate and yield stress tables just as there are for steel in its longitudinal or rolled direction. "There are no publications by the steel institutes or in steel design booklets indicating the different strengths in steel's different directions," says Hanskarl Bandel, principal with consulting engineer Severud-Perrone-Sturm-Conlin-Bandel, New York City.

William Milek, AISC director of engineering and research, says, "Designers should recognize, with their academic training, that differences in strength exist in steel." In research, the American Iron and Steel Institute is presently sponsoring a $60,000 research program at Lehigh University. Major producers of large plates, United States Steel Corp., Bethlehem Steel Corp. and Armco Steel Corp., claim they have research on the subject under way.

The research, however, lags behind present design and owners' demands for longer spans and more dramatic structures. Lawrence H. Daniels, a structural engineer who is Kaiser Steel Corp.'s marketing development manager, says that in the past five years, design of welded steel structures has departed from precedent and it has become apparent that the pace of research has not kept up with changes in design. Says Ralph Webb, a U.S. Steel metallurgist: "Designers have gotten ahead of materials research. Some of the complex welded connections came up unexpectedly."

For the present, designers are finding ways to get around the problem. L. E. Robertson, principal in the Seattle structural engineering firm of Skilling, Helle, Christiansen and Robertson, says, "We try to organize plates so that their through thicknesses are used minimally. We also specify ultrasonic scanning of critical pieces at the shop." AISC's Milek says a [bolted-web], welded flange-type connection is favorable. For a 56-story office building in Dallas, engineers specified vacuum-degassed steel for critical members, which cost 3.5% more on that job. Steel producers say other solutions, requiring new types of equipment and new processes to eliminate inclusions, would be costly and uneconomical. One U.S. Steel spokesman said: "It's like spending a million dollars on a 10-cent problem."

Eight months later, in May 1973, the American Institute of Steel Construction (AISC) admitted that the steel industry had a problem. The topic led off the AISC's national engineering conference in Philadelphia, and took the largest block of time at the meeting.

"The recent increased concern about lamellar tearing is a direct result of

Figure 6-3 El Paso's civic center under construction, May 1972. Cracks first appeared in joints of the ring girder. *(Robert E. McKee, Inc.)*

Figure 6-4 Actual construction photos taken in December 1972 and January 1973 show sections of the ring girder of the El Paso civic center. Above, the diaphragm plate has been removed and replaced with weld material. Below, sections of the web plates have been removed to provide access for inspection and repairs at welded girder intersections. *(Robert E. McKee, Inc.)*

the trend in architectural style and structural concepts which require heavy welded connections between thick materials and produce the conditions in which lamellar tearing is more likely to occur," noted AISC chief engineer Robert O. Disque, in a letter to the editor soon after the meeting (ENR, June 14, 1973, p. 5).

In El Paso, the city's public works department spent more than $150,000 to ultrasonically inspect welded joints between connections in the civic center's cable roof compression ring. The contractor, Robert E. McKee, Inc., spent a similar amount on quality control. The structure, originally estimated to cost $5 million, was a year behind schedule by the time the AISC met.

Also in the wake of the AISC meeting, the Bureau of Reclamation stopped construction on twenty transmission-line towers meant to bring power from a new Grand Coulee powerhouse. Only one tower had been erected, but it was taken down when lamellar cracks were discovered. Twelve other towers also showed cracks in their welded frames, even though they had not yet been set into place. The lamellar tearing was a surprise to professionals, because the steel used ranged in thickness from ⅜ to 1¹⁄₁₆ inches. The cracking had not been previously reported in plates that thin.

The towers had been designed as tripods with welded tubular steel columns and rectangular tapered steel crossarms. At each crossarm connection, a rectangular box girder was to tie the tripod legs together and support the arms themselves. Tearing occurred in edges of the diaphragm plates that continued through the box girder and between the column legs. The towers are from 100 to 175 feet tall; each supports 2 miles of double-circuit 500-kilovolt transmission lines. The towers were redesigned to avoid plates running through the box. BuRec paid $950,000 for the old towers, and another $952,000 to rebuild them.

H. G. Arthur, BuRec director of design and construction, said the bureau's design personnel were not familiar with lamellar tearing when the towers were

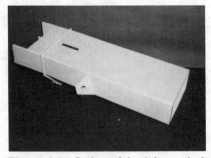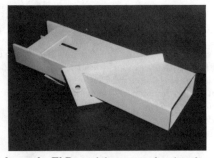

Figure 6-5   Scale models of the cracked girder at the El Paso civic center, showing the intersection of two segments. The view at left shows the girder as originally designed with its roof cable lug attachment. Note that the diaphragm plate, at right angles to the box, penetrates the full length and width of the box sections. As redesigned (right) the roof cable lug attachment and diaphragm plate have been removed to the back side of the flange plate and replaced with weld material. *(Robert E. McKee, Inc.)*

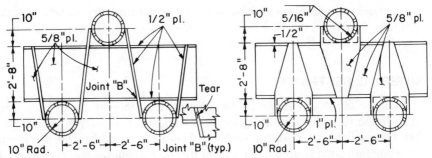

Figure 6-6 The old design of the towers near the Grand Coulee Dam, left, called for the girder of the crossarm to be pierced by welded plates that also were to hold the tripod legs; the new design, right, uses diaphragm plates that do not penetrate the girder. *(Interior Department.)*

designed in 1970. "The American Institute of Steel Construction was pretty quiet about it," Arthur said.

On September 13, 1973, ENR reported on AISC's first major advisory study, in a document that left many questions unanswered:

AISC Juggles Sizzling Potato in Report on Lamellar Tearing

A 9-page report on lamellar tearing of steel makes clear that the report's author and the American Institute of Steel Construction (AISC) have hold of a hot potato. The report, described by a special AISC task force, is contained in the third-quarter issue of AISC's *Engineering Journal....*

The document, the work of a special AISC task force, cautions, "information on this subject [lamellar tearing] is incomplete and research is continuing throughout the world." The report further warns, "While every precaution has been taken to insure the information is as accurate as possible, the American Institute of Steel Construction disclaims responsibility for the authenticity of the information herein and does not guarantee that in specific applications any of the material contained in this paper will prevent lamellar tears."

And although the document offers 13 statements under the heading, "Recommendations," the authors early in the paper say "no attempt is made to make specific recommendations at this time." AISC's explanation is that the key word in the statement is "specific," since the statements described as recommendations are "general in nature," and give neither precise dimensions nor specifications.

The document also emphasizes that it is not intended to be a complete guide covering all potential difficulties (such as brittle fracture, underbead cracking, fatigue) that may result from improper joint designs.

INTERNAL RESTRAINT

The paper says "it is important to recognize that joint restraint . . . is not the connection restraint that designers count upon in the analysis of rigid frame structures. Properly designed restrained connections which transfer frame bending moments from one structural member to another do not generally induce localized strains responsible for lamellar tearing. The restraint that is of concern is *internal* restraint (within a connection made up of several joints) which inhibits the small *total*—but large *unit*—localized strains resulting from weld shrinkage."

The paper says because the various design codes and specifications tend to focus attention on the relationship between calculated and allowable stresses, "there is often lack of recognition that under certain conditions localized *strain* is significantly more important than *stress*."

Figure 6-7   How magnetic flux detection is done. Having laid out the scanning lines (the one closest to the column is the weld face), the technician calibrates a Magnaflux ultrasonic testing instrument by placing the transducer on a test block that has the same characteristics as the weld. When scanning the flange, he will use soapy water to couple the transducer to the surface. *(Magnaflux Corporation.)*

THE RECOMMENDATIONS

The authors say "successful highly restrained connections require an understanding of the phenomenon and attention to detail on the part of the designer. Good materials and workmanship cannot assure success on poorly conceived and designed or specified connections." The suggestions offered as "representative of possible means to minimize or avoid lamellar tearing" are:

- Select electrodes which deposit weld metal with the lowest yield strength adequate to carry design loads. Use of excessively high yield strength weld metal can force strains above yield point in the connected material.
- Design connections to minimize accumulation and concentration of strains resulting from weld metal contraction in localized areas.
- Where possible, arrange connections so as to avoid welded joints which induce through-thickness strains due to weld shrinkage.
- Make connections with welds having the minimum throat dimension required to carry the stresses and having a minimum practical volume of weld metal. Lower strength fillet or partial penetration welds may often be used to join higher strength steels when the joint is designed for shear.
- Design corner joints with proper consideration of edge preparation.
- Consideration of the use of soft wire cushions or other means to permit contraction of weld metal without producing high concentration of stresses may be helpful in difficult situations.
- Whenever practical, completely weld subassemblies prior to final assembly of the connection. Sequence the welding of individual joints so that restraints will be minimized on the largest welds. Tack welds should be limited to a minimum size and number.
- Do not use prequalified joints without considering restraints provided by the complete connection assembly.
- Fully research and utilize available experience and knowledge on specific design details that might be potential sources of lamellar tearing.
- Do not use larger welds than are necessary to transfer calculated forces.
- Do not specify stiffeners when they are not required by design calculations. Stiffeners induce restraint. When they are required, make them and the welds by which they are attached only as large as required by calculations.
- Before making repairs to highly restrained connections, determine whether the repair will be more detrimental than the original cause for repair. Usually a repair must be made under greater restraint than the original weld. It is often better to tolerate a minor imperfection than to create conditions that will cause a lamellar tear. If the discontinuity is a lamellar tear, consider the modifications to the welding procedure or the details which are needed to avoid reoccurrence of lamellar tears in the repaired connection.

- The designer should selectively specify ultrasonic inspection *after fabrication and/or erection* of those specific highly restrained welded connections critical to structural integrity that he considers subject to lamellar tearing.

The uncertainty was handled in different ways by different designers. Joseph Colaco, director of design and compter operations for Ellisor Engineers, Inc., of Houston, went to bolted connections for a 32-story tower near Detroit (ENR, Nov. 1, 1973, p. 16). The 110-story Sears tower, with more than 100,000 pounds of weld in its connections, was exhaustively tested by Magnaflux Testing Laboratories. More than 775,000 tests and inspections were necessary.

In July 1976, Nippon Steel Corp. announced the availability of special steel with very low impurity levels and very low sulfur content to reduce the chance of lamellar tears occurring. The steel is used on critical connections for offshore oil platforms in the North Sea.

Earlier that year, steel cracking was reported in the frame of an 8-story, $60 million office building in Stevens Point, Wisconsin. No one connected with the project was willing to confirm that the cracks—in cantilevered beams at the corners of the building—were due to lamellar tearing. But the welded joints involved were redesigned using steel gusset plates and bolts.

The same secrecy ultimately befell the El Paso project as well. In March 1975, the general contractor, McKee, sued the city for $2.3 million. Also sued were sixteen subcontractors and the project's architects. The city, in turn, sued the structural engineer, the steel supplier, and the AISC for the same $2.3 million, plus another $247,603. By that time, the project was 2 years overdue.

In February 1980, 5 years after the suits were filed and 2 weeks before they were to go to trial, the parties settled their dispute. All sides shared the blame. From the February 7, 1980, issue:

Tom Diamond, a registered professional engineer and an attorney with Diamond, Rash, Anderson, Leslie and Smith, El Paso, represented the city in its lawsuits. "The interesting thing about this case," Diamond says, "is that the whole spectrum was involved—the contracting team, the design team, the owner and the industry [code] specifying side—to attempt to resolve the responsibility for lamellar tearing.

"There are four different ways of looking at lamellar tearing and who is responsible for it," he says. "Is it a design problem, construction problem, materials problem or nobody's specific problem that the owner should pay for?"

The recent out-of-court settlement left that question unanswered. Nearly all parties involved agreed to pay a collective $1 million to McKee, which will distribute some of that money to subcontractors.

FIRMS PAID JOINTLY

According to Diamond, the many sources contributing to the settlement (all in amounts of $100,000 or more) include the City of El Paso; the American Institute of Steel Construction; steel supplier Armco Steel Corp.; the three joint venture architects, Garland & Hilles, Carroll, Daeuble, DuSang & Rand and Barnard Mulville; structural engineers A. B. Peinado & Son, Inc., and Severud-Perrone-Sturm-Bandel. Even the contracting side took some of the penalty, Diamond says, as some subcontractors withdrew or lessened the value of their claims.

"Lamellar tearing is still a recent phenomenon," Diamond says. "Even with this litigation concluded, you can't say who in the industry bears responsibility for the expenses it can cause."

Research continues to this day into ways of preventing lamellar tears. As the article below (ENR, June 24, 1982, p. 12) suggests, the research is bearing fruit. We know what makes steel weak, and we can repair torn joints. But firm design advice, written into standards, will have to wait.

A three-year research program has identified causes and means of preventing lamellar tearing of heavy-section steel weldments. The phenomenon is not prevalent, according to the American Iron and Steel Institute, but it has occurred in a variety of structures, often requiring costly repairs.

The study was carried out at Lehigh University under the direction of two professors in the metallurgy and materials engineering department, Robert D. Stout and Alan W. Pense. It was funded by AISI and the findings are available from the organization's Washington, D.C., office. . . .

According to researchers, tearing is triggered by decohesion or shattering of nonmetallic material in the steel under strain developed in the plate parallel to the plane of rolling as the weld contracts during cooling. Silicate and sulfide impurities are the biggest culprits. They can initiate tears in or immediately adjacent to the area subjected to welding heat, generally within 5 mm of the weld face.

The Lehigh team tested more than 100 weldments of A572 and A588 high-strength steels. It found that the welding method used had the greatest influence on the susceptibility to lamellar tearing. The samples embodied four processes—gas metal arc, submerged arc, shielded metal arc and flux-cored metal arc. The first two produced welds that were more resistant to tearing than the others. The researchers say that is apparently because of hydrogen in the electrodes of the latter two. Reinforcing that finding, when moisture was introduced to the arc atmosphere, it greatly reduced tear resistance.

As a remedial measure, the team recommends either grooving out and replacing the heat-affected area of base metal or covering it with two layers of weld metal, a technique called "buttering." The weld metal has higher ductility than the base metal and can better accommodate shrinking strain. In one test, buttering increased failure stress from 48,000 to 85,000 psi.

Researchers also found that with some welding processes preheating the steel improved tearing resistance. And, in some cases peening the plate helped overcome contraction strain.

Bailey's Crossroads and Progressive Collapse, 1973

At the same time lamellar tearing was embarrassing the structural steel industry, concrete structures were failing with alarming regularity—often while still under construction. In May 1968, a gas explosion on the eighteenth floor of the 22-story Ronan Point housing project in London blew out one of the load-bearing wall panels. That, in turn, began a chain-reaction collapse of an entire corner of the building, all the way down to the first floor; the building reacted much the way a child's tower of wooden blocks would have. Four people died. In 1970, England tightened its building standards to provide for alternative means of support even if a major structural member were to be removed or were to fail. Steel bracing with floor-to-wall connectors was mandated, along with a minimum tensile strength of 3000 pounds per foot across the length and width of floors and roofs (ENR, Apr. 16, 1970, p. 12).

In March 1970, a 300 X 45-foot reinforced-concrete platform collapsed under the weight of 800 factory workers in Japan; 260 were injured, 7 seriously.

January 1971, saw the collapse of a sixteen-story luxury apartment building being constructed in Boston; four workers died. The causes: poor-quality concrete and failure to follow the building's plans as designed. Insufficient reinforcing steel and inadequate allowance for settling doomed the roof of a reinforced concrete exhibition hall being built in Belo Horizonte, Brazil, that February. Sixty-five workers died.

Twenty-four died waiting in traffic in downtown Rio de Janeiro when a concrete viaduct collapsed above them in November 1971. The viaduct span split under the weight of a 2.5-ton concrete mixer, carrying 8 tons of concrete. Poor-quality concrete, the weakening effect of inspection openings not called for in the plan, and poor grouting all contributed to the failure of the 402-foot, 3-span section.

No collapse was as visible as the one which occurred at Bailey's Crossroads, Virginia, just outside Washington, D.C., in March 1973. The failure started as concrete was being placed on the 24th floor of the new structure, while shoring was being removed from new concrete at the 22d-floor level. The weight of the

Figure 6-8 This rooftop parking area in Miami totally collapsed after poor-quality concrete gave way in one beam. *(ENR.)*

concrete from the 22d, 23d, and 24th floors, as well as the weight of a crane on the 24th, ripped a top-to-bottom gap through the building. The first article discussing the cause of the collapse appeared in ENR a month later, in the issue of April 19, 1973:

Collapse Blamed on Premature Shoring Removal

The possible premature removal of shoring between the 22nd and 23rd floors of a 26-story building under way in a Washington, D.C. suburb apparently caused the collapse of a portion of the cast-in-place reinforced concrete structure [ENR, Mar. 8, 1973, p. 12]. The accident killed 14 workers and injured more than 30 others.

The finding was contained in a consultant's report to Robert F. Horan,

Jr., the attorney for the Commonwealth of Virginia, which hired a consultant to study the collapse in [Bailey's] Crossroads, Va. Horan said this week that the findings will be presented to a grand jury.

The report said: "It appears to be premature removal of shores between the 22nd and 23rd floors in the area known as 'Pour Number Three.' Unassisted by shoring to the 22nd floor, the concrete on the 23rd floor had not obtained sufficient strength to carry the load imposed on it."

The structure, 386 X 76 ft in plan, was one of two identical apartment buildings under way in a $200-million residential-commercial complex. Two climbing cranes were positioned in the building, and one of them crashed to the ground when the failure occurred. The collapse ripped a top-to-bottom gap about 60 ft wide in the building, leaving standing two separate sections.

The collapse of the concrete and the crane also collapsed the completed portion of a planned 340 X 395-ft post-tensioned garage under way between the two residential buildings.

The consultant, Ingvar Schousboe, a civil engineer and a professor at University of Illinois, Urbana, and others will testify before the grand jury, which will be looking for possible criminal violations, Horan said.

The owner is Charles E. Smith Companies, Washington, D.C. The concrete contractor is Miller & Long Construction Co., Bethesda, Md.

Figure 6-9 The Bailey's Crossroads condominium tower before the collapse. *(ENR.)*

Figure 6-10 The collapse at Bailey's Crossroads started on the twenty-second floor and dropped concrete through the building, leaving this wide gap. At first glance, it looks like the two sections of the structure had always been separated. *(United Press International.)*

A month later, the building's general contractor, Charles E. Smith Construction; the concrete subcontractor, Miller & Long; and the job superintendent, Roger Gilbert Arnold, were indicted by a Fairfax County Grand Jury. Their legal problems were only just beginning, as this article from the May 31, 1973, ENR issue shows:

Indicted Subcontractor Also Faces OSHA Action

The concrete subcontractor for a high-rise apartment building that collapsed while under construction at [Bailey's] Crossroads, near Washington, D.C., has been charged with willful violation of the Occupational Safety and Health Act (OSHA).

The subcontractor, Miller & Long Co. of Virginia, Inc., Bethesda, has also been indicted by a grand jury, which probed the March collapse that killed 14 men working on the 26-story reinforced building [ENR, Mar. 8, 1973, p. 12].

If the OSHA charges stand, the company will be subject to a total of $13,000 in penalties, the most ever sought by the Labor Department's

Occupational Safety and Health Administration. Company attorneys say the charges will be contested.

OSHA says Miller & Long is responsible for the premature removal of forms from the 23rd floor of the building and the failure to have tests conducted to insure that the concrete had become strong enough to support the load without forms.

OSHA's citation also says the company used damaged shoring timbers on the 22nd and 23rd floors and failed to place guard rails on the open sides of the 20th and 21st floors.

A $2,000 penalty was proposed for the alleged repeated violation involving the lack of a standard guard railing on the 20th and 21st floors. This violation is called repeated because Miller & Long was cited Dec. 20, 1971, for not having appropriate guard rails on an Arlington, Va., construction project.

Fairfax County is considering a total revamping of its building codes as a result of the accident. A consultant, Ingvar Schousboe, of the University of Illinois, Urbana, was to have given to county supervisors this week his suggestions for changing the codes and whether the standing portion of the building should be razed.

His appearance was canceled after a state court ordered that all county and company officials remain silent. The court said discussion of the collapse may endanger the rights of Roger Gilbert Arnold, a job superintendent for Miller & Long, who was also indicted. He is charged with involuntary manslaughter, a felony punishable by one to five years imprisonment [ENR, May 3, 1973, p. 16].

Charges against the contractor, Charles E. Smith, were dismissed in June 1973 after a county judge ruled Miller & Long responsible for the concrete work. The Smith firm had not been aware of code violations, the judge noted. In July, Miller & Long was fined the maximum—a mere $300—for its role. Arnold was found not guilty of involuntary manslaughter that same November; he could have gone to prison for as long as 5 years.

Who, then, would be held responsible? The only ones left were the architect and the engineer, who were judged negligent for not watching the construction proceed. ENR carried the story on January 16, 1975:

A-Es Held Liable to Worker in a Collapse

A construction worker who was injured when a building under construction collapsed has successfully sued the building's architect and engineer for $500,000 in damages.

The verdict, returned last week by a federal jury sitting in Alexandria, Va., stemmed from the February, 1973, collapse of a high-rise, cast-in-place concrete apartment building at [Bailey's] Crossroads, Va., a suburb of Washington, D.C. [ENR, Mar. 8, 1973, p. 12].

The jury heard testimony charging that the architectural firm and two engineers were negligent and that the negligence was the proximate cause of injury.

Attorneys representing the designers said the award will be appealed.

The plaintiff, an elevator worker at the time of the accident, was one of 35 construction workers injured in the collapse that also killed 14 employees. He suffered two broken arms, skull fracture and lung damage.

Sued as defendants were the architect, Weihe Black Jeffries & Strassman, and engineers Arthur Heinzman and Henry Clifton of the firm of Heinzman, Clifton and Kendro. Both firms are in Washington.

In earlier judicial and regulatory proceedings, the collapse was blamed on the premature removal of shoring in the structure's upper floors. As a consequence, according to earlier testimony, recently poured concrete that had not cured could no longer support a climbing crane and gave way.

In the new federal court case, witnesses told the jury that under the applicable building codes, the designers were required to visit the job site and inspect the work. The jury was also told that the designers were responsible for warning the contractors that curing times listed in the drawings were adequate for normal weather, but perhaps inadequate for cold or wet weather.

The general contractor and building owner, Charles E. Smith Co., Washington, was not brought into the suit because the plaintiff had earlier received an award under the Virginia Workmen's Compensation Act.

The plaintiff's attorney says he will file similar suits for 20 other workers injured in the collapse.

By that time, owner-builder Smith had been given permission to resume construction on the $200 million residential-office complex. In the April 17, 1975, issue of ENR, the American Concrete Institute addressed the problem:

Progressive Collapse Causes Examined

Examination of progressive collapse of some types of high-rise, reinforced concrete buildings indicates that "we are treading in dangerous territory." That warning, involving primarily flat plate high-rise construction, came from Richard E. Elstner, of Wiss, Janney, Elstner & Associates, consulting engineer, Northbrook, Ill.

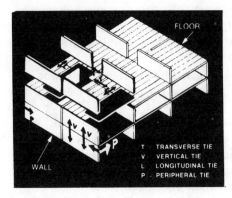

Figure 6-11 American Concrete Institute design recommendations call for ties between various panel sections to avoid progressive collapse. *(ENR.)*

Speaking at a symposium on progressive collapse at the annual convention of the American Concrete Institute (ACI) in Boston, he suggested that when designing such a building, engineers adopt a principle applied in some types of bridge design: that the construction loads be the governing loads.

Elstner said, "We, as design engineers, seem to forget that a structure must be built, and how it will be built should be taken into consideration." He noted that "in bridge design, the construction loads are the governing loads for many members of that structure. And I think that especially with apartment and office buildings that same criterion will apply; construction loads are governing loads."

He warned that unless "we come to grips with the problems we can predict similar catastrophes will occur." The collapses to which he referred were the progressive collapse of a 16-story reinforced concrete apartment building under way in Boston in 1971 and a similar failure of a 26-story apartment building of flat plate design at [Bailey's] Crossroads, Va., a suburb of Washington, D.C. At the time of this collapse, concrete placement on the 386 X 76-ft building had reached the 23rd floor. . . .

SUDDEN PROBLEM

Referring to a paper in the November, 1974, *ACI Journal* that reported, "Field measurements confirmed that construction loads are often greater than the design load of the structure," Elstner said, "If it were my prerogative, I would add, 'and with present design and construction practices they can approach failure load'."

He said that excessive cracking and deflection of floors "are the rule rather than the exception. Many experts feel the cause is shrinkage. In my opinion, the pattern of cracking is related to overload of the slab at early age during construction rather than volume change."

The apparent suddenness of the problem when design and construction practices have improved is because "structures are constructed faster with less materials," Elstner said.

The actual factor of safety has decreased he said, but adding, "although today's structures are adequately safe for intended service loads, they no longer have the inherent fat in design, which previously gave sufficient protection for uncalculated situations such as overload during construction."

Elstner also recommended that it be required that designers "indicate in contract documents the method of shores and reshores for which the structure was safely designed." He also suggested that design and construction codes be modified to permit some degree of overload during construction. He called attention to the ACI building code that states: "No construction loads exceeding dead plus live load shall be supported on any unshored portion of the structure under construction."

He added, "If this provision were enforced, most high-rise work should stop immediately if shores are not provided all the way to the ground."

TOO DANGEROUS

At a symposium on safety, John H. Stender, assistant secretary of Labor and head of the Occupational Safety and Health Administration (OSHA), called construction "far more dangerous than it need be, with about one of every five workers on a construction job facing the prospect of being injured or killed every year."

Although conceding that many situations in the field are beyond the control of designers, "I believe that they have a moral, if not legal responsibility, to exercise their best professional experience and judgment to provide a safe base, which in turn will enable the contractor to do the job safely."

Better construction techniques and closer inspection have drastically cut the number of such failures during construction. The Housing and Urban Development Department specifies that as far as construction using large panels is concerned, design must "avoid" progressive collapse. And the Portland Cement Association (PCA) and the Prestressed Concrete Institute have both issued design guides.

The PCA "alternative path" methodology calls for tying building elements together and increasing ductility so that the building elements can better sustain deformations from the failure of a portion of the building's structure. Transverse ties create cantilever action from adjacent walls. Vertical ties provide suspension from panels above, peripheral ties hold floors together, and longitudinal ties string floor planks—large prestressed panels—together.

Hancock Tower Facade Glass, 1972

Way back in November 1972, a pane of glass popped out of the nearly completed John Hancock Tower in Boston. Few people took much notice. After all, glass still falls with some regularity from other high rises; Hancock is hardly unique. But the sleek tower *was* designed by the renowned architectural firm of I. M. Pei, and testing later turned up deficiencies in the building's foundation and framing. To top it all off, the American Institute of Architects (AIA) bestowed one of its annual awards on the tower's architect, praising Pei's "attention to detail."

The structure came to be known as the "plywood palace" locally, thanks to all the unsightly plywood sheets that replaced broken panes. The palace stood empty for 4 years, until 1976, while the experts figured out how to replace the plywood with glass. The costs of the delays, the design modifications, and even the personnel who watched the tower continually to warn passersby of new cracks, probably doubled the structure's original $95 million tab. In short, those popping panes added up to one of the most expensive construction disasters in history.

Other notable glass failures:

- Tall new buildings in New York City shed glass in strong high-level winds, all through the early sixties. In 1963, Emery Roth & Sons specifies heavier glass—$\frac{5}{16}$ inch thick instead of the prevailing ¼-inch plate—for the new Chemical Bank–New York Trust Building in midtown Manhattan.
- High winds create negative pressures on the lee side of the 60-story Chase Manhattan Bank Building near Wall Street; by 1964, some fifteen panes have been shattered.
- The Merchants National Bank and Trust Co. building in Fargo, North Dakota, begins losing tinted, heat-absorbing panes from its new building in the fall of 1964. The reason: Glass in direct sunlight gets hot, but portions of the panes in shadow, or near the building's cool walls along the panes' edges stay relatively chilly. The uneven expansion cracks the glass. Each pane costs $1200 and measures 10 X 14 feet.
- In 1966, the glass-enclosed grandstand and clubhouse of a trotting track near Chicago loses most of its panes—sheets of glass ranging in size from 8 X 18 to 8 X 26 feet. The owner sues for $400,000 damages.
- That same year, Chicago's 31-story civic center begins losing sheets of bronze-colored glass. Architect Skidmore, Owings & Merrill (SOM) notes that wind tunnel tests on the Chase Manhattan structure—which it also designed—lead to calls for stronger glass at corners, where wind stresses are greatest. But SOM never publishes the results for the benefit of the profession as a whole.
- In 1970, the 23-story Knights of Columbus International headquarters in

Figure 6-12 Boston's John Hancock Tower, nicknamed the "plywood palace" by local residents. *(ENR.)*

New Haven, Connecticut, begins losing clear glass plates 8 X 10 feet across; a total of about forty such plates are lost.

- In 1971 the newly completed Gulf & Western building in New York loses two panes.
- A storm in 1970 brings down three panes of the 39-story One Oliver Plaza building in Pittsburgh.
- In Houston, the 35-story United Gas Building loses two panels in February 1972.
- Ceramic-backed spandrel glass cracks in two high rises—one in Chicago (30 North LaSalle Street) and one in Philadelphia (1818 Market Street), starting in 1975.
- High winds smash forty-three panes in the 110-story Sears Tower in February 1974.
- A window wall in a state office building in Hauppauge, New York, peels away from the frame in 1977.
- A federal court awards $5.8 million in damages to the owner of three 11-story pyramidal towers in Indianapolis; cracking had started in 1972 and was traced to faulty gaskets and supports.

- In the spring of 1981 the state of Virginia refuses to accept a new office building until spandrel glass cracking is fixed.

Through much of this period, the Hancock Tower was shedding glass. Four years after it all began, ENR reported in the issue of May 13, 1976, that the reason had been found:

Hancock Glass Breakage: A Combination of Errors?

It still may be the best kept secret in construction, but clues to the cause of extensive glass breakage in the 60-story Boston headquarters of the John Hancock Mutual Life Insurance Co. are slowly surfacing.

As the building takes on its first occupants and the case over the breakage goes to court, the owner and lawyers continue to muzzle all those involved in its design and construction until the delicate lawsuit is settled.

In the meantime, though, some insights into the problem came in a recent speech given to the Boston Rotary Club by Hancock president J. Edwin Matz. And his comments seem to point to a combination of reasons for the breakage of the building's original glass that led to replacement of all 10,344 lights and increased the building's cost. . . .

But even after a three-and-a-half-year delay, with the first phase of Hancock's move of 374 persons into the building completed, the building is still running into problems. Recently, Boston building commissioner Francis W. Gens threatened to order evacuation of the tower if the owner did not prove that it is safe for its occupants and for pedestrians. Gens' statement came after a single pane broke, the 11th since all of the new glass was installed.

BLUNT REFUSALS

Gens received only information proving the safety of the new curtain wall but did not receive anything on why the original glass broke, which started in November, 1972. Hancock and its designers and contractors refuse requests for information on the structure's extensive tests.

In the reams of legal papers filed in court so far many allegations are made but they do not go into the technical data to support them [ENR, Nov. 13, 1975, p. 19]. That, lawyers are holding for the courtroom.

With the cause not revealed, rumors abound, with one going as far as to say that the building is settling and tons of grout are being pumped into the foundation and disappearing into caverns below the building.

Figure 6-13 This photo taken from across Copley Square shows how thin the Hancock Tower is. The reflecting glass had been chosen to "hide" the building's bulk by reflecting the landmark Trinity Church beside it. *(John Hancock Mutual Life Insurance Company.)*

SOME HINTS

In his speech, though, Matz reveals that wind tests showed that the highest pressures sustained on the building are negative pressures caused by the wind turning a corner of the building. According to Matz, much of the original 4.5 X 11-ft, double-pane glass in the building was rated for pressures from 35 to 40 psf while the new, tempered glass in the building, not only in places where pressures are high, but also in places where instrumentation and wind tunnel pressures were low, is rated for 220 psf.

Further tests were made to determine the building's period of motion and the extent of its vibrations. Matz said,

> There were instruments that measure acceleration, and for good reason. I mentioned that the building, any building, vibrates a little. But what human beings feel, and maybe what determines in some measure the way a building reacts, is not how far it goes or how fast, but how fast it picks up speed.

Included in the tests were lasers mounted at the bottom of the building to follow movement.

Previously announced modifications to the building related to movement include huge dampers installed in the core and stiffeners added to the core.

STRUCTURAL MODIFICATIONS

Matz said thorough examination of the building's steel structure

> ... disclosed that under the most extreme conditions visualized, maybe the 100-year storm, the building might be deficient in strength, not in a narrow dimension, but in the long dimension, where there was relatively light horizontal bracing steel. Because we wanted every precaution to be taken we have gone through the process of installing something like 1,500 tons of steel in the elevator shafts and in the stairwells surrounding the core of the building.
>
> In his speech, Matz mentions that deflection instruments were installed on the building that showed how much the skin of the building was moving under stress, and window racking sensors to find whether the window frames were twisting and putting stress on the glass. Another modification to the building announced last summer was installation of additional anchors between about 100 window frames and the building frame in critical turbulence areas [ENR, June 12, 1975, p. 12].

The newly installed panes continued to pop. In 1977, Hancock stationed two security guards to watch the glass from the street between 6 A.M. and mid-

Figure 6-14 The architects turned to wind-tunnel testing at MIT to determine forces acting upon the Hancock Tower. Frank Durgin, assistant director of the facility, watches as the smoke stream makes eddies visible around the model structure. *(Massachusetts Institute of Technology.)*

Figure 6-15 A new glass pane being installed on the John Hancock Tower. Each pane weighs nearly 500 pounds. *(John Hancock Mutual Life Insurance Company.)*

Figure 6-16 Boston's downtown skyline and the Public Garden are reflected in a new glass pane being installed on the Hancock Tower; in all, some 13½ acres of glass were replaced, in 10,344 panes. *(John Hancock Mutual Life Insurance Company.)*

night. The guards watched continually, scanning the tower for panes that had lost their reflectivity. The glass loses its reflectivity upon fracturing, but remains in place for 5 or 10 minutes before falling. In June 1980, the watchers were replaced by automatic electronic sensors to detect window cracks and notify maintenance personnel to reverse the building's air conditioning system, causing the panes to fall into the building rather than down to the street.

The Hancock's visible problems led to increased use of wind testing for models of new buildings. The trend was described in the March 27, 1980, issue of ENR:

Wind Analysis: Preventive Medicine for Cladding, Structural Problems

Codes less precise than wind engineering.

A wind tunnel study performed on Boston's John Hancock tower to help determine why its glass curtain wall failed showed that actual wind loading on the facade was as much as three times greater in some places than the facade had been designed to handle. Many believe the discrepancy contributed to this now classic case of curtain wall failure.

In 1978, structural engineer William J. LeMessurier convinced officers of Citicorp, the New York City–based banking concern, to spend about $1 million to weld additional steel wind bracing into the 914-ft office tower of Citicorp Center, which he had designed. The measure, carried out after construction was nearly complete, was intended, LeMessurier says, to mobilize the lateral load-carrying capacity of 240 connections in the structural steel frame.

Today, in New York City, designers of a new 644-ft-tall office and apartment building are making plans to run wind tunnel tests on a model of the structure, partially because of their concern over possible wind turbulence created by a cluster of other new tall buildings nearby—at least a half dozen are planned or under construction within blocks of each other.

Certainly, the experts disagree over exactly what caused the problems at Hancock, whether Citicorp really needed more wind bracing, and what structural implications stem from the effects of groupings of buildings. But what they do not disagree about is the importance of wind engineering in the design of tall buildings, and the notion that although this discipline has been practiced and refined for more than a decade, problems stemming from the effects of wind on tall structures still persist.

"It's in its infancy," Leo Plofker says of wind engineering. Plofker, a partner in the New York City structural engineering firm of The Office of James Ruderman, structural designer of the Boston Hancock tower, says candidly that "it's because we were involved in Hancock" that he insisted on extensive wind studies on structures he recently designed for sites in New York City. "Few people have the expertise," he says, to develop accurate wind loading information and "to use it properly."

The growing sensitivity of engineers such as Plofker to the importance of wind engineering has been a bonanza for a handful of experts who are combining the science of fluid dynamics, the study of climate and the behavior of wind close to the earth, the use of computers for information processing and the application that all of these have to the structural engineering of tall buildings.

These experts test scale models of buildings in wind tunnels and the leading ones, including those at Colorado State University in Fort Collins, Colo., and at Canada's University of Western Ontario in London, Ontario, have backlogs of so many buildings that engineers sometimes have to wait months for test results. Fees for studies at these and other facilities can add up to hundreds of thousands of dollars—from minimums of $35,000 for simpler rigid model work to $70,000 to $100,000 for more complex aeroelastic studies. Further, points out one engineer interviewed, the complexity of the modeling and computer technology involved can mean that the building's structural engineer is in a position of "relying on a very few people who insist they can model the wind within 10 to 15% accuracy."

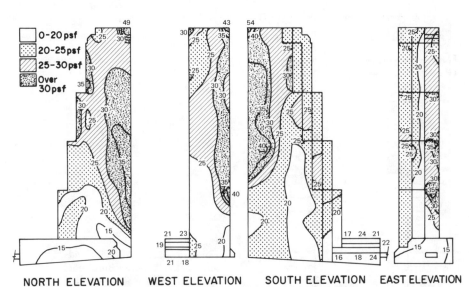

NORTH ELEVATION   WEST ELEVATION   SOUTH ELEVATION   EAST ELEVATION

Figure 6-17   Contours illustrate test results showing that wind pressure on the facade of this building varies widely. *(ENR.)*

MODELING THE WIND

The issue of modeling the wind is key to the state of the art of wind engineering. As New York City structural engineer Paul Weidlinger puts it, "We now have no problem finding out what happens to a building in wind if we know what the wind is. The problem is in the input, the meteorology, what is the character of the wind. It has become a very complicated issue."

This threshold of wind engineering has to do with the problem of amassing accurate data about just what the wind has done and is likely to do at any given location, and then recreating such conditions in a test situation. These efforts are already impacting on codes—the American National Standards Institute [ANSI], for instance, is making important revisions in the wind section of the revised building code standard (A58) that it plans to propose later this year. And, for some, it offers exciting prospects for the application of computer technology to the field.

In addition to helping create an accurate model of the wind, it is hoped the computer will be able to replace use of models and wind tunnels altogether, thereby cutting costs and allowing some buildings to be tested much faster and with greater accuracy.

"We have begun to move beyond the point where every model we build and every test we run is a new adventure," says Alan G. Davenport, director of the Boundary Layer Wind Tunnel Laboratory at the University of Western Ontario. "We're looking for ways to do things rapidly [to] bypass some of the [wind tunnel] studies." Davenport says that his engineering team at Western

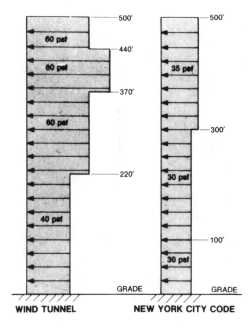

Figure 6-18 These charts compare facade design loads anticipated from wind-tunnel tests, with the loads mandated by the New York City code in 1980 (right). *(ENR.)*

Ontario is working now to develop computer representations of buildings that can reflect the fact that "the center of pressures will be orbiting all over the face [of the building] and the magnitude will be changing. . . . We need ways to get this information much more rapidly. It's getting awfully close."

To many involved, the need for such speed and accuracy is made more immediate by several other factors, including:

- A resurgence of building construction occurred following the recession of the early 1970s. In New York City, for instance, one 10-block-long section of midtown Manhattan has nine buildings planned or under way. Although many engineers believe wind testing is not always necessary, the process of handling those that are to be tested is time consuming. Current practice is to design a building to code specifications and then redesign it as necessary according to test results.

- The continuing trend toward use of high-strength steels, light-weight flooring systems and more flexible interior partitions means that buildings are still becoming lighter and more flexible, with less natural damping than was typical of heavy masonry or steel and masonry buildings. Citicorp Center's tower, for instance, notes Jack Cermak, who heads the Colorado wind tunnel laboratory, weighs about 8 lb per cu ft, compared to the Empire State Building's approximately 23 lb per cu ft. Designers now are under greater economic pressure to conserve on use of steel.

- An architectural trend toward increased use of unusual shapes—such as the canted corners of Houston's Texas Commerce Plaza or the so-called broken pediment top on architect Philip Johnson's American Telephone & Telegraph headquarters in New York City—can complicate facade loading problems, changing, for instance, patterns of pressure or suction that could contribute to facade failure.

- Many local building codes are based on elementary perceptions of wind conditions and loadings on structures, with the result that they may be inadequate.

"Very simplistic codes still exist in parts of the country," says Weidlinger. The New York City code, he notes, up until about 10 years ago, assumed "amazingly low wind pressures." Up to 100 ft in height, for instance, the code assumed a 0 psf wind loading. Largely because of the extensive wind research that was conducted by designers of the 1,350-ft World Trade Center towers, the New York City code was substantially revised.

STATIC AND DYNAMIC BEHAVIOR

Briefly, building wind analysis as now practiced produces two main categories of data—the static behavior and the dynamic behavior of buildings under wind loading. This information is developed by placing a model (scaled 1 to

300, 400, 500 or some other convenient size) of the structure in a wind tunnel. Both the model and the tunnel are intended to closely simulate the true possible conditions that will occur. The model for dynamic analysis, for instance, is designed to replicate the real building's characteristics, such as mass, flexibility and natural frequency. The tunnel, similarly, must seek to replicate the wind.

Here, a crucial difference arises between an atmospheric wind tunnel and the type needed for testing buildings. The latter, called a boundary layer wind tunnel, seeks to recreate the part of the wind that is slowed down and made turbulent by natural and man-made objects on the earth's surface.

The boundary layer wind tunnel at the University of Western Ontario, for instance, is a 6 X 8-ft space 100 ft long with a 60-ft test section and an 8-ft-dia, 36-hp fan to create simulated wind. The boundary layer is simulated by series of short wood blocks (Styrofoam or other materials could be used) set along the length of the tunnel to create surface roughness and by a detailed model of the city in which the building to be tested is located. The city model is erected on a turntable so that the building can be tested at various angles to the wind.

When tests begin, an instrumented model of the building is set in place on the turntable and the fan is activated. The building is then subjected to simulated winds striking it with different intensities and at different angles— all of which are determined by researching meteorological data—and sensors begin feeding information into a computer.

For determining the building's static response to the wind, a rigid model is wired with pressure taps that show what loadings of positive and negative (suction) pressure the panels will experience. These tests also can record wind turbulence at the base of the building, an annoyance for pedestrians.

The building's dynamic response to the wind, however, is illustrated by far more elaborate studies that require constructing a model mounted on springs and dampers so that it can experience lateral and torsional loading as well as acceleration. Because of the expense and time-consuming nature of these tests, known as aeroelastic modeling, they are the focus of Davenport's efforts to introduce computer modeling as an alternative.

In both cases, the task of developing the model, simulating an accurate wind environment, running the tests and compiling the computer output is the job of the wind tunnel staff. Once the work is complete, the engineer who requested the studies is supplied simply with a document that gives the lateral and torsional loadings on the structure and the pressure on the facade cladding that the building has to be designed to resist. Rigid model tests produce a detailed picture of, for instance, loads on facade cladding. These are often represented visually as contours on a facade [see Figure 6-17]. Aeroelastic model tests reveal any unusual loads the structural frame must resist.

CODE INCONSISTENCIES

Often, the numbers that turn up through wind tunnel tests differ appreciably from those cited in local building codes. According to engineers interviewed, codes generally are sufficient for wind loadings on the structure, but are less so for loadings on cladding.

In one recent case, tests using 176 pressure taps on a rigid model of a 38-story, 500-ft-tall office building planned by The Continental Corp. for a waterfront site in New York City showed that wind loading on the facade would reach up to 80 psf in some spots under certain conditions. And yet the New York City building code called for design for a maximum facade loading of just 35 psf near the structure's top [see Figure 6-18].

"A lot of architects and engineers that are not knowledgeable say it's okay because the code says it's okay," says Charles H. Thornton, president of Lev Zetlin Associates, Inc., and its subsidiary, Thornton-Tomasetti, P.C., which is Continental's project structural engineer. Thornton adds, however, that worst case loading on which the code is based is infrequent.

"A speculative developer who can find an architect who's willing to put his name on the line will go with the lower loads," he says. "And in most cases, he'll be okay. It's rare that an 80-mph wind will hit New York City."

Sometimes, the situation is reversed and wind tunnel studies show that code requirements are unnecessarily high. Such was the case with Weidlinger's 720-ft-tall Georgia-Pacific headquarters building in Atlanta. Loadings, says Weidlinger, "were very similar for wind on the broad side, but for the short side, the wind tunnel showed the load was much lower."

Such discrepancies prompted ANSI to make several significant revisions in the wind section of its A58 standard, which is widely used as a component of building codes nationally. The standard was last revised in 1972.

As part of the revised version that it hopes to publish late this year, ANSI is upgrading its national map of basic wind speeds—and related design loadings listed for both cladding and structure—to reflect more recent meteorological data. Brownsville, Tex., for instance, which was listed in 1972 as having a 50-year recurrent wind of 80 mph, will be revised upward to show a wind of 108 mph. Miami's basic wind speed will rise from about 110 to 120 mph. Most changes affect Gulf Coast regions; many areas of the country, including New York City will remain unchanged, and some will have their wind speeds lowered, according to Bruce R. Ellingwood of the National Bureau of Standards, which is overseeing the revision.

Among other important changes is the recognition—and recommendation for—wind tunnel testing for so-called wind sensitive buildings. Although the exact definition of wind-sensitive buildings is under discussion, this generally refers to those structures with a height-to-width ratio so great that the building's resonant frequency is low and dangerously close to that of the wind's. Buildings, say five times as tall as they are wide, have a greater possibility of beginning to sway in coincidence with the wind than do buildings which are stouter. Buildings that sway with the wind may experience what is called negative damping. Early wind analysis showed, for instance, that the twin towers of the World Trade Center were so wind sensitive that they might undergo this type of fluctuation. As a result, 15,000 friction-producing dampers were designed into their flooring systems. To counteract wind sway, buildings must either be stiffened to raise their frequency, or have damping added to dissipate energy.

"Wind-sensitive structures really should be looked into in detail by the designer," as the standard will now recommend, says Ellingwood. "Before, we never recognized the wind tunnel as an alternative to the standard."

HANCOCK

Perhaps the problems that can result from discrepancies between codes, wind tunnel analysis and the interpretation of data is no where better illustrated than by the Hancock Tower. A raft of lawsuits stemming from the failure of its glass facade and the need to add steel bracing to its structural frame are [not entirely settled]. Several experts involved in that litigation have, however, shed some light on conditions that they believe contributed to the problems.

Wind tunnel tests conducted at the Massachusetts Institute of Technology indicate, for instance, that actual wind pressures on the facade were up to three times greater in some places than what was required by the architect's design wind load and the local building code. Further, the higher loads were primarily closer to the base of the structure, where the overall thickness of glass was thinner than that at the top, where it had been assumed the higher wind loads would occur.

These problems developed despite the precaution of conducting a wind tunnel study at Purdue University. According to George M. Palmer, director of Purdue's Aerospace Sciences Laboratory, who conducted the Hancock studies as a private consultant, the purpose of the tests was to determine what the mean loadings on the facade would be, not the peak loadings. At the state of technology then, he says, "that's all that [the glass companies] were interested in."

At least one engineering team involved in the case believes that this use of mean load values instead of the peak values that can occur during periods of gustiness could have led designers to conclude that lower design loadings would be sufficient.

Further, notes another expert involved, in Hancock's wind tunnel analysis "the question of recreating the boundary layer was not a focal point."

Not everyone will say that Hancock's problems stemmed even partially from wind engineering. Leslie E. Robertson, the New York City partner of

Skilling, Helle, Christiansen, Robertson who has been involved closely in wind engineering since his days studying wind effects on the World Trade Center, will argue semantically that it's not wind but rather a structural problem.

Still, says Weidlinger, "Hancock . . . was comparable to the Tacoma Narrows Bridge . . . it really changed that whole aspect of building engineering. It was a symbol."

There was one key difference between the Tacoma Narrows case and the John Hancock Tower, however. While Tacoma data were discussed in public and at great length—despite the presence of lawsuits—much of the data for the plywood palace may never be discussed in public. In August 1981, John Hancock Mutual Life Insurance Company settled out of court on almost all the suits pending between it, glass supplier Libbey-Owens-Ford, I. M. Pei & Partners, general contractor Gilbane Building Co., and the structural engineering firm The Office of James Ruderman, Inc. Only the glazing contractor, H. H. Robertson Co. of Pittsburgh, refused to settle.

As part of the agreement, all parties agreed to keep details secret. Libbey-Owens-Ford did admit, however, that beyond product liability and warranty reserve funds, it lost $6 million in the settlement. That, by the way, is about what the Tacoma Narrows Bridge cost to build in its entirety from 1938 to 1940.

Facade Failures, 1980

Failures in building facades cause payment of more insurance claims than any other construction defect except bad roofing. But while roofing may damage a building and its contents through leaks, falling facades can cost lives as well. Sifting back over the years, the causes of most facade failures are obvious: incompatability of materials, lack of attention to detail in design, and poor workmanship.

For those who need a lesson, the ENR issue of December 1, 1938, contains one:

How to Build Leaky Brick Walls with Good Materials

A. B. MacMillan   *Vice President, Aberthaw Company, Boston, Massachusetts*

No attempt will be made here to describe how to produce good brick walls. The problem after all is reasonably simple, and therefore capable of solution.

Figure 6-19 Serious cracks are apparent in the brick facade of this pre-World War II building. *(An ENR photograph by G. Burns.)*

However, judging from examples on every hand, much effort has gone into the production of leaky walls, even though carefully specified and selected materials were used. Up to the present time, in so far as the writer knows, there has been no concerted effort to educate the public to understand exactly how poor walls may be produced at will. There are a number of steps in the process; for some the owner and designer are responsible, and for some the builder may take all credit.

Without attempting to place the responsibility for any of the steps individually on either of the several participants, let us consider what these steps are.

First, there is compatability of materials. Just as incompatability in marriage leads to divorce, so in building materials it leads to separation. Each material used has characteristics peculiarly its own. For instance, the coefficient of expansion of brick masonry is approximately 0.0000031; that of limestone 0.0000044; and that of concrete 0.0000067. This simply means that in a length of 100 ft. with a temperature change of 100 deg., neglecting the effect of moisture, brick masonry if unrestrained would expand or contract ⅜ in.; limestone ⁹⁄₁₆ in.; and concrete ¹³⁄₁₆ in.

PLAIN ARITHMETIC

It is evident then that if an artificial stone (concrete) coping is placed on top of a brick wall and the end joints between adjacent stones are filled with a hard mortar, the stone in its endeavor to move twice as far as the supporting brickwork, in response to temperature changes, must either be restrained and prevented from moving by the brickwork or else will crack the brickwork or slide on the brickwork; in either case openings will be made through which water can enter the wall. Obviously, if limestone were used for the coping, the movement would be much less, and the marriage might prove successful.

Having thus insured the formation of fissures, the next step is to try to prevent the water going any further. This can be done with flashings. Naturally, if the flashing is laid on a smooth bed of dry mortar with elastic cement at the outer edge; if the outside edge of the flashing is turned down ½ or ¾ in. to form a drip; if the edge on the inside is turned down two courses for a cap flashing, or up if required as a cutoff elsewhere in the wall; if the joints in the copper are made by first tinning the edges of the sheets, then locking them together and soldering the seams so that the joints are thoroughly filled and covered with solder; if all these things are done penetration of water will be stopped at this point.

But as this is not what we want to accomplish, let us lay our flashing on the top of the rough brickwork, keeping the edge ½ in. or more back from the surface of the wall so that it will not mar the appearance of the outside face. Next, let us simply lap or, at most, form lock seams without tinning and soldering the copper sheets when they lap. This will insure that any water which penetrates to the copper can readily go through the several joints or, if by any chance they happen to resist the flow of water, it can find its way to the outer edge of the flashing and thence down into the irregularities in the masonry below.

Another excellent way to assure a leaky wall is never to seal the copper flashings around and against the wall columns. This is particularly effective in the case of steel columns where the space between the flanges is usually filled very roughly with brick bats, mortar, and empty pockets so as to form a natural channel for the passage of moisture.

In laying up the brickwork, after the mason gets his line stretched and mortar bed laid, simply butter the outer edge of the brick to be placed and tap it into place. This will appear to give a full joint on the outside and if the owner happens to notice that it is not full all of the way back just tell him that this is common practice and that when the next bed of mortar is laid it will be squeezed down and fill the joint. Never admit to him or anyone else that the pocketed air will prevent this filling, because if all joints were thoroughly filled it might hinder getting what we are striving for—a poor wall with good materials. To insure further that the wall will be poor, lay up several courses of brick without changing the line or plumbing the face, then

Figure 6-20   Popped bricks can be caused by trapped water. *(ENR File.)*

rack the wall until it is plumb and true. Doing this will guarantee that joints will be opened; also it saves money in laying.

There are still a few more precautions that should not be forgotten. Don't parge the back of the face brick; this might act as a barrier and stop some leaks. In laying the back-up bricks simply slap them into place on the mortar bed when no one is watching, without buttering the ends or sides, and cover the top face with more mortar as fast as possible so that the inspector can't see that the joints are not filled. Naturally, a little mortar must be used at vertical joints on the inside face of the wall because if these were left entirely open someone might notice it.

These notes could be further amplified to cover the use of membrane flashings, how to treat windows, doors, etc., but sufficient hints have been given so that any careless or unscrupulous builder who follows them can be sure to produce a poor wall with high maintenance cost at will, however excellent the materials used may be.

E. L. McFalls of the Master Builders Company, Cleveland, replied in a letter to the editor (Jan. 19, 1939):

We know of only one other measure that might be taken, and very frequently is, to increase the likelihood of leakage: The use of as wet a mortar mix as can be handled, which results in excessive initial shrinkage and can be relied on to break the bond between mortar and brick, even if the mechanic is conscientious in filling the head joints.

Some of the materials have changed since then, and so have some of the expansion coefficients mentioned. But the problems have not entirely gone away, as the ENR issue of January 24, 1980, made clear:

Facades: Errors Can Be Expensive

Often result from lack of training.

In Chicago, six sheets of marble, each covering over 22 sq ft, topple from the 13th floor of a high-rise building to the sidewalk.

In New York, a young woman is killed when she is struck by a piece of stone window framing that has worked loose from a university building.

The State of New York sues a contractor for $28 million, claiming faulty installation of marble on one of the buildings of the Nelson A. Rockefeller Empire State Plaza. On two buildings in the complex, marble has cracked, spalled and pulled loose from its anchors.

The University of Massachusetts at Amherst closes its 28-story library to investigate brick shards falling from the facade. The library partially reopens, but students must enter the building through tunnels for protection. Pieces of brick have been falling for seven years.

Four marble slabs tumble from the face of a New York City department store. Discovering that all of the building's marble may be overstressed, the store's management decides to strip the entire facade and replace the marble with metal panels, at a cost that has been estimated at $1 million.

These failures have caused, or could have caused, serious injury to passersby. All [are] expensive to repair. Lawsuits are being hurled at architects, contractors and engineers. And all of this has happened just within [1979 alone].

These are a few notable examples of a serious and frequent problem: the failure of building facades. Many instances reach the public eye each year. But for every facade failure that sets off a hullabaloo of nervous news reports and lawsuits, probably several are discovered and repaired without publicity, in the nick of time, before falling stone or brick can arouse public curiosity.

Yet even though a falling facade can be dangerous and expensive and can result in the loss of license or bankruptcy for building designers and contractors, facades and their particular problems are met largely with ignorance and lack of concern on the part of the building industry.

"There are four basic causes of building facade failures: ignorance, carelessness, negligence and greed," says engineer Dov Kaminetzky, whose New York City firm, Feld, Kaminetzky & Cohen, P.C., is a frequent investigator of cladding and its problems. "Ignorance is the only one we can hope to improve."

COURSES LACKING

Dean C. Patterson, assistant chief engineer with the Brick Institute of America, blames part of that ignorance on a change in responsibility. Masonry and stonework are both very old building materials, he says. They were formerly the business of craftsmen who learned the trade from their fathers or through apprenticeship. Nowadays, cladding design has fallen into the hands of architects and structural engineers.

But a student architect or civil engineer looking for a course devoted to building cladding design will discover quickly that it's about as hard to find as gargoyles on a glass box office building. Education in building exteriors has made some gains, but improvement is slow in coming. "We now have some undergrad courses for the first time. We feel it will be a great boon to us," says Patterson. But he admits that courses are "still a little scattered."

Research into cladding problems is also lacking. "Cladding has historically not been given much attention" as a research subject, says Barry J. Goodno, associate professor of engineering at the Georgia Institute of Technology. "It's catching up with us. Cladding is a very, very expensive part of a building." Goodno estimates that cladding can cost as much as 10 to 20% of a building's initial cost. If that facade is improperly designed or installed and serious repairs are needed, they can cost many times more than the original cost, because of the difficulties of facing a building that is already in use, and the additional cost of removing the faulty facing.

Goodno suggests that building research emphasizes framing and the primary structures of buildings rather than cladding. "It's not a glamour part of research," he says, and as a result, "we're not far enough along to understand failures. Right now we still need to know how cladding behaves in normal day-to-day situations."

Because cladding is still not given its due attention, several experts interviewed report that many architects and engineers do not fully understand such cladding problems as the expansion of brick due to moisture and direct sunlight, the effects of freezing and thawing and problems stemming from insufficient firing of brick. This can result in bad designs and detail drawings that produce faulty buildings, they say.

SHRINKING AND SWELLING

The classic case of a faulty facade is inadequate brick cladding on a concrete frame building. The concrete will tend to shrink with time while masonry will swell. With the brick and frame pulling against one another, serious stresses can build up if there are not enough shelf angles for support and sufficient horizontal expansion joints in the wall to let the building components move independently.

Another important cause of failure is water. "If there is insufficient drainage the wall will deteriorate very quickly," Kaminetzky says. "It's one of the biggest problem causers," particularly when water trapped behind the facade freezes and expands during the winter, dislodging the brick. The importance of freeze-thaw cycling in causing facade deterioration is evidenced

Figure 6-21 The close-up (right) and the circled area (left) show a large vertical fissure that appeared December 13, 1971, on the north wall of a building facing 32d Street near Broadway in Manhattan. *(ENR File.)*

by the almost complete limitation of facade failures to areas where winters are harsh. Failures are relatively rare in warmer areas.

Moisture that reaches steel columns also takes a toll on facades. When the steel rusts, it flakes and expands, pushing out brick and forming long vertical cracks that can be found at the corners of many masonry buildings, says Peter Corsell, president of New York City consultant Peter Corsell Associates, Inc., a building exterior specialist. Proper coating of the column so it cannot rust if exposed to water and waterproofing to prevent water from reaching it are two solutions to the problem, he says.

Parapets, among the most vulnerable parts of a building, must be carefully detailed, cladding experts say. Parapets are subject to wind-driven rain and freezing on both sides, and must be well protected.

Designers occasionally take insufficient care where two materials meet, where a metal railing connects with a stone parapet for example. Since the materials expand and contract at different rates with temperature changes, they must be able to move independently without building up stress.

Frequently, according to Kaminetzky, designers provide too few masonry ties, or anchors that are too weak to bear the load or that are not corrosion resistant. Expansion joints must allow sufficient movement.

Movement has become an especially critical concern in modern building design, says Corsell. As building frames become lighter, the easier movement of buildings and the resultant jostling of cladding panels becomes a crucial concern to designers.

THE HUMAN ELEMENT

And yet, says Corsell, an adequate design often suffers from bad construction. "Even if the detailing and the drawings are good, often that's not what we find in the field," he says. Kaminetzky agrees. "Much of the problem usually is the human element of constructing the building," he says.

Construction crews commonly fill in expansion joints with mortar, negating the joints' intent. Also common are shelf angle supports whose effect is ruined because the contractor does not extend them around corners or bolt them down adequately, or troublesome pieces of brickwork that are supported by too few ties.

One example of a contractor's error having serious consequences is the Lyndon Baines Johnson Library at the University of Texas in Austin. Seven months after the building opened in 1971, university officials noted that some of the building's 2,000 travertine panels were loosening. An investigation revealed that the masonry contractor had used the wrong kind of mortar, one that expanded when exposed to water. Every panel had to be removed, cleaned and reinstalled with different mortar. Cost: $1.7 million and three years of work.

Kaminetzky says the problem with inadequate construction is often an incomplete understanding of how building cladding behaves. Better training for foremen and supervisors and a freer flow of information within the industry are needed, he says.

INSPECTIONS NEEDED

Once a building is completed, concern for the health of its exterior should not end or another group of avoidable problems may result, engineers interviewed say. Responsible care of the facade is required to take advantage of the full amount of endurance inherent in the cladding materials. Frequent and thorough inspections are necessary to find cracks, movement, leakage and improper drainage, says Corsell. These deficiencies, if repaired early, will have little effect on the building exterior. Once water leaks behind a wall and is trapped there by an undetected clogged weephole, for example, a few winters of freezing and thawing can do some expensive damage.

Figure 6-22 Wind ripped away the metal panels that covered this apartment building wall. Many other panels were loosened (note the vertical bars holding them at the windows). *(ENR File.)*

Corsell also emphasizes that building components such as calking, sealants, mortar and weatherstripping are not indestructable. Failure to replace them will bring greater expenses later on.

"Proper preventive maintenance is the key," says Corsell. He cites as examples New York City's Chrysler and Empire State Buildings. Both are tall buildings, constructed a year apart. Both must withstand the same climate. All things being equal, one would expect them to exhibit roughly the same deterioraton of age. Yet the Empire State Building is still in good shape at the age of 49, while the Chrysler Building is not. As a result of the Chrysler Building receiving inadequate preventive maintenance compared to the well-cared-for Empire State Building, it has required millions of dollars in repairs, Corsell says.

Aware of the importance of facade maintenance, and spurred by an incident five years ago in which a pedestrian was killed by falling terra-cotta, the Chicago Department of Buildings is now enforcing a city ordinance that requires periodic inspections of building exteriors by qualified engineers. The requirement doesn't become effective until September, but notification has already been sent out, according to John Power, records administrator with the department. Although some building owners have already expressed reluctance to comply, Power says the inspections will benefit owners by early identification of problems that might show up as serious trouble 10 years from now if not repaired. . . .

Keeping a wall in good repair need not be expensive, cladding specialists surveyed say, as long as proper care is taken at all steps of its construction. This requires architects and engineers who take care that all necessary protection has been designed into building exteriors, detailers who understand proper connections and are careful to include them wherever necessary, contractors who are sensitive to the requirements of facades and take pains to follow them thoroughly, owners who keep the exteriors of their buildings sealed tight and in good repair, and inspectors watching at every step of the way to see that the same attention is given to cladding that is given to the rest of the building.

As persistent cladding failures show, sufficient concern is not always there.

Progress has been slow on the legal front. Only when a passerby gets in the way of falling pieces does a facade failure rate time on the evening news. Chicago passed an inspection ordinance in the wake of a 1974 incident in which a person was killed by a falling piece of decorative terra-cotta. The ordinance, passed in 1978, requires that an architect or engineer inspect the exterior of every building more than 5 stories in height for signs of imminent failures. It was only after 6½-ton marble panels started blowing off the city's 76-story Water Tower Place in March 1979, however, that the ordinance was enforced.

Following initial inspections, buildings are to be inspected every 10 years until they are over age 35, and every 5 years thereafter. Chicago's buildings commissioner has the authority to force owners to make the required repairs.

In March 1981, Shand, Morahan and Co., of Evanston, Illinois, a large underwriter of professional liability insurance, helped run a major symposium on the problem. The firm's motivation was simple: Facade failures jumped from 15 percent of all claims in 1960 to 33 percent in 1980.

The meeting was reported in the April 9, 1981, issue of ENR:

Coordination Could Prevent Building Facade Problems

Charles H. Thornton, president of Lev Zetlin Associates, Inc., New York City, charges that incompatibility of building systems due to lack of coordination among members of the building team are behind most exterior wall and enclosure failures. With owners, architects, designers and engineers all trying "to establish their mark," untested systems are used at the potential expense of building durability, he says. But even well-tested systems used with high-strength, lightweight structures lead to subtle variations that must be considered in designs, he says.

Thornton recommends "a more formalized" education of architects and engineers in "the coordination, behavior and compatibility" of building systems. In addition, he says, structural engineers should be more involved in the selection, design, installation and quality control of enclosure systems. "Blind reliance on the recommendation of non-qualified material suppliers who are not intimately aware of the structural behavior of a building should be eliminated," he says.

But Paul M. Lurie, an attorney with Chicago-based Fohrman, Lurie, Sklar & Cottle, Ltd., says that without top management's support quality-control programs will never get off the ground. Quality assurance "must be designed, financed, marketed, sold and managed" and, therefore, should be a "line item" in the budget. But Lurie admits that selling this idea is a problem. "Design professionals tend not to be team players and believe no one else is more knowledgeable to check their work."

Until quality control becomes an integral part of the design and construction process, Lurie recommends that to curb liability claims, designers:

- Include a limitation-of-liability clause in contracts, which holds down the extent of responsibility to a predetermined dollar figure.
- Eliminate performance guarantees, which indicate that a product or system will meet a certain performance level.

· Distinguish in the contract between supervision, as in control, and observation of the contractor. Lurie contends that avoidance of the word supervision is not sufficient to avoid a lawsuit. If the word observation is used to suggest "how a contractor is to do something, and that suggestion appears to be wrong, you may still find yourself responsible for your suggestion," he says.

· Advise owners of the consequence of construction compromise resulting from insufficient funds, as well as adding allowances in contracts for possible extras.

The seminar also covered problems of masonry and curtain walls. Panel participants emphasized interaction among the members of the entire design team from designer to mechanical engineer, before the construction process begins. "Liability aspects have escalated so drastically that it's obscuring our vision. Construction requirements are not spelled out early on because of fear of changes," says Eugene P. Holland, president of Chicago-based Coder, Taylor Associates, Inc. "Eventually we'll have to get back to developing buildings, not contracts."

7

Roofs

No construction failures cause more problems—nor more claims—than roofing that leaks, cracks, collapses, or blows away. Sometimes the failures accumulate a few at a time. Dow, for instance, once had special problems with built-up roofing over Styrofoam insulating cores. Outer membranes cracked, causing leaks. Yet the same design in Europe suffered few failures.

Sometimes even traditional materials are not up to the task. Old New England buildings lost thousands of roofs in the great hurricane of 1938. The high wind lifted the heavy plank roofs a few inches. Unsecured supporting columns wobbled and fell beneath them, and the roofs came back to rest on non-existent columns, collapsing into rubble. Building codes now take such uplifting forces into account, and require anchors and ties, even for massive roofs.

In the late seventies, 2 years of especially heavy snow (the winters of 1978 and 1979) caused a new rash of failures. And two especially spectacular collapses of modern long-span roofs—the Hartford Civic Center Coliseum and the Kansas City Kemper Arena—focused renewed attention on design and fabrication problems.

For the winter of 1978, for example, Connecticut's Office of Civil Preparedness reported seventy-nine roof failures due to heavy snow on warehouses, department stores, and factories, for a damage total of almost $9 million—not including the Hartford Coliseum collapse in January of that year. Several hundred residences also lost their roofs that winter in Connecticut, causing even more damage.

In Chicago that winter, more than 32 inches of snow fell in January, compared to a norm of 9.4 inches. The ENR issue of February 9, 1978, described some of the damage:

WALL TRAPPED SNOW

Snow piles up [to] 11 ft deep on a 36-ft-wide roof of a truck loading dock in suburban Lyons, Ill., brought down a 300-ft-long section. According to

Figure 7-1 This college roof on Long Island fell 43 feet. The dome was 171 feet across. *(United Press International.)*

Kolbjorn Saether, president of Kolbjorn Saether & Associates, Inc., Chicago, which designed the structure, the loads on the roof were as much as 165 lb per sq ft, far exceeding its 66-lb design. The loading dock roof adjoined a higher roof in stair-step fashion, and snow drifted against their common wall. Eight-in. wide-flange steel columns and bar joists supported the roof.

Two other collapses occurred in Chicago, says Patrick J. Noonan, the city's chief construction inspector. Both were one-story older structures with timber trusses supporting arched roofs. One roof was 150 ft square with 40-ft spans and the other was 125 X 100 ft with 100-ft spans, but only portions of them failed.

Indianapolis received 48 in. of snow last month, and heavy accumulations are blamed for roof failures of two warehouses and a loading dock, says chief structural inspector Otto C. Guedelhoefer. Both warehouses were constructed of concrete block walls and metal panel roofs bearing on bar joists. The roofs were 100 to 150 ft long and about 50 ft wide with decorative mansards jutting up about 24 in. above roof level. Guedelhoefer says the roof failures were most prominent behind the mansards.

DEEP DRIFTS

In Kalamazoo 2 ft of snow is thought to have collapsed a 25 X 40-ft bay covering part of a shopping mall. "It was a case of a low roof adjacent to a higher roof," says Howard Linders of Carl Walker & Associates, Kalamazoo, which is investigating the failure. The consultant reports that the wind piled a 12 to 15-ft-deep drift atop the lower roof, which was a metal deck supported by bar joists.

It was more of the same the following winter in Chicago, where snow loads reached 50 pounds per square foot and more. The city's building code specified

Figure 7-2 The Madisonville school gymnasium (above) collapsed Christmas day, 1969. Below, structure identical in design and construction to the Madisonville gymnasium, 12 miles away in Tellico Plains, fell the morning after Christmas. (Knoxville News-Sentinel.)

only 25 pounds per square foot, with obvious results: More than 100 roofs failed, and another 1000 were damaged. A committee investigating failure patterns in Chicago noted that the most likely structures to fail were wood bowstring trusses, steel bar joists, and the roofs of pre-engineered metal buildings.

Evidently, the prefabricated roofs were designed for specified loads that were exceeded in Chicago. Roofs designed and built for specific sites often had reserve strength built into them either for ease of calculation of stresses or to make up for possible construction errors.

The quest for longer and longer unobstructed spans on tight construction budgets led to many collapses of school gymnasiums in the 1960s and 1970s. In one 24-hour period during Christmas recess in 1969, two steel-framed, hexagonal gyms that had been designed by the same architect and built by the same contractor failed. Because of the holiday, they were unoccupied. They served the high schools of two towns, 12 miles apart, near Knoxville, Tennessee.

Both were steel-framed with brick veneer on block walls. The roofs, which failed first, bringing down the walls, were supported by inclined steel trusses spanning between six steel columns in the outside walls and a steel ring, which acted as a compression ring at the top and a tension ring at the bottom.

The gyms failed at the same points: Four of the six lower connections of the center ring and the trusses failed in each building. The trusses had been joined to the ring through bolted steel plates. The plates—not the bolts—failed.

The two roofs each had about 3 inches of wet snow on them when they fell. One design problem identified later was that water near the drains could cause fairly large deflections at those points, making drainage rather slow. The gyms had stood for about 2½ years before failing.

Less than 9 months later, a post-tensioned, reinforced concrete roof over a high school gym in Henrico County, Virginia, began sagging. A girls' basketball team practicing beneath the roof ran for safety moments before the roof caved in. Eight girls were slightly injured by flying debris. Officials were secretive when ENR first reported the incident in the September 24, 1970, issue:

County attorney J. Mercer White clamped a tight lid on the release of all information regarding the design, construction and collapse of the building and refused to allow reporters to talk with the team of consulting engineers retained to investigate the accident.

The gymnasium, designed by Richmond architect Thomas A. Hanson & Associates, under a subcontract from J. Henley Walker, Jr., the Richmond architect who designed the entire high school complex, is rectangular in plan with corridors and lockers located on its perimeter. Four reinforced concrete columns supported a reinforced concrete A-frame along each face of the building. Each frame was tied across the building to its opposite counterpart by a post-tensioned, reinforced concrete ridge beam. The roof is a four-quadrant, hyperbolic paraboloid.

ENR learned from a set of microfilmed blueprints, on file with the Virginia State Department of Education, that the gymnasium was 153 x 162 ft with 100-ft-square floor in its center. Its reinforced concrete sidewall framing beams canted outward 4.5 ft.

The plans show post-tensioned tie-beam dimensions as 14 in. wide by 16 in. deep. But Hanson says the tie beams were increased to a 22-in. depth after conducting model tests of the design. Specifications called for a 3.5-in-thick lightweight concrete shell roof reinforced with steel mesh. R. L. Bulifant & Co., Inc., Richmond, built the high school in 1962 under a $1.8-million contract.

The county has closed two other high school gymnasiums of similar design and by the same architect. Officials of nearby Bedford County also closed a gymnasium, which is similar in design.

It turned out that the structure had been built according to accepted practice, but that over time, slight deflections and flattening built up what the investigators called "secondary moments or stress" that eventually overwhelmed the design. Two similar structures that had not failed were also found to have roofs that had begun to flatten, thus redistributing the forces acting upon structural members. The roofs were shored.

Such roofs are a form of "space frame," in that they are three-dimensional in their ability to withstand and redistribute the forces acting upon them. Their use had begun to expand in the early 1950s, as engineers learned how to perform the complex calculations necessary to design them. Among the spectacular structures incorporating space frames are the exhibition hall in Denver (ENR, Sept. 22, 1966) and the "crystal cathedral" of the Hour of Power television ministry near Los Angeles (ENR, Jan. 3, 1980, cover story).

As the two failures discussed in the remainder of this chapter make clear, however, complex designs must be shepherded through the detailing and construction process, lest fatal but nonobvious errors creep in.

Hartford Civic Center Coliseum, 1978

If 6000 spectators had been watching a hockey game in the Hartford Coliseum when the roof caved in, 4000 would have died. Instead the spectators had been home for 4 or 5 hours when the roof, one of the largest space frames in the United States, collapsed under the weight of a major snowstorm on January 18, 1978. Here's how ENR described the aftermath in the January 26 issue.

Figure 7-3 This stadium in Rosemont, Illinois, collapsed in August 1979 while under construction. The failure killed five people and injured more than a dozen. (Chicago Tribune.)

Space Frame Roofs Collapse Following Heavy Snowfalls

As a clamshell crane last week began tearing loose jagged and bent steel sheathing from the collapsed 2.5-acre space frame roof of the Hartford Civic Center Coliseum, investigators continued to sift through the debris in a search for clues of what caused the near-record-size roof to fall. No one was injured in the accident which occurred Jan. 18 following a snow storm that hit many East Coast areas.

That same night, roofs fell in two other Connecticut towns and one in Poca, W. Va. A wire factory roof collapsed in Jewitt City, Conn., killing one worker, and a roof topping a K-Mart department store in Manchester also gave way. The West Virginia failure involved a food store's steel lattice joist roof.

Three days later, following a second heavy snowfall, another space frame roof collapsed. That 171-ft-dia domed roof topped a 3,500-seat auditorium at C. W. Post College in Brookville, N.Y. No one was hurt [see Figure 7-1].

Failure of the 360 X 300-ft Hartford civic center roof occurred just before dawn. Hotel night clerks and a parking garage attendant near the five-year-old building reported they heard a rumble and then a boom just before the collapse. The 25-ft-deep roof sagged in the center, dropping 83 ft to the 12,000 seats and arena below. All four corners, which cantilevered 45 ft beyond reinforced concrete columns, kicked upward.

During the night before the collapse, snow began falling and then changed to rain. According to Fraioli Blum Yesselman Engineers PC [FBY], whose Hartford office designed the roof, the structure was designed for snow loading of 30 lb per sq ft, as required by Hartford's department of licenses and inspection. Tests done one day after the collapse by a team from the U.S. Army cold regions research and engineering laboratory showed that snow across the street from the coliseum weighed 23 lb per sq ft.

City officials have appointed a three-member city council panel to handle the investigation. The panel, in turn, has retained New York City consultant Lev Zetlin Associates, Inc. [LZA], to determine the cause of the collapse and develop a demolition procedure. That probe is expected to take about three months. Two other consultants hired by the city, Loomis and Loomis, Inc., Consulting Professional Engineers, Windsor, Conn., and Buck & Buck, Hartford, are checking to see if other areas of the civic center are damaged.

Figure 7-4 Hartford Civic Center Coliseum the morning after the collapse. Notice the buildup of snow that triggered the failure. *(United Press International.)*

OTHER AREAS UNTOUCHED

Preliminary examinations show that the only damage is in the coliseum area, according to a city spokesman. This area covers 25% of the $75-million civic center complex. Shops and convention space surrounding two sides of the coliseum appear to be virtually untouched.

Bethlehem Steel Corp., Bethlehem, Pa., erected the $1.4-million roof in 1972. At that time the space frame roof was second only in size to that covering an activities center at Brigham Young University in Provo, Utah. Clear spans on the Hartford roof were 270 and 210 ft.

Bethlehem crews fabricated the roof on the ground, then jacked it in stages from temporary steel towers to slightly above its eventual 83-ft height. Reinforced concrete columns were built within the temporary towers. Then crews lowered the roof onto bearings atop the columns and bolted it and grouted it in place.

FRAME DESIGN

The erector used high-strength bolts to connect the space frame components, which consist of triangular bracing between top and bottom chords. Bethlehem shop-bolted some sections of the chords and main web members before shipping them to the field. Without roofing materials, mechanical systems or metal sheathing attached, the space frame weighed 1,400 tons.

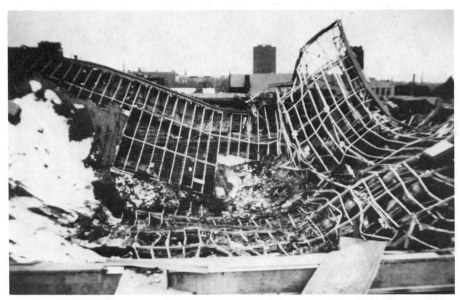

Figure 7-5 Twisting of relatively thin structural members forming the space frame of the Hartford Coliseum is very obvious here. *(ENR.)*

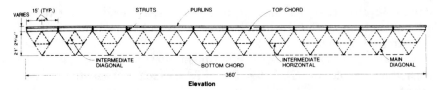

Figure 7-6 The top and bottom chords of the Hartford Coliseum consisted of steel angles shop-bolted back-to-back. The purlins sit atop struts, separate from the trusses making up the space frame itself. *(ENR.)*

According to a Bethlehem spokesman, ASTM A572 Grade 50 steel was used for the roof structure's highly stressed members while A36 steel was specified for the remainder.

Welded to the top chord of the frame were steel posts that supported a framing system for the 3-in.-thick wood fiber composition roof. Space frame designers Werner Blum and Philip Wesler wrote in a January, 1974, article in *Civil Engineering.*

> By having the posts bear directly on main panel points, or subpanel points, bending stresses due to gravity loading are eliminated from the top chord lattice members.
>
> However, to simplify both fabrication and assembly, no camber of the space frame was provided. The computer results indicated that a downward deflection of about 13 in. would occur at the midpoint of the roof, under all dead and live loads, and an upward deflection of about 6 in. at the extreme cantilevered corners. These deflections were considered in establishing the true heights of the [roof system posts] to maintain positive drainage under all conditions.

Though specific reconstruction plans aren't yet solid, City Manager James B. Daken says the structure, the keystone of downtown redevelopment, will be rebuilt "bigger and better." And, he says, it will probably have a different roof.

What had gone wrong? After all, the roof had stood for 5½ years. Yet no one had been concerned enough about obvious sagging to do anything. The preliminary report of Lev Zetlin Associates was shocking. As summarized in the April 6, 1978, issue of ENR:

Design Flaws Collapsed Steel Space Frame Roof

Design deficiencies caused the collapse of the 2.5-acre steel space frame roof over Hartford's Civic Center Coliseum. The 1,400-ton truss began failing the day in late 1972 that jacks lifted it into place. Actual loads on the roof were 1.5 million lb more than assumed design loads and some main members were overstressed by as much as 852%.

That is the conclusion spelled out in an interim report by New York City consultant Lev Zetlin Associates, Inc. (LZA), which is spearheading the investigation for the City of Hartford. Also involved in the probe are Loomis and Loomis, Inc., Windsor, Conn., and Buck and Buck, Hartford. A final report is due about May 1.

In testimony last week before a city council committee, LZA president Charles H. Thornton said a comparison of the design and as-built conditions of the space frame revealed three "basic design errors that occurred together with an underestimation of the actual dead loads of the roof." A buildup of snow and ice during the early morning hours of Jan. 18, though less than the roof was designed to carry, was sufficient to drop the 360 X 300-ft structure 83 ft to the 12,000 seats below.

Designed by Fraioli-Blum-Yesselman, Norfolk, the space frame had typical top and bottom chords and main diagonals that consisted of lengths of

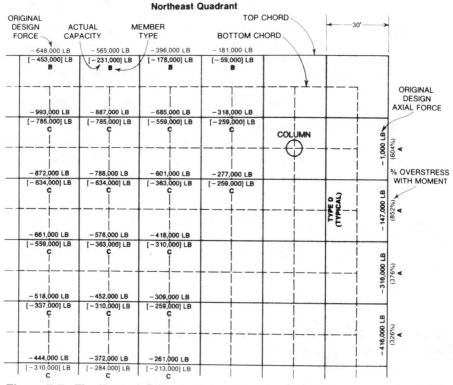

Figure 7-7 The Hartford Coliseum design, symmetrical along two axes, quadrupled the problems. The member type corresponds to the drawings in Figure 7-8. *(ENR.)*

steel angles shop-bolted back to back to form a cross. Bolts connected some of the angled members where they were separated by tie plates. These main members consisted of 8 X 8-in. to 3.5 X 3.5-in. angles. Intermediate members were single 5 X 5-in. angles. Bottom chords were set back 15 ft from the top chord and the entire truss was 21 ft deep.

WHAT THE FLAWS WERE

The three major design flaws cited by LZA involved inadequate bracing. According to LZA's computer analysis of the original design:

- Exterior top chord compression members on the east and west faces were overloaded by as much as 852%.
- Exterior top chord compression members on the south and north faces were overloaded by as much as 213%.
- Interior top chord compression members in the east-west direction were overloaded by as much as 72%.

In addition, says Thornton, "interior top chord compression members in the north-south direction would be similarly overstressed but for the bracing effect at the midpoint of the member due to the strut/purlin assembly." Steel struts of varying heights bore atop panel points on top of the truss to support the roof purlins. There was no cross-bracing between these struts.

In a preliminary report to the city's investigative committee in February, LZA criticized this aspect of the roof design. The configuration of the roofing system, in particular the placement of the purlins, struts, cementitious deck, roofing and waterproofing "as a separate system, with no contact to the space frame other than the vertical struts at certain panel points of the space frame, makes the . . . space frame susceptible to buckling or instability of top chord space frame compression members."

Ordinarily, according to the report, such a purlin system is placed directly on the space frame top chord. Separating these purlins from the top chord and placing them atop the struts minimizes the diaphragm action of the roof.

DETAIL DIDN'T MATCH DESIGN

The space frame consisted of a series of 30-ft-square bays. According to LZA, the original design calculations provided for an unsupported length of 15 ft for top chord members. This would have meant a brace at the midpoint of every such member. But when the structure was detailed, the exterior top chords were unbraced for their entire 30-ft length. Interior top chords were partially and inadequately braced at their midpoints.

"Where and how the omission occurred is hard to say," says Thornton.

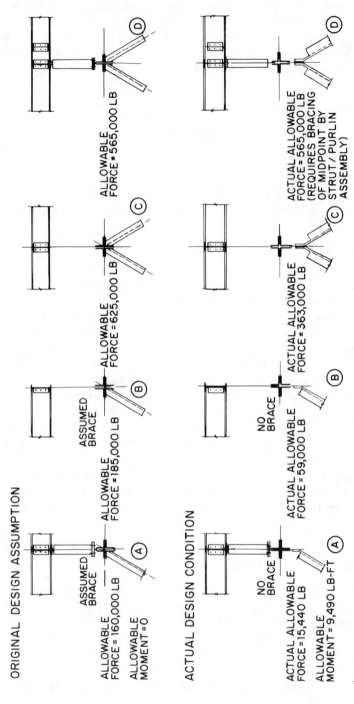

Figure 7-8 Bracing details along exterior and interior top chord members at the Hartford Coliseum don't match the design, which assumed diagonals through the working point. See Figure 7-7 for placement of various types of joints on the actual roof plan. (*ENR.*)

This inadequate bracing in both exterior and interior chords, coupled with the underestimation of actual dead loads and eccentric forces from some purlin-carrying struts that were placed at the unbraced center point of some top chord members resulted in the overloaded condition.

Thornton backed up his testimony with drawings of midpoint bracing details along typical exterior and interior top chord members. In general they illustrated that the connection as contemplated in the original design was different from that actually constructed, resulting in significantly reduced load-carrying capabilties. Typically, diagonal bracing beneath a purlin-carrying strut intersected beneath rather than through the working point of the connection as assumed in the design.

Examination of bottom chord elevations recorded by a contractor during erection of the truss in January, 1973, shows that the problem began during construction. By that date, according to LZA, the bottom chord had deflected 8.4 in. under dead load alone. Without the cementitious deck and permanent roofing, which would add 9.2 and 11 lb respectively, the deflection had already exceeded the total design load deflection of 7.35 in. By April, 1975, the deflection measured 12 to 13 in. Design calculations show it should have been 8.5 in. at this point.

In explaining the excessive deflection, Thornton says:

- The design contemplated a space frame weight of 18 lb per sq ft while actual weight was about 23 lb. This is 20% higher than the design anticipated.
- Bowing of top chord compression members shortened their length, further deflecting and distorting the entire truss.
- Design analysis apparently was not repeated after some of the space frame members were reduced in cross-section.

During his testimony, Thornton produced a photograph taken during truss fabrication that showed obvious bowing in two top chord members. "This amount of bowing should have been a red flag indicating there was a problem."

EVERYTHING IS OK

Correspondence among nearly everyone involved on the project, says Thornton, states that "although the deflection and loads are greater than originally anticipated, everything is O.K." Adds Thornton, "They simply didn't know how bad the problem was."

Another indication that the frame was deflecting significantly were problems with fitting the steel framing supports for fascia panels on the exterior of the truss. Some of the supports had to be coped and others refabricated in order to fit. According to a source close to the investigation, this problem was spelled out in correspondence between the subcontractor responsible for attaching the fascia supports and coliseum general contractor Gilbane Building Co., Providence. Gilbane's answer, the source says, directed the subcontractor to deal with the problem or be responsible for delays.

According to Gilbane executive vice president Paul Choquette, it had been informed that whatever deflection occurred and whatever coping was required was to be expected.

MYSTERY CABLES

Field checking after the collapse turned up ⅜-in. steel cables strung through the truss in both directions. The investigation source speculates that they were added during installation of the fascia supports to force the truss back into shape to ease fascia frame installation. But the contractor responsible for that portion of the work, Standard Structural Steel Co., Newington, Conn., denies that it installed the cables.

These cables, which previously were thought to have been left in place as painting scaffold supports, do not appear on any working drawing. Just who installed them and why remains a mystery.

In any case, says the LZA report, "the presence of these cables at strategic locations at the most deficient portions of the space truss indicates

Figure 7-9 One plane of failure at Hartford; note the uniform folding. *(ENR.)*

that parties involved during construction should have detected these cables and questioned their presence. These cables should have pointed to excessive distortion and deficiency in the structure."

In addition to design defects, LZA's investigation also turned up some construction deficiencies. According to the report, several connections were found for which welding of filler plates substantially reduced the capacity of the connections.

Where the collapse began is still undetermined. Because the truss was symmetrical about two axes, "any understrength member in one quadrant is also present in the three other quadrants; thus there are always four understrength members," according to the report. This symmetry, it states, makes it difficult to determine which of any four understrength members buckled first.

FAILURE SEQUENCE

LZA's design analysis indicates that the collapse happened like this: The most highly overloaded members at the exterior top chords buckled, redistributing loads to other top chord compression members, which in turn buckled. As top chord members buckled, the forces in many bottom chord members changed from tension to compression, and these members buckled. Then the most highly overloaded top chord members in the east-west direction failed. A major fold along a north-south grid line developed and total collapse followed. There were two major folds.

LZA's report concludes that "there should have been a resident specialist structural engineer with full-time involvement during the assembly and erection of the space truss roof."

Project architect Vincent G. Kling, of The Kling Partnership, Philadelphia, said he hasn't yet seen the consultant's report and cannot comment. Danos & Associates, Hartford, was the associated architect.

Attempts to obtain comments on the report from structural engineer Fraioli-Blum-Yesselman were unsuccessful. A spokesman for Bethlehem Steel Corp., Bethlehem, Pa., which fabricated and erected the truss, said the company wouldn't comment until after the final report is out. Construction manager William L. Crow Construction Co., New York City, declined comment.

The final report (ENR, June 22, 1978, pp. 36–37) confirmed LZA's view that design deficiencies were the cause of the collapse, and narrowed the major problems to a lack of adequate bracing along the top chord compression members. But construction errors also contributed to the failure, the final report said.

In a report to the city manager, however, Charles J. McSheffery, director of Hartford's Department of Licenses and Inspection, said that ice-clogged drains alone could have caused the collapse. In some areas of the roof, overloads of more than 5 percent were calculated.

Paul Gossen, who headed the investigation team from LZA, said even an overload that great would not have led to failure if the structure had been designed properly. Computer analysis calculated actual loads of 66 to 73 pounds per square foot on the roof, including snow loads of 12 to 19 pounds per square foot, and that the capacity of the roof was only 69 to 74 pounds per square foot. "It is therefore apparent that failure could occur," he said. "The minimum design load should have been 84 psf average load, including 30 psf live load. With a safety factor of 1.67 the roof should have had a capacity at failure of 140 psf."

LZA also complained about the slenderness of built-up diagonal members, of four steel angles connected back to back, in violation of the American Institute of Steel Construction code. Some members had holes punched through, whose area was more than 85 percent of the total area of the members—also a code violation.

LZA noted a possible deficiency in the code itself: "The outstanding legs of all angles at all connections were not connected to the main gusset plates. The observed failures at many connections due to shear lag effects indicates that the AISC code requires revision to compensate for that mode of failure."

In reply, the structural engineer disputed every point. The June 29, 1978, issue of ENR contained the following article:

Collapsed Roof Design Defended

Collapse of the steel space truss roof over the Hartford Civic Center Coliseum last January was not due to improper design, according to its structural engineer. While calling the cause of the collapse "at best speculative," the engineering firm says it "performed its services in a professionally sound manner and is not responsible" for the failure.

In its first public response since the collapse of the 360 X 300-ft truss, Fraioli-Blum-Yesselman of New England (FBY), Hartford, the structural engineer, says the report of a consultant hired by the city to investigate the accident is "overstated and contains erroneous, unsupported and misleading conclusions." FBY's statement says, " . . . we suggest that Dr. Thornton has declined or failed to consider, adequately or at all, in his final report, major theories of causation which appear more supportable as a matter of fact and engineering judgment."

Charles H. Thornton is president of New York City–based Lev Zetlin Associates, Inc. (LZA), Hartford's consultant. LZA's final report blames the collapse primarily on design deficiencies involving inadequate bracing of top chord compression members. But its 400-page report also points to other, minor design flaws, code violations, questionable design practices, construction problems and inadequate inspection [ENR, June 22, 1978, p. 36].

FYB's statement says it "continues to take strong issue with the contents of Dr. Thornton's report insofar as it persists in its charge that Fraioli-Blum-Yesselman is responsible for the collapse." Specifically FBY says the conclusions of LZA's final report "represent significant changes in tone and substance from those . . . in his preliminary report. . . ."

One example FBY cites are mysterious steel cables strung through the truss which, it says, LZA's earlier report "insinuated" were "introduced to restrain alleged instabilities in the structure." LZA's final report, says FBY, "simply dismisses this phantom issue by confirming the 'cables were installed by the painting subcontractors to support scaffolding.'"

FBY says LZA's preliminary report "erroneously sought to place virtually exclusive blame for the collapse of the roof on those charged with its design." But in the final report, says FBY, "Dr. Thornton concluded that the construction manager, the space frame contractor, the inspecting engineers and, indeed, the city itself may have been contributors to the failure of the roof."

In addition, says FBY, "We believe that many areas of investigation and much physical evidence have either been overlooked or too lightly considered. . . ." The structural engineer says LZA's report does not consider "stresses introduced during fabrication and construction by the contractors and others. . . ."

As to the results of FBY's investigation, the firm says it has been advised not to disclose "the substance of our own expert team's efforts" due to probable litigation. That team includes: Wiss, Janney, Elstner & Associates, Inc., Chicago; Weidlinger Associates, New York City; Computerized Structural Design, Inc., Milwaukee; and Macchi Engineers, Hartford. FBY has also retained Lev Zetlin, of Zetlin-Argo Corp., New York City, who sold his interests in LZA a few years ago.

The Hartford City Council's own investigation committee agreed with LZA, but also criticized the city's Department of Licenses and Inspection for not arranging an independent design review of the roof. The council also faulted the construction manager, William L. Crow Construction Co. of New York, claiming the firm was "inadequately staffed to perform the structural inspection of the space truss" and that this "contributed directly to the apparent failure of Crow to detect the distortion of exterior top chord members."

Some months later, in the November 30, 1978, issue of ENR (p. 10), Joseph Goldbloom, manager of the specifications department for Parsons Brinkerhoff Quade & Douglas, disputed that last point, saying: "Technical inspection of construction should be performed by its designer, who is the one best qualified to assure that the materials and workmanship meet the contract requirements. Assigning this responsibility to a construction contractor is, in my opinion, asking for problems."

This was not to prove the last word, however. Another report refining theories about what went wrong was issued in June 1979 by an unexpected party— a consulting firm that had been a subcontractor to LZA, but had disagreed with some of the points in the LZA report. This new development was covered in ENR on June 14, 1979:

New Theory on Why Hartford Roof Fell

Torsional buckling of compression members rather than bowing of top truss chords may have brought on the collapse of the Hartford Civic Center Coliseum's 2.5-acre space truss roof in January, 1978. Even if designers had corrected the inadequate bracing of top chord members, blamed as the most significant cause of failure in an investigating consultant's final report, the roof most likely still would have fallen.

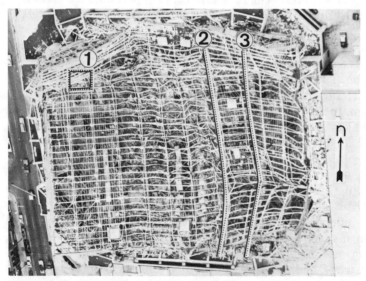

Figure 7-10 The origin of the Hartford Coliseum collapse was near the corner support pylon (1), says consultant Loomis and Loomis. Academic investigators put the start of the failure along the north-south line near the roof center (2). LZA's report placed the prime failure line further east (3). *(ENR.)*

These are the conclusions drawn by consultant Loomis and Loomis, Inc., Windsor, Conn., after performing its own technical analysis of the collapse.

Both the Loomis and LZA analyses blame design error on the part of Fraioli-Blum-Yesselman, Norfolk, Va., the structural consultant to architect Vincent Kling and Associates, Philadelphia. Both also agree the roof began failing the day it was raised in 1972.

But Loomis and Loomis's theories differ significantly from conclusions drawn by LZA and an academic task force working for the mayor of Hartford, not only in the mode of collapse but in the location of collapse origin. LZA said the collapse occurred when overstressed top chord members in the truss buckled laterally under compression loads, and said the collapse originated along a north-south line three bays in from the eastern edge of the roof [ENR, June 22, 1978, p. 36]. The academic task force agreed that inadequately braced top chord members buckled laterally and started the collapse, but put the collapse origin farther west, just east of the roof's center line.

Loomis and Loomis says that according to its own computer analysis, the collapse was more likely the result of torsional buckling of cruciform diagonal members under compression and that the collapse originated somewhere around a support pylon in the northwest corner of the roof.

FROM DAY OF COLLAPSE

Loomis and Loomis, along with consultant Buck and Buck, Hartford, was involved in the coliseum investigation from the day of the collapse, Robert L. Loomis says, first to check for damage in the other civic center buildings, and later as subcontractor to LZA. Although LZA did most of the analysis work, Loomis and Loomis became so involved in its own analysis that Robert Loomis, his brother Raymond and son Richard decided to go ahead with it, spending $20,000 of their own in man-hours and computer time. They were also concerned that torsional buckling wasn't being looked into thoroughly enough.

Noting the extensive amount of twisting in the cruciform members that made up most of the space truss, the Loomises suspected that that mode of failure could have been a significant collapse factor. Using torsional buckling theories from two sources—*Buckling Strength of Metal Structures,* by Frederich Bleich, and *Torsional Buckling of Compression Members,* by Edwin H. and Charles N. Gaylord—computer runs showed that 74 truss members should have buckled from the dead weight of the roof alone, and that the center of the truss should have been deflected about 11.7 in., very close to the 12 to 13-in. deflection measured during construction. That analysis also showed that top truss chords near the center of the roof and compression diagonals around the four support pylons were reaching their torsional buckling capacity.

The Loomises determined that with these chords and diagonals at torsional failure load, the roof would have been able to take about 12 to 15 psf of live load, again agreeing with field conditions. Estimates cited in the LZA report say the snow load on the roof the night it fell was somewhere between 14 and 19 psf.

The Loomises say torsional buckling is so uncommon a problem that it is not covered by building codes and only by a few textbooks, so most designers don't bother to look for it. With most types of compression members it is not a problem, but some types of cruciform sections are susceptible, they say. Most members of the Hartford truss consisted of four angle sections bolted together heel to heel to form cruciform sections.

FAILURE SEQUENCE

The Loomises theorize the collapse happened in this way:

- Even before any live load was added to the structure, east-west top chord members close to the center of the truss and compression diagonals around support pylons were near critical load.

- As snow and ice loaded the roof in the range of 12 to 15 psf, the compression diagonals around support pylons were loaded to their torsional buckling capacity. Those in the northwest corner of the roof buckled first, bringing the roof to an abrupt collapse just south of the northwest pylon. The resulting severe fold there twisted the cantilevered corner into an almost vertical position.

- As the northwest corner of the roof caved in, it took the rest of the roof along with it, throwing support bearings at the northwest, northeast and

Figure 7-11 Many structural steel plates were torn apart as the stress that had built up in the Hartford Coliseum roof was released. *(ENR.)*

southeast corners off their supports to the west, where they were later found. As both eastern bearings tore loose, the roof folded along a north-south line near the center. Since top chord members in this area were near their failure loads, "the center section virtually exploded as joints, chords, and beams unloaded their pent-up energy."

The Loomises give evidence that they feel shows that torsional buckling theory fits the physical evidence better than lateral buckling:

· Lateral buckling theories of the collapse puts the collapse origin in the top chords along a north-south axis. If the collapse occurred along a north-south line, say the Loomises, there should have been some symmetry in the damage occurring on both sides of that axis. There is no reason to expect the damage that actually resulted, with the northwest corner the most badly mangled and the southwest corner almost unscathed.

· If a failure occurred along a north-south line, there is no reason to expect that the three ejected bearings would have been thrown westward, or to expect the general westward drift of the roof observed during collapse investigations.

The Loomises emphasize that their theory of the collapse is not meant as a criticism of the others, but another angle that should be considered. The inadequate bracing cited in the other reports still would have to have been corrected to prevent collapse, they say.

REBUTTAL

Charles H. Thornton, president of LZA, refutes the methods the Loomises used to obtain their results. The texts they based their computer models on are design texts, he says, and as such are admittedly oversimplified and conservative. Thornton points out places in the text where the author's simplifications make his methods conservative by as much as a factor of three. That Loomis and Loomis were able to match actual loads and deflections with their model which has such gross inherent errors does not mean much, Thornton says.

There is also no verified visual evidence that 74 members were buckled under dead load, he says.

University of Connecticut civil engineering professor Howard Epstein, one of 10 academics who studied the collapse for the mayor of Hartford, also refutes the Loomises' results. While the method they used can be used for analysis as well as design, he says, they were misapplied in this case.

Both Thornton and Epstein say that the evidence of thrown support bearings and asymmetrical damage is inconclusive since once the collapse started it is nearly impossible to say how and in what sequence the roof failed.

Figure 7-12 Structural members at the corners of the Hartford Coliseum roof were pitched sharply upward. *(LZA.)*

Regardless of its merits, the Loomis theory will undoubtedly not be the last of present alternatives to the conclusions of the LZA report. A paper is expected within the next few weeks from consultant Hannskarl Bandel . . . that reportedly disagrees with both the LZA and Loomis theories.

That report was published in the July 19, 1979, issue of ENR:

Hartford Collapse Blamed on Weld

A newly completed investigation of the Hartford coliseum collapse concludes that what brought the roof down under its load of snow and ice was not a design fault but failure of a weld connecting the scoreboard to the roof. The conclusion conflicts with those of other structural investigators, who have generally agreed that a design error was at fault, although they have disagreed as to what that error was [ENR, June 24, 1979, p. 13].

Structural consultant Hannskarl Bandel undertook the independent investigation for the CNA Insurance Co., which insures the coliseum architect, Vincent Kling and Associates, Philadelphia.

In a terse, four-page report, Bandel says that estimates by other investigators of the roof's capability to support snow loads are "unrealistically lower than the actual capability." Bandel says rigid end connections of compression members and extra bracing from the roof deck made the space truss about 30% stronger than some have maintained.

Bandel says his investigation of the Jan. 13, 1978, collapse showed that although "three of the four scoreboard framing connection plates were badly bent, the fourth . . . was unscratched and its welding had separated neatly . . . I have concluded that, on the night of the collapse, the largest load ever experienced by the coliseum roof stretched the bottom chords to their longest length ever, and upon failure of the defective weld on the scoreboard framing, an explosive release of 150,000 lb created an impact force which triggered the collapse." Other weak welds also contributed to the collapse, the report contends.

Charles H. Thornton, president of Lev Zetlin Associates, New York City, which investigated the collapse for the City of Hartford, stands by the theory that a design error was responsible for the collapse. "If you look at the relative weight of the scoreboard compared to the weight of the roof, the thought that that caused the collapse doesn't seem to hold much water. . . . We did look at it," he says.

Figure 7-13   One consultant said that this clean weld split was the cause of the Hartford collapse; it may have released explosive force initiating the failure. *(An ENR photograph by J. Dimitri.)*

Bethlehem Steel declined comment. Some designers do, however, feel that despite the scoreboard's relatively small weight, its structural members might have stored enough energy in deformation to trigger the collapse, once the weld failed—if, indeed, the failure started at the weld at all.

Sixteen months after the collapse, reconstruction was started on an enlarged coliseum with 4000 more seats and a roof covering 30 percent greater area. The city wouldn't go along with another space frame, however. The new roof is a simple truss.

Before construction began, project architect Donald Eyberg said, "we intend to do a considerable amount of deflection monitoring during and after construction and before occupancy and maybe even during occupancy to test the adequacy of our designs." The roof was checked by three computer programs, STRESS, Control Data's EASE, and McDonnell Douglas's STRUDL.

Former President Ford wouldn't accept computer modeling for the space frame roof of the Gerald R. Ford museum in Grand Rapids, Michigan. The space frame had been chosen for it before the Hartford collapse. In September 1980, the roof was covered with wooden boxes lined with plastic. The boxes were then filled with water while deflection measurements were made at 20 points.

The unusual test cost about $40,000 and proved the design to be worthy of a president—deflection under 8 inches of water was only 1.25 inches, in a roof that covered more than 27,000 square feet.

Kemper Arena, 1979

Just as the wreckage was being cleared in Hartford for an enlarged civic center with a new roof, another modern arena's lid failed spectacularly. Like the Hartford roof, the Kemper roof was supported by a space frame. But the similarity

Figure 7-14   The Kemper Arena frame is on the outside, rather than the inside; the roof is suspended from the exterior trusses. *(Kemper-Crosby Arena.)*

Figure 7-15 This interior view of Kemper Arena before the collapse shows lightweight trusses supporting the roof deck. The Republican National Convention was held here in 1976. *(Kemper-Crosby Arena.)*

ends there. The Kemper Arena roof did not fail in the frame; the external frame remained in place, but the bolts connecting it to the roof deck suspended below the frame sheared away.

Two nights earlier, more than 13,000 people had filled the arena for a show. Mercifully, no one was inside when disaster struck. There was one interesting irony, however. The collapse occurred just hours after the American Institute of Architects opened its annual meeting across town. The opening ceremonies included an award for another building by the arena's designer, Helmut Jahn of the Chicago architect-engineer firm C. F. Murphy Associates. Jahn had received an honor award from AIA for the Kemper Arena itself in 1976.

Architects viewing the collapse tended to blame the bad weather—wind and heavy rains had added to the roof's load—or faulty structural engineering. "It doesn't help the public's respect for architects," said John Sheehy of the Architects Collaborative in the June 14, 1979, issue of ENR, "But the real question here is where does the responsibility lie. I don't have negative feelings about C. F. Murphy" (p. 12).

Quoted in the same issue, Thomas H. Teasdale, a newly elected AIA vice-president, said in reference to the two spectacular failures: "When you put two things like that back to back it's got to have tremendous impact.... There's no way we can ignore them" (p. 12).

AIA president Ehrman B. Mitchell, Jr., noted that the collapse could bring into question the design-build contractual arrangement under which the arena was built, with the designer technically working for the builder, J. E. Dunn Construction Co., of Kansas City.

The City of Kansas City, Missouri, wasted no time in hiring a consultant to investigate the collapse—James L. Stratta, a 58-year-old fellow of the American Society of Civil Engineers who had been active in failure investigations for the Earthquake Engineering Research Institute and other clients. He was quoted in an article in ENR's issue of June 14, 1979:

Failed Bolt Connections Bring Down Arena Roof

A series of bolted connections supporting the suspended roof system at Kansas City's 17,600-seat Kemper Arena failed last week, allowing more than two-thirds of the roof to rip away and crash 95 ft to the arena floor. The

Figure 7-16   This view of Kemper Arena from the air the day after the collapse shows the supporting struts to be in perfect shape. *(United Press International.)*

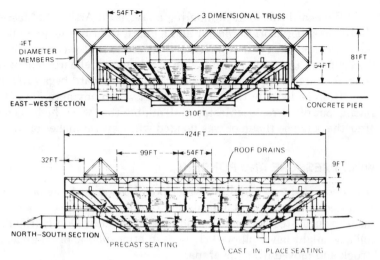

Figure 7-17 Details of the general structural plan of Kemper Arena. Three space trusses rise over the arena to carry its 424- by 310-foot roof. *(ENR.)*

collapse occurred during an intense wind and rainstorm and left twisted steel trusses, metal deck roofing and scoreboard and lighting equipment tangled in a heap of rubble.

The cause of the collapse is now under investigation by California engineer James L. Stratta, retained by city officials within two days of the failure, which occurred shortly after 7 p.m. on Monday, June 4. Stratta said he may conduct wind tunnel tests on models of the structure to determine whether it was subjected to unusually high wind loads exceeding even those created by 80-mph gusts that were recorded nearby.

Although stressing that it is too early to draw conclusions, he said after his initial inspection of the site that he found remains of bolted connections that formed the link between the suspended roof and three huge three-dimensional trusses that carry it, and that the bolts appear to have experienced tension failures.

"The bolts broke at the root of the thread," Stratta told ENR. "It appears to be a direct tension failure. They pulled apart," indicating a tremendous downward force on the roof. The cause of that force, whether differential wind pressure inside and outside the structure, ponding of rainwater, vibrations, structural defects or a combination of these, is not yet known.

Stunned by the disaster, officials quickly closed off the $23.2-million arena, where two nights earlier 13,200 people had attended a truck show and where in 1976 the Republican Party had held its national convention. One maintenance man and two guards were at the arena when the roof collapsed, but they were not injured.

"We heard this loud thundering noise," said Arthur LaMaster, the afternoon supervisor. LaMaster and a guard went to the arena floor to check the noise, and then saw two tremendous streams of water pouring down from the center of the roof on either side of a huge scoreboard. The water came down for three or four minutes before the scoreboard began to fall, he said.

"It broke loose in the center. I didn't watch anymore. I was too busy getting out of there," LaMaster said, adding that when he looked back inside after the collapse the floor was flooded with several inches of water.

WIND PRESSURE AND PONDING

Deflection of the roof and rainwater ponding was just one of the theories advanced in the rampant speculation that swept Kansas City last week. Other theories suggested by some, including city engineer Don Hurlbert, indicated collapse might have followed changes in atmospheric pressure as the storm struck and moved over the arena.

Project designer Helmut Jahn of Chicago architect-engineer C. F. Murphy Associates, said at the site, "It had to be something like a vibration, an oscillation. It was an absolute wind and rainstorm."

Stratta said the effect of wind pressure is also evident at curved overhanging corners of the structure where soffit panels and insulation were blown out in a splayed pattern. Further, he said, the light steel framing that supports the arena's metal panel cladding was bowed outward.

"The pressure of the wind is really quite evident," he said.

Crosby Kemper Memorial Arena was completed in 1974 under a $12.6-million design-build contract awarded to J. E. Dunn Construction Co., Kansas City, Mo. A dramatic, award-winning structure, its 424 X 310-ft enclosure is carried by three three-dimensional, or "space," trusses that rise up one side, cross over the top and continue down the other side. Comprised of tubular members up to 4 ft in diameter, these space trusses are 54 ft wide and stand in a row 99 ft apart. They bear on either side on pairs of conical concrete piers supported by pile foundations.

PRIMARY STRUCTURE SOUND

Suspended from and running perpendicular to these primary structural trusses are seven secondary trusses that together with long-span joists spanning between them carry the arena's metal deck roofing. It is part of this roof that collapsed, leaving the giant tubular trusses looming alone over a gaping hole.

The secondary, or roof, trusses vary in depth from 5 to 9 ft. The joists, spaced 9 ft c-c, span the 54 ft between the trusses except at the sides where the span is 45 ft. This roof system is suspended from the tubular trusses by 10-in.-dia pipe hangers bolted to the top chord of the secondary roof trusses.

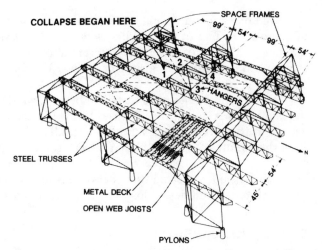

Figure 7-18 The failed area of the Kemper Arena roof (dotted lines) dropped from bolted connections. *(ENR.)*

Each tubular truss carries seven pairs of pipe hangers, so that each roof truss is picked up by six hangers. The roof trusses cantilever 30 ft at each end of the arena. Overall, the structural steel weight was 23.5 psf.

Steel mullions 18 ft c-c around the structure carry 3-in.-thick metal panel cladding. Inside, a combination of cast-in-place and precast concrete comprises an independent seating substructure.

The collapse left the tubular trusses, seating, exterior walls and outer perimeter of the roof in place. But in a nearly square area roughly at its symmetrical center, the roof ripped free of its bolted pipe hanger supports.

OVERDESIGN

The apparent tension failure of these bolts, according to Stratta, "may have been a secondary failure . . . the bolts may have failed because of something else." He cautioned against quick conclusions, saying, "We don't want to get into the DC-10 problem (a reference to the recent airline crash) where investigators said the bolt created the problem and then a week later said the problem created the sheared bolt.

According to drawings obtained last week, each hanger connection typically has four 1⅜-in. A490 friction bolts through steel plates, indicating each has a load-bearing capacity of 320.72 kips for the typically 4,131 sq ft area carried. Since even if a foot of water had ponded over that area it would weigh only 257.70 kips, the connection appears to be well over-designed for that type of live loading. However, actual dead loads that would also bear on specific connections could not be learned.

According to Myron Calkins, the city public works director whose office approved plans for the arena, wind tunnel tests on it showed that wind pressure at the face of the building is twice as great as it is 40 ft out from the building. Calkins attributed this differential in part to the arena's curved corners and its location in a river basin near the confluence of the Missouri and Kansas rivers.

Before wind baffles were installed, he said, wind pressure at the face of the building was so bad that it was difficult to open the doors, which are located at the curved corners. Baffles 8 ft tall and projecting out about 6 ft from the building face were placed at each set of corner doors to break the wind.

Still, he said, the structure "met or exceeded the codes," which for the arena call for a wind design load of 40 to 45 psf and a snow load of 25 psf.

STORM "NOT UNUSUAL"

Although the precise behavior of the storm at the arena site is not known, winds gusting up to 70 mph were recorded at Downtown Airport about 2 miles away and up to 80 mph at other locations nearby, according to Frederick P. Ostby, deputy director of the National Severe Storms Forecast Center in Kansas City.

A storm with winds of this severity occurs "about once a year" in Kansas City, he said. "It's not unusual to have gusts of 70 mph in a severe thunderstorm. It's certainly something one would want to engineer for." Ostby said further, "We're pretty confident there was no tornado involved. It's doubtful there was any kind of rotary action . . . there was no particular damage [to buildings] anywhere around the arena."

In about the first hour of the storm, beginning at about 6:30 P.M., some 3.5 in. of rain fell in the area of the arena, Ostby said. If 3.5 in. of rain had collected on the 131,440 sq ft roof, the total weight on the roof could have amounted to 2,392.2 kips (almost 1,200 tons). On a pitched roof, this weight would accumulate in a smaller area, intensifying weight per sq ft dramatically.

According to William H. Dunn, Jr., head of the general contracting company that built Kemper, the roof was designed to have eight "flow control design" drains. These include 4-in.-dia pipes leading from the roof into 5-in.-dia pipes and finally into 8-in. pipes that carry runout into storm sewers. The drains are centered on the roof between the middle and outer space trusses, four to a side. There is a 6-in. pitch to the roof from the outer edges toward the drains. A 5-in.-high coping rises around most of the roof perimeter. It is lower at the far edges.

None of the involved parties interviewed said they had any indication of whether one or more of the drains were clogged.

Dunn said he was considering hiring an independent engineer to analyze the collapse.

C. F. Murphy Associates has declined to discuss the arena's structural details.

UNLIKE HARTFORD

Although it involved space truss type members, the Kemper collapse bears little resemblance to the January, 1978, collapse of the Hartford Coliseum roof, according to Charles H. Thornton, president of Lev Zetlin Associates, the firm the City of Hartford retained to investigate the collapse. At Hartford the 9,500-seat arena's primary structural system—a 360 X 300-ft, self-supporting space frame that roofed it—failed, Thornton said. The failure at Kemper, however, occurred in the roof structure suspended from the primary support system.

According to Stratta, a visual inspection showed no structural failure of the primary trusses. These trusses have bolted connections of a custom design developed for ease of fabrication and erection. The steel subcontractor was KC Structural Steel, Kansas City.

Home of the Kansas City Kings basketball team, the arena is used in summer months mainly for concerts and circuses. "It's a facility we will be putting back into use . . . just as quickly as possible, the mayor said.

The final report confirmed that fatigue weakened the bolts that supported the roof as it hung from the space frame trusses—and also confirmed that the city would not be able to get the arena back into service as soon as it had planned. From the August 16, 1979, issue of ENR:

Rocking that Fatigued Bolts Felled Arena Roof

Fatigue weakening of high-strength bolts to as little as 20% of their original maximum load-carrying capacity precipitated the collapse last June of the roof of Kansas City, Mo.'s Kemper Arena.

In reaching this conclusion, investigating engineer James L. Stratta says he found that recurrent movement, or rocking, of structural members in the wind subjected the bolts to dynamic loading that they were never intended to carry. Over the building's five-year life, the motion fatigued and loosened the bolts, which were in tension, to the point that they failed under the shock of an intense wind and rainstorm, he says.

"They really had deteriorated," Stratta says of the bolts. "They apparently failed at between one-fourth and one-fifth of what they should have been able to carry. They were ready to go."

The roof of Crosby Kemper Memorial Arena, the $23.2-million, 17,600-seat hall where the Republican Party held its national convention in 1976, collapsed when empty on the evening of June 4. Its distinctive exoskeletal design of three huge tubular space frames carrying a suspended roof was acclaimed at the time of its opening in 1974.

But according to Stratta, the Menlo Park, Calif., structural engineer hired by Kansas City to determine why the roof fell and whether it could be repaired, the 42 bolted pipe hanger connections that linked space frames to the suspended roof were subjected to rocking and prying action that they were not designed to withstand.

"If it had not been for that connection, wind pressure would not have been a problem," he says. "Specifications for those bolts suggest they be used only in static conditions and not dynamic conditions. The problem was [repeated] relative motion."

FRAME REUSABLE

To the relief of the Kansas City officials, Stratta does say, however, that the primary structural space frame system is sound, and that the roof can be rebuilt simply by redesigning and replacing all of the pipe hanger connections. One redesign under consideration, he says, would consist of plates welded through the top flanges of the trusses that make up the suspended roof.

Each connection consists of a 10-in.-dia. pipe hanger welded to a 1-in.-thick steel base plate that, together with a [¼-in.] layer of Micarta (a resin-containing plastic material) and other steel plates, is bolted to the top flange of the secondary truss by four 1⅜-in. A490 bolts. With design loads of 26 psf for dead load and 25 psf for live load, each connection should have been able to carry 51 psf for its 4,130 sq. ft tributary area, or 210,000 lb. The capacity of the bolts was well above this at some 80,000 lb apiece, or 320 kps. And yet, according to Stratta, two of those bolts, in a connection near the center of the roof, failed under much less loading, initiating the collapse.

Figure 7-19 At Kemper, the plate ripped when the adjacent hanger broke. *(ENR.)*

Figure 7-20 This view of the truss after the failure of the roof at Kemper Arena shows the rods from which the roof was suspended. *(ENR.)*

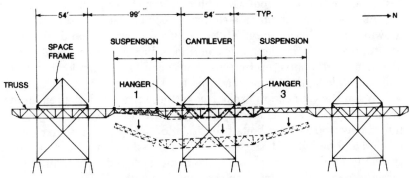

Figure 7-21 The center trusses at Kemper fell with a hingelike action, creating air pressure that bulged the walls outward. *(ENR.)*

Importantly, however, because the high-strength steel with which A490 bolts are made is brittle and has low ductility, their allowable loading in tension is good only under static conditions. Under dynamic loading, A490 bolts in tension deteriorate dramatically, as research cited by Stratta in his report to the city shows. Failure of the bolted pipe hanger connections was evident after the collapse [ENR, June 14, 1979, p. 10], but what caused the connections to fail was the subject of Stratta's two-month study.

In particular, Stratta refers to studies documented by John W. Fisher and John H. A. Struik in their 1974 book, *Guide to Design Criteria for Bolted and Riveted Joints*. In a graph appearing on p. 63, the researchers show that in tests, ⅞-in. A490 high-strength bolts, when tightened and loosened five times, failed at a load one-third of what they originally could have carried.

"This is typical of high-strength steels," says Stratta. "They do not like to be pushed back and forth."

In his report, Stratta says that wind loading on the exterior space frames "imposes a moment [in the] connection on top of the steel truss [causing] a rocking motion to this inverted tee [connection]. This rocking action creates increases and decreases in the loads that must be carried by the A490 bolts [which] cannot withstand dynamic loading or relaxation and reapplication of loading."

POOR BOLT INSTALLATION

Stratta points out further that the bolts were apparently too loose to begin with, that in erecting the connections the bolts were never tightened enough to bring all of the structural plates in the connection into full contact with each other. This, however, only aggravated or hastened the failure that was inevitable because of the tendency of the bolts to gradually deteriorate under dynamic loading. In short, as in the January, 1978, collapse of the Hartford Civic Center Coliseum roof, the failure began the day the roof went up.

As a result, two bolts in a center connection (see location No. 1 on drawing above) began to fail at "somewhere between 30 and 40 kips per bolt," Stratta told ENR. Under static conditions, he says, "they should have been able to carry 160 kips [each], plus or minus." The design load of each A490 bolt was 80 kips; the failure load was 160 kips.

When the connection broke free of these two bolts, the remaining two bolts had to take all the load. Bending occurred when the base plates were forced downward as the bolts tried to hold, finally failing under the combined tension and bending. Because of the lack of redundancy in the framing system used, the failure of one hanger will cause redistribution of the load directly to the other hanger on the space frame holding the same truss, causing it to fail also. In other words, when one hanger fails, the load, instead of spreading, goes directly to the other hanger. Thus, the hanger at location No. 3 ripped in half. Seconds before, the hanger at location No. 2 had failed under the additional load imposed on it because of the failure of hanger No. 1. The sequence brought down the center sections of the middle trusses, ripping joists, metal decking, and a 15,800-lb scoreboard down with them. Crashing 95 ft to the arena floor, the hinge-like, outward motion of the falling trusses created air pressure so great that it blew out corner soffit panels and caused the arena's metal panel walls to bulge out as much as 14 in.

The collapse began at location No. 1 in part because this area at the center of the roof is where the dynamic loading, or the relative motion between the space frames and roof (through the hangers), would have been greatest, Stratta says. But proof that it began with two northern-most bolts in this connection is provided by examining markings in the Micarta plate, showing it was not in full contact with other plates in the assembly, he says.

"Due to those Micarta plate markings . . . we can pretty much make the firm statement that it was that way originally," says Stratta, adding that the

Figure 7-22 The roof construction of Kemper Arena was remarkably light for its span, because the exterior members carried the weight. *(ENR File.)*

reason the Micarta plate was included is not clear as it would absorb about 40% of each bolt's torque load and tend to render each bolt more subject to dynamic loading.

The two north bolts of the hanger at location No. 1 "did not have proper contact and over a period of five years of water loading and unloading, plus dynamic wind loading and unloading, these bolts became fatigued and failed," he concludes.

TORQUE TEST

In erecting the connections, steel subcontractor KC Structural Steel, working under subcontract to design-build general contractor J. E. Dunn Construction Co., both Kansas City, Mo., used the "turn of the nut" method rather than a calibrated wrench to torque the bolts, according to Stratta. Although it is an accepted industry procedure, use of this method may have left some of the connections loose, with insufficient torquing to bring all plates into full contact, he says.

In fact, when two other connections were removed from the arena for testing at the University of Missouri at Columbia, a torque load of only 400 to 750 ft-lb was necessary to loosen the bolts, says Stratta. If installed properly, a torque load of up to 2,800 ft-lb would have been necessary to loosen them.

Although his analysis points to design deficiencies, Stratta declines to say that the collapse resulted from design error on the part of the arena's architect-engineer, C. F. Murphy Associates, Chicago.

The collapse includes together, he says, "a materials problem, an installation problem and a design problem."

Both Stratta and city engineer Donald D. Hurlbert point out that the limitations of A490 bolts in tension under dynamic loading are indicated in the American Institute of Steel Construction's handbook *(Manual for Steel Construction)* only by a footnote. And although, as Stratta shows, it was documented by Fisher and Struik, the arena was designed a year before that work was published.

The structural engineer at C. F. Murphy who handled Kemper, Sherwin P. Asrow, now of S. P. Asrow Associates, Chicago, was not available for comment concerning use of the bolts under dynamic loading or of the Micarta plate, according to his office. However, Asrow told ENR shortly after the collapse, "It just doesn't seem possible. Everything that could have been considered was considered."

Asrow suggested then also that the collapse might have stemmed from "very bizarre wind loading." But, according to Stratta, not only does weather service data confirm that no such loading could have occurred, but the roof could have collapsed eventually in a lesser storm because of deterioration of the bolts. Also, while some ponding of rainwater occurred before the collapse, its maximum possible weight as a static load was far below what the bolts could carry, Stratta says. He adds also that none of the roof drains was clogged.

A490 AMBIGUITY

In an interview with ENR, Stratta noted that although the design of the roof's pipe hanger connection was unsuited in this case, a certain amount of ambiguity concerning uses of A490 bolts also contributed.

"Structural engineers that I have talked to have been amazed to hear about this tremendous drop, the fantastic drop these bolts have in tensile strength after being jerked around. . . . I don't think enough emphasis is

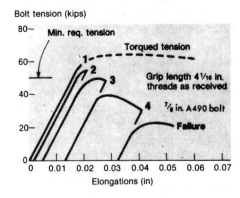

Bolt tension (kips)

Figure 7-23 This graph, originally published in 1974, shows that A490 bolts in tension weaken under dynamic loading. *(American Society for Testing and Materials.)*

Figure 7-24   This test assembly has loose bolts. *(ENR.)*

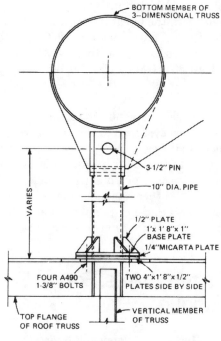

BOTTOM MEMBER OF
3–DIMENSIONAL TRUSS

3-1/2" PIN

10" DIA. PIPE

1/2" PLATE
1' x 1' 8" x 1"
BASE PLATE

1/4" MICARTA PLATE

VARIES

FOUR A490
1-3/8" BOLTS

TWO 4" x 1' 8" x 1/2"
PLATES SIDE BY SIDE

VERTICAL MEMBER
OF TRUSS

TOP FLANGE
OF ROOF TRUSS

TYP. HANGER DETAIL

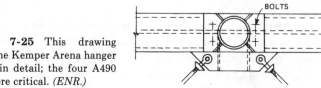

BOLTS

Figure 7-25 This drawing shows the Kemper Arena hanger system in detail; the four A490 bolts were critical. *(ENR.)*

placed by AISC on this type of steel." Stratta noted further that many designers do not tend to consider wind load a dynamic load, and thus might mistakenly use the bolts in a dangerous application.

"Anybody who has these bolts now where they are used in pure tension only with a possibility of dynamic loading introduced by wind should seriously consider replacing some and testing [the rest] for possible fatigue," he says.

City attorney Aaron Wilson says that suits against various parties involved in design and construction of the arena are "under serious consideration," but that the "first order of business" is to "review the Stratta report and make plans to rebuild the arena."

Originally, the city had hoped to have the facility back in use in time for a horse and livestock show held there annually in early November. Now, there is no certain date for reopening, according to Kansas City Mayor Richard L. Berkley.

Already, the city expects to lose more than $500,000 as a result of the collapse. Although it recently won a dispute over its insurance claim on the arena with the Great American Insurance Co., which had first refused to pay, the city still must spend its $250,000 deductible amount. Revenues lost from canceled concerts, sporting events and relocation of the horse show will cost at least $300,000 by Nov. 30, officials say.

Those comments about high-strength bolts being misused raised more than a few eyebrows in the engineering world. When the bolts had been introduced in the early 1950s, they had been billed as extremely well suited for joints subject to fatigue from dynamic loading. In the 1960s, the AISC and other groups warned of potential problems, but the warnings never matched the splash of earlier announcements. This article from the August 2, 1951, ENR issue was typical of the early praise for the bolts. *It is printed in full to give the exact, original flavor. Its advice should not be heeded today.*

Bolted Joints Found Better under Fatigue

T. R. Higgins   *Director of Engineering, American Institute of Steel Construction, New York, New York*

Laboratory tests and field experience have demonstrated the superiority and economy of structural steel connections made with high-tensile steel bolts. In comparison with ordinary riveted and bolted connections, these bolts are particularly advantageous for structures subjected to widely fluctuating dynamic loading.

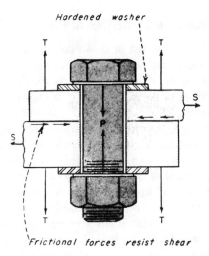

Hardened washer

Frictional forces resist shear

Figure 7-26 The original caption for this drawing from the 1951 ENR article by T. R. Higgins read, "Connection made with high-strength bolt resists shear through friction on contact surfaces. Plates do not bear on bolt." *(ENR File.)*

Placed in holes of larger diameter than that of the bolt shanks, the bolts clamp the components of a joint together under high pressure. This enables the joint to resist shear through friction at the contact surfaces.

Design and fabrication of such connections is covered in a specification, "Assembly of Structural Joints Using High-Tensile Steel Bolts," which was adopted early this year by the Research Council on Riveted and Bolted Structural Joints.

FIELD EXPERIENCE

Test installations of high-strength bolts under severe conditions have been under observation for more than three years by the research staff of the Association of American Railways. One installation is in the riveted ore bridge of the Pennsylvania Dock Co. at Ashtabula, Ohio. Under the dynamic loading to which this structure is subjected, rivets often work loose, creating an expensive maintenance problem. To alleviate this nuisance, high-strength bolts were substituted for rivets in some trolley-stringer and bracing connections. These joints now are entering their fourth season of bridge operation without need for maintenance.

Similar behavior was observed for this type of connection in other ore bridges and in railway bridges.

High-strength bolts also may be used in structures in which fatigue resistance is unimportant, when the bolts show greater economy. An example is a 21-story building now being erected for the Mayo Clinic, Rochester, Minn., for which field riveting was ruled out because of the noise. After a comparative cost study, the contractor elected to use high-strength bolts instead of field welding.

BOLTS MAY BE CHEAPER

While the cost of these bolts is much more than that of corresponding plain, undriven rivets, savings in the cost of installation often more than make up the difference. This is particularly true where a relatively small number of rivets or bolts, perhaps quite widely scattered throughout a structure, must be installed at some remote site where costs incident to assembly and use of riveting equipment would mount rapidly. However, even under conditions favorable to riveting, high-strength bolts may be competitive.

One of the first buildings to be assembled with such bolts is a 14-story hospital at the University of Illinois. The bolts were late in arriving. Rather than hold up the job, the contractor used standard erection bolts, which he later had to replace with high-strength bolts. The final cost was $6 to $7 per ton more than if the structure had been riveted, including the higher cost of the bolts. If the bolts had been available as erection bolts, however, there would have been a net saving in time.

There are numerous other cases of friction connections being selected after cost comparison with other types. For one 8-story building, such action showed a net saving of 11% for the erection, based largely on the following factors:

1. Elimination of temporary erection bolts.
2. Elimination of transportation of riveting equipment.

Figure 7-27 Test samples pictured in Higgins' 1951 ENR article. They show that such joints always fail in fatigue, away from the bolted "net section" area. *(ENR File.)*

3. Two-man crews to bolt up after erection.

4. Normal production per crew of 400 bolts per day.

The bolts were installed with air impact wrenches and were spot checked with a torque wrench. Even when impact wrenches are used, the noise is much less than that due to rivet guns; hand-torquing, of course, is noiseless.

TESTS FAVOR BOLTS

Nearly a quarter of a million dollars was spent on research on riveted and bolted joints, the first tangible result being high-tensile bolt connections. This investigation of friction joints was carried out as Project IV of the Research Council for Riveted and Bolted Structural Joints. Like the Welding Research Council, this [four-year-old] organization, upon the recommendation of the American Society of Civil Engineers, is sponsored by and functions under the Engineering Foundation. Other contributing sponsors include the Association of American Railways, American Institute of Steel Construction, American Iron and Steel Institute, Illinois Division of Highways, Industrial Fasteners Institute and Public Roads Administration.

In addition to the financial support of these groups, substantial contributions of intrinsic value have been made by Purdue University, Northwestern University, and the Universities of Illinois and Washington—in whose laboratories the experimental programs are being carried out.

A notable feature of Project IV, distinguishing the council's work from that of earlier investigators, is the extensive use of fatigue testing. Prior to the formation of the council, exploratory work performed on special machines had already indicated that fatigue testing is often the most effective approach for evaluating structural connections of different design. The testing machines, which were developed during the last decade, are large enough to perform fatigue tests on full-scale joints containing more than four common-size rivets or bolts.

Tests made by the machines show that if joints of different geometry but with nearly the same behavior under static loading are subjected to many cycles of loading, the endurance limit of some may be larger than that of others. This is of great significance in the design of structures to sustain widely fluctuating loading. Some parts of most bridges and all parts of some industrial equipment come within this category.

Tests also show that high-strength bolts, substituted for an equal number of rivets of the same diameter, exhibit superior behavior under fatigue loading:

Fastener	Fatigue strength—psi 2,000,000 c, full reversal
Cold-driven rivets	14,700
Hot-driven rivets	15,820
High-strength bolts	17,200

These fatigue strengths are typical; actually, the difference in stress at failure under a specified number of cycles may be small or large, depending on the design of the joint.

These test results led to field installations to verify the conclusion that high-strength bolts require less maintenance than rivets in structures subject to cyclic loading. As mentioned previously, field experience favored the bolts. The next step was preparation of a specification.

NO SLIP IN JOINTS

Salient points covered in the specification adopted by the council last January are these:

1. High-strength bolts may be substituted for an equal number of American Society for Testing Materials A141 rivets of the same nominal diameter. Though shear is actually resisted through friction at contact surfaces, the bolts are allowed the same "shear" stress as the rivets.
2. Construction should conform, in general, to existing codes for riveted structures.
3. When the bolts are used, holes may have the customary ⅟₁₆-in. clearance associated with ordinary riveted work and with unfinished bolts.

Tests show that any slip that occurs is far too small to bring the sides of the holes into bearing against the bolts. Obviously, this favors the bolts by eliminating bending stresses from them. For all practical purposes, they sustain only a static tension stress, producing no fatigue.

Appreciable slip will not take place in joints having contact surfaces with ordinary mill scale and clamped with high-strength bolts torqued nearly to the proof load, unless the applied loading on the joint is at least a third greater than the design loading. For the plates to bear against the bolts, applied loading must be at least twice the design loading.

BOLT CHARACTERISTICS

The specification requires that bolts meet the requirements of ASTM Tentative Specification for Quenched and Tempered Steel Bolts, A325 (yield point 74,000 to 90,000 psi and tensile strength 105,000 to 125,000 psi, depending on bolt diameter). They must also conform to American Standards Association's standard for Regular Semi-finished, Hexagonal, Head Bolts, ASA B18.2, with respect to threads and other dimensions. However, the radius of the fillet under the bolt head must be at least ⅟₃₂ in. for bolts larger than ⅝-in. dia and at least ³⁄₆₄ in. for bolts larger than 1-in. dia.

At least one carburized or quenched and tempered washer must be installed under each nut and bolt head.

HIGH CLAMPING FORCE

All nuts must be tightened to reproduce a bolt tension of not less than 90% of the elastic proof load of the bolt. It is interesting to note that the clamping force recommended is about three times that which would be required to completely compress ordinary spring washers. It is little wonder, then, that in no case to date, either in the laboratory with as many as 8,000,000 cycles of loading, or in closely watched field installations, has one single nut shown the slightest tendency to back off. Yet, no particular measures have been taken to restrain the nuts.

The specification further requires that a certain proportion of the bolts be checked for tension by a procedure of loosening and retightening under controlled conditions. The exact number of bolts is to be determined in advance by the engineer in charge, but for the present, between 5 and 10% is the recommended proportion.

Joints are to be spot checked regardless of the method of applying the torque to the bolts. According to one school of thought, equipment and techniques should be developed that would record or control the amount of torque. According to another group, calibrated devices would be made available at the construction site so that each iron worker can practice until he acquires the feel for the predetermined torque. With new work employing high-strength bolts now pending, there should be ample opportunity in the next few months to see which is the more practical approach to this problem, which intimately involves the human equation.

In the meantime, research is progressing toward improving the specification and increasing the economy of the friction joint.

The point was further explored in ENR in a series of letters and replies beginning on December 6, 1979:

Kemper Q&A

I was quite interested in your article on failure of the Kemper Arena roof [ENR, Aug. 16, p. 10]. However, the investigation [by James L. Stratta] left questions unanswered:

- Since the specifications of the Research Council on Riveted and Bolted Structural Joints (RCRBSJ) have required for some time that "bolted steel parts shall not be separated by gaskets . . ." why was there a Micarta pad ¼-in. thick used in the critical joints?
- Could the pad have been subject to creep under the 1⅜ in. bolts with their high tensions (installed by turn-of-the-nut) and thus over the last five

years allowed all of those bolts to suffer a considerable loss in internal tension or "prestress"?

It has been known for many years that well fit-up steel joints have small bolt tension relaxation with time; joints subject to fatigue loadings and prying may have somewhat more relaxation. But a joint containing a pad which might creep could have much higher losses in bolt tension. Thus, a residual torque of 400 to 750 ft-lb to loosen the bolts might not be unexpected.

Since there was no mention that these large 1⅜ in. A-490 bolts were torqued and then retorqued, the diagram you reproduced (from the Fisher and Struik study) seems of little consequence. Similar behaviors exist for A-325 bolts and A-490 bolts when installed, removed and reinstalled. That is why the RCRBSJ specifies "bolts shall not be reused." A more appropriate figure might be that enclosed from the February, 1963, *ASCE Structural Division Journal* ST 1, Paper 3411, p. 63. This shows the dramatic decrease in fatigue strength under tensile loadings with reductions in bolt pre-load. The diagram was for A-325 bolts, but a similar pattern can be anticipated for A-490 bolts.

Further discussion of the topic of bolt tension and prying was presented in *ASCE Structural Division Journal* ST 2, Paper 10373, February, 1974, pp. 351–372. And there may be other data sources on this subject which I have not mentioned.

Specifications on A-490 bolts limited their use in direct tension to static loads only. Later versions of these specs have prescribed reductions in design load (stress) for fatigue, depending on the number of cycles and amount of prying action expected. Of course, those specifications assume well fit-up joints, no gaskets, and properly tightened fasteners.

Eugene Chesson, Jr.   *Professor of Civil Engineering,*
University of Delaware,
Newark, Delaware

I am in receipt of your letter to *Engineering News-Record.* You are absolutely correct in all of your statements, and I hope that the following answers your comments to your satisfaction.

I will reply in the order in which you brought up the questions:

First, the purpose of the Micarta pad was to function as an insulator to prevent condensation from occurring on the trusses and creating a dripping situation. I agree that such a gasket in torque situations should not be used.

Second, the amount of torquing absorbed by the Micarta plate is approximately 40% of the total torque load, if one considers the thickness of materials and moduli of elasticities of the compressed layers.

Finally the report states: "Granted we do not have repeated installation but due to the circumstances and location of this detail, we had static loading during rainstorms and dynamic loading during wind storms. This occurred over an extended period resulting in similar characteristics." The main purpose and objective of including the graph from Fisher and Struik's book was to point out the extreme sensitivity of brittle steels to dynamic loading conditions.

Engineering News-Record carried a fine overall presentation of the report, but not necessarily an in-depth study. Further, rightfully or wrongfully, I did not want to appear hypercritical of all of the design problems, as has sometimes been done in the past by other investigators of failures. The primary function of the report was to find the cause of the failure. The redesign will eliminate the failure modes.

James L. Stratta   *Menlo Park, California*

And from the ENR issue of December 13, 1979:

"Turn-of-the-Nut" Criticized

The article concerning James L. Stratta's investigation of the Kemper Arena roof collapse [ENR, Aug. 16, 1979, p. 10] questioned the suitability of using A490 bolts in tension under dynamic loading conditions. He indicated the AISC Manual of Steel Construction, in a footnote, recommends the use of A490 bolts in tension for static loads only. The "Specification for Structural Joints Using ASTM A325 and A490 Bolts" approved by the Research Council on Riveted and Bolted Structural Joints dated Sept. 1, 1966, is the basis for the footnote. The commentary to the 1976 specification explains that research on dynamic tension loading for A490 bolts was incomplete, therefore, static loads only were recommended.

The February, 1976, specification allows both A325 and A490 bolts to be used in dynamic tension, subject to stress reductions depending on prying force and number of loading cycles. The 1976 commentary states, "Properly tightened A325 and A490 bolts are not adversely affected by repeated application of the recommended working tensile stress, provided the fitting material is sufficiently stiff, so that the prying force is a relatively small part of the applied tension." Specification allowable stresses are such that even for connections with high prying forces and subject to over 500,000 cycles (275 times per day for five years), the reduced stress shall be 50% of that allowable for static load conditions or 40 kips for each $1\frac{3}{8}''$ 0 bolts. Even if the bolts were subjected to 275 stress cycles a day for five years (doubtful), the bolts should have carried more than the failure load reported by Stratta if tightened properly.

Research quoted in the "Guide to Design Criteria for Bolted and Riveted

Joints" by Fisher and Struik, p. 267, listed a ¾″ 0 A490 bolted connection loaded dynamically in tension from zero to full load 3,000,000 times without failure and one with 20% prying force carried 592,000 cycles before failure.

The key to the problem is the phrase "properly tightened." Very little increase in actual bolt tension occurs in a properly tightened connection when subjected to tensile loads until the applied tension exceeds the fastener tension in the tightened bolt (see p. 257–260 in the "Guide" by Fisher & Struik). The bolts in the arena connection were probably not "properly tightened" due to the use of the "turn-of-the-nut method" in combination with the compressible Micarta plate. Thus, the bolts were subject to fatigue loadings from internal tension stresses they were unable to carry.

Stratta's conclusions appear sound; however, the article places doubt upon the use of A490 bolts in dynamic tension. The true cause of failure might well be improperly tightened connections rather than an inherent weakness of A490 bolts in dynamic tension. The article also quotes Stratta as castigating AISC for ambiguity concerning the use of these bolts. The 1976 specification for A325 and A490 bolts, endorsed by AISC, should remove the ambiguity.

Harold E. Costley   *Consulting Structural Engineer*
Torrence, Dreelin, Farthing & Buford, Inc.
Richmond, Virginia

The Kemper Arena reopened in March 1980, with a redesigned roof hanging from steel bars. The slope of the roof was increased to improve runoff, and the eight drains were increased to twenty. The four bolts, two steel plates, and Micarta pad in the original design are replaced with a single A36 steel bar for each hanger. The bars are 2¼ by 6½ inches in cross section, and are each about 10½ feet long. They run from a steel pin connection at the base of the space truss down through the secondary truss to its bottom chord, where it is welded to the truss diagonals.

These new, much more ductile connections are designed by Stratta and the Kansas City engineering firm of Bob D. Campbell & Co. The reconstruction was performed by the original builders, J. E. Dunn Construction and KC Structural Steel.

Six months later—in August 1980—Kansas City began fact-finding for a possible lawsuit against C. F. Murphy Associates and the structural steel firm. The suit alleges almost $9 million in damages—$6 million for the reconstruction and the remainder for loss of business. The city's position is that the design was negligent and that construction errors hastened the arena's demise, mainly due to improperly tightened bolts.

The suit is still pending as this was written.

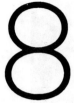

Details, Details, Details

Complex designs require complex, sophisticated ways of checking to make sure that details are carefully laid out by the designer and carefully followed by builders. No section of the book shows this requirement more clearly than this chapter. The five failures discussed here range from the almost trivial—$25,000 damage and no lives lost— to the tragic (113 lives lost at the Kansas City Hyatt). Three of the five involve failures during construction, a particularly common occurrence. All were particularly galling to the public and to the technical professionals involved, not only because of the money, but also because the problems looked so simple once they were exposed.

Nevertheless, they were not all that simple after all. Each involved new designs or new technology, pushing architects, engineers, and contractors into uncharted waters—waters where lack of communication and lack of respect for natural forces proved disastrous.

Considering all the new construction methods and new designs that have been introduced in the past generation, it is amazing how few such problems there really are.

Boston Rockers, 1952

After World War II, highway and bridge designers began experimenting with devices to replace the expensive, hard-to-maintain roller nests used in expansion joints. Steel rockers soon became a favorite choice. But this seemingly simple solution turned out to have some quirks that had not been fully anticipated by the profession

On May 22, 1952, a modest elevated highway span in Boston collapsed while under construction, due to faulty rocker design and placement. Although the mess caused a massive traffic jam, no lives were lost. The lessons of the "Boston Rockers" might never have been broadcast to the profession if it had not been for the controversial nature of the highway's design (elevated expressways were rare in urban areas at the time), the detailed reporting of *Engineering News-Record,* and some thoughtful follow-up letters to the editor.

Figure 8-1 In this view of a highway span in Boston, rocker assemblies are visible at the top of the bent, still supporting a short span that stayed intact when the longer span fell. *(ENR File.)*

The 96-foot-long span that collapsed was made up of seventeen I-beam steel stringers. The end that fell was supported by a three-column steel bent. The supporting bent was "freestanding," in that the adjacent span it supported was also resting on rockers. Concreting of this shorter adjacent span had been completed on the day of the collapse.

The rockers had been designed to stand approximately vertical under typical full dead load on the spans, and at a mean temperature of 60°F. For erection purposes, therefore, they were inclined away from each other and toward the centers of their respective spans. After the failure, the freestanding bent was found to be inclined away from the collapsed span with two anchor bolts sheared off and two others deformed.

Although damage would total only about $25,000, no fewer than five investigations were set off in the politically charged atmosphere of Boston. ENR reported on their conclusions in the June 19, 1952, issue:

Bridge Collapse Traced to Rockers

Five consulting engineering firms blamed the May 22 collapse of the 96-ft span of the new Sullivan Square overpass in the Charlestown section of Boston, Mass., on the rocker support of the beams. State Department of Public Works officials concurred in this finding.

Four engineering firms expressed the opinion that the Lehigh Structural

Steel Co., of New York City, to which the steel erection had been subcontracted, had placed rocker supports improperly under the ends of the 17 steel girders in this span, causing a thrust on the three-column steel bent. This, the consultants claimed, led eventually to the rocker-supported girder ends falling to the ground.

William F. Callahan, commissioner of the State Department of Public Works, reported the possibility that disturbances of extraneous origin might have caused the rockers to tip excessively and drop the beams.

D. B. Steinman, consulting engineer of New York City, retained by Lehigh, said there was "no faulty fabrication of steelwork or faulty erection or construction of the structure." He attributed the failure to "inherent instability" of the bent on which the rockers were supported, in conjunction with the rocker detail. In other words, if the rockers had been installed vertically to begin with, only a slight deviation from the vertical, brought about by any cause whatsoever, would cause them to continue to tip, exerting larger and larger forces on the bent, until it deflected sufficiently to drop the beam ends.

BENT NOT SUPPORTED AT TOP

The overpass consists of steel bents, spaced at varying distances, founded on spread footings and capped with deep steel girders, on which the longitudinal floorbeams rest. The beams, in turn, carry a four-lane concrete pavement.

Figure 8-2 This overpass failure in Boston was attributed to horizontal thrusts caused by excessive tipping of the rocker supports under the beams. *(ENR File.)*

At one end of the 96-ft span, each beam is riveted to a bent; at the other end, the beam is supported on a rocker designed to permit expansion and contraction of the deck and floorbeams. The bent that supported the rocker end of the span that collapsed also carried the rocker end of the adjoining span. Thus, this particular bent was "free-standing."

Prior to the accident, all the steel had been erected. Concrete had not yet been placed on the span that failed but had been cast on the other span carried by the free-standing bent.

No work was under way on the span at the time of the collapse, 8:15 pm on May 22. But during the day, in the vicinity, piles had been driven, steel had been riveted on the adjacent elevated railroad structure, which also had carried trains that set up vibrations, and a heavy volume of automobile and truck traffic had passed by.

Commissioner Callahan reported that these disturbances might "have caused a movement of the rockers from the position in which they were left by the steel erection company to a more angular position, creating a great horizontal thrust. . . .

ROCKERS WERE TIPPED

After the accident, engineers of the State Department of Public Works investigated. The department also engaged Charles T. Main, Inc., consulting engineers, of Boston, to report on the adequacy of the design and the cause of the failure. Thomas Worcester, Inc., who designed the structure and supervised construction, requested the engineering firms of Fay, Spofford & Thorndike and Hayden, Harding & Buchanan—all of Boston—also to determine independently the cause of the structure's failure.

All subsequently agreed that the steel erection subcontractor had installed the rockers at the end of the span that collapsed at a relatively large angle with the vertical, to allow for anticipated temperature changes and pavement loads. This created "a great horizontal thrust which resulted in the collapse of the rockers and the beams resting thereon."

WHAT ONE ENGINEER FOUND

Typical of the opinions expressed by the consultants is that of R. A. Moncrieff, of Charles T. Main:

> Temperature change was not . . . a major cause of failure. We are therefore led to believe that the rockers were placed out of line, inclined from a vertical position, at the time of erection.
> This belief is confirmed by an examination of the rockers after the collapse. After steel erection, the rockers were painted, and since that portion inside the receiving groove at the top end of the rocker was not easy to reach, the paint stopped on a horizontal line which was not at a right angle with the axis of the rocker and therefore provided visual evidence that the rockers were not placed

in a vertical position at the time of erection, nor corrected for proper position prior to painting.

Twenty-one of the rockers were examined, and the deviation from a vertical position varied up to 18 deg, with an average of about 10 deg. In other words, they were 'tipped' toward the center of the span, and when the weight of the bridge beams was placed on them, the rockers "kicked" against the top of the bent in varying amounts, depending on the weight supported and the inclination of the rockers.

The "kick" of the rockers induced a thrust at the top of the supporting bent and initiated a series of changes which resulted in the collapse of the floorbeams. These changes were briefly:

1. The thrust at the top of the beam induced a bending moment in the columns of the bent.
2. The bending moment resulted in the deflection of the bent outward.
3. The deflection of the bent increased the inclination of the rocker.
4. With the increased inclination of the rocker, the thrust at the top increased and the series of changes (1, 2 and 3 above) was repeated. Finally the increasing thrust and the bending columns in the bent reached a point where the elastic limit of the steel bolts holding the bent upright was exceeded; the bolts stretched, the bent tipped outward, and the ends of the beams, having no further support, fell to the ground.

STEEL MAN'S VIEW

Leo I. Bruce, general sales manager of Lehigh, ridiculed the use of paint lines to measure the angle at which the rockers had been left by the erector.

A hard-working southpaw painter . . . would make a very different angle with his brush than a right-handed easy-going workman. But even more important, the rockers of the adjacent span, which were among the group that were examined by the consultants, had been painted before those rockers were plumbed. After the failure, there was no way of associating the rockers with their beams.

Actually, the steel could not have been erected if the rockers had been left at the angles claimed. . . . The beams would have been too long to fit between the supports.

CONTRACTOR HELD LIABLE

William F. Callahan, commissioner of the Department of Public Works, reported the engineers' findings to the state Senate on June 9. He added:

It is therefore my intent to enforce the conditions of our contract with the general contractor (M. DeMatteo Construction Co., of Qunicy, Mass.) for the furnishing of a satisfactory and acceptable completed project, at no added expense to the Commonwealth.

Cost of repairing the damage is estimated to be $25,000.

After the investigation reports were published, numerous ENR readers asked for more details about the rockers themselves. Typical among them was a letter from Truman P. Young of Hanly & Young, Cincinnati. In the July 24, 1952, issue he wrote:

The blame is laid on the tipping of the rockers.

Since these are commonly designed with the center of the rocker surface at the center of the pin, the rocker is merely a segment of a wheel, and its reaction (neglecting friction) is normal to the bearing plate. Tipped rockers might result from either a discrepancy in span length or careless setting of a shoe where no provision for an alignment pin or tooth is made. In either case, no lateral load is applied to the column unless the shoe is tipped so far as to bear on the edge of the turned face.

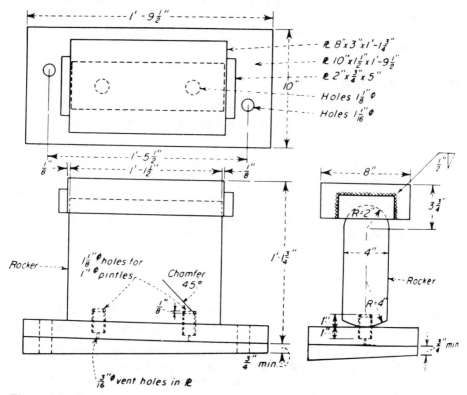

Figure 8-3 Detail of rocker support for the collapsed beams in Boston. Notice the restraining pins (lower left drawing) and the different radii in the rocker itself (right). *(ENR.)*

In response, ENR obtained drawings of the rocker detail, showing that the two ends were not segments of the same wheel; the top had a radius of only 2 inches, while the bottom had a radius of 4 inches. "From this fact," ENR said, "the conclusion may be drawn that when tipped away from the vertical, the rocker exerts a horizontal thrust against its support" (July 24, 1952).

This stimulated a 1200-word letter from Ray M. Boynton, then an associate (and later to become a partner) in D. B. Steinman's firm. It was published on August 7, 1952:

The conflicting reports of consultants, miscellaneous suggestions and assumptions by some of them, and the interjection of conditions extraneous to the fundamental problem, so becloud the issue that the basic problem of the stability of the bent, in combination with the type of rockers used, should be reexamined and the critical weakness reemphasized.

UNLIKELY EXPLANATIONS

The following suggestions and assumptions are largely extraneous or minor aggravations to the basic stability problem involved and may be eliminated:

1. The suggestion that a freestanding bent is unstable is untenable. Many such bents, properly designed and loaded, have been constructed and have given satisfactory service.

2. The suggestion that expansion rockers, without a common center of curvature for top and bottom bearing surfaces, were the sole cause of the accident is equally untenable. While this type of rocker should generally be avoided, it may be properly used when the structure carried and the support against which it reacts are sufficiently rigid to effectively overcome the thrusts produced.

3. The suggestion that vibrations from adjacent elevated electric trains, and even heavy highway traffic, caused the failure has little merit. The stability of a highway bridge should not be jeopardized by such relatively insignificant forces.

4. Citing the failure of the anchor bolts at the base of the bent as the cause of failure is merely jumping to a conclusion. Such failure may be merely an after-effect, or a minor contributory effect, as distinguished from the initial or basic cause of failure. In the present case, failure of the bent would have ensued even if the anchorage had been infinitely strong.

5. The suggestion that both sets of rockers tipped in the same direction so that their thrusts no longer counterbalanced each other gives the unwarranted and optimistic impression that stability might have been obtained by proper counterbalancing of thrusts. In the present case, suggestion of

such balance is academic, since the reactions of adjacent spans were unequal. Also, the lengths of adjoining connected girders subject to temperature effects were unequal, being 148 ft on one side and 46 ft on the other. These unequal lengths produce correspondingly unequal tilts of the two sets of rockers, such motion amounting to about ¾ in. and ¼ in., respectively, for a temperature change of 60 F. Only a highly mechanized arrangement could be expected to balance such unequal loads, unequal expansion movements and resulting thrusts.

6. The assumption that the rockers were improperly installed, causing a great horizontal thrust, merely diverts attention from the basic cause of the collapse. If the rockers were erected within reasonable limits of accuracy, as one must assume and as reports indicate, then such tilt, if any, would merely augment the critical inherent weakness of the system. Temperature effect would soon produce the same, similar or perhaps more severe tilt of the rockers, even if they had been erected in perfect position originally.

ROCKER-BENT DETAIL ANALYZED

What is of more significance is the basic stability problem of the combination of a pin-ended column (or rocker with two centers of curvature, which may closely approximate such a column) and a flexible free-standing column, which supports the pin-ended column on the free end.

Figure 8-4 shows schematically a basic structural system [along with] the forces developed and the resulting deformations caused by a (even an infinitely small) relative displacement d of the two hinges. Such a movement necessarily results from the effect of temperature. The equilibrium of the upper column and the deflection of the lower column may be expressed in two equations, respectively as follows:

$$d = \frac{Hh}{P} \text{ and } d = \frac{HL^3}{3EI}$$

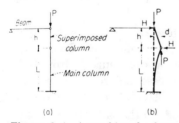

(a)   (b)

Figure 8-4 A two-hinged column supported on a freestanding column may have to carry a horizontal force as well as a vertical one. *(ENR.)*

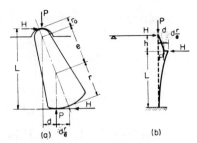

Figure 8-5 A rocker with different centers of curvature for top and bottom surfaces may act like the hinged column in Figure 8-4. *(ENR.)*

The critical load P_c for the system may be obtained from this equation:

$$P_c = \frac{3EIh}{L^3}$$

It should be noted that the critical load is independent of the initial displacement, d, and hence infinitely small displacement initiates a rapidly progressing failure.

SIMILAR CASES OF INSTABILITY

This represents a condition in which initial displacement with resulting thrust causes a deflection, which in turn augments the initial displacement and resulting thrust causing still greater deflection. The phenomenon is similar to the aerodynamic instability of structures, where, after some initiating force has started oscillations, such oscillations of the structure itself repeatedly augment the preceding aerodynamic forces, cycle after cycle.

This stability problem is also analogous to that commonly encountered and unquestionably sometimes with disaster, when a falsework bent is supported upon a group of flexible (unbraced or inadequately braced) piles. The bent corresponds to the upper column and the piles to the lower column in the preceding basic problem. Usually the bent is substantially pin-ended, and relative displacement of its two ends may result from the effect of temperature, erection stresses, improper erection or other conditions. The resulting thrust on flexible piles may cause collapse. I am convinced that several major disasters have resulted from such a system of falsework.

CRITICAL LOAD COMPUTED

Rockers with more than one center of rotation may introduce many variables. One typical type is shown in [Figure 8-5]. The travel of the rocker, development of forces and the resulting deflection caused by any relative displacement of the bearing surfaces of the rocker are shown in [Figure 8-5]. Omitting negligible influences such as the very small eccentricity of application of the load on the lower column, the derivation of the critical load is as follows:

$$d = \frac{Hh}{P} \quad \text{and} \quad d\left[1 + \frac{r}{e}\right] = \frac{HL}{3EI}$$

$$P_c = \frac{3EIh}{L^3}\left[1 + \frac{r}{e}\right]$$

The formula shows that the critical load increases with decreasing value of e, becoming infinite when e equals zero as in the case of a round roller. This indicates that in such a case even an infinite vertical load would develop no thrust, and the Euler load would become the governing critical load.

The punishing and catastrophic effect of the thrust of the rockers may be comprehended by the following comparison of the critical loads for a column of the bent in the Sullivan Square viaduct that failed:

The Euler load for the column is approximately 1,980,000 lb.

The critical load for the column loaded with rockers of the type installed, assuming perfect design, fabrication and construction in all other features, and no development of thrust by other influences such as temperature change, was only 204,000 lb, or only about 10% of the Euler load. Therefore, the actual critical load from this column as constructed and acted upon by various and ever present outside influences would be considerably less.

A flexible column and a rocker of the type used are each individually sound structural units. To use them in combination, without extreme precautions, only invites disaster.

The last word was provided by Lewis E. Moore, a Boston consulting engineer, who noted the foolishness of using different radii on the top and bottom of such rockers, and who also complained about the way rockers were typically attached to the tops of bents. His letter was published in ENR on October 2, 1952:

Rocker Should Be Wheel

In the reader comment columns (ENR, Aug. 7, 1952 p. 7) there was quite an extensive letter concerning rockers and their reactions. It seems that certain considerations which were not mentioned enter into the picture.

A rocker is intended to be a better device for allowing expansion than the old-fashioned roller nest. It must meet certain requirements:

1. It must keep the roadway surface at the same elevation for all positions of the rocker.
2. It must avoid caus ng bending stresses in the supports.

To accomplish these results the rocker must, in principle, be a wheel supporting the movable end of the structure upon its axle. Because of the small amount of movement the complete wheel is not needed so a sector is used.

For a wheel to be a success its periphery must have the same center as its axle. Then the load upon the surface on which the periphery bears will always be vertically under the center of the axle, and there will be no horizontal thrust upon the support.

A rocker in which the curvatures of the top and bottom surfaces are not concentric will, as indicated in the comment referred to, exert a decided thrust upon the support. A further consideration is that when the angle d/L becomes equal to the angle of friction of dry steel on steel (about ¼) the rocker will snap out of place suddenly and drop the span. It may be restrained by the dowel often used, which is inserted loosely in holes in the rocker and the support. Incidentally, it is hard to conceive of a cruder mechanical device than this dowel. Further, the hole in the support will fill with water and rust the dowel away in not too many years.

If the reader will consider carefully the rocker illustrated in the August 7 issue, he will see that the distance L will be different for every different angle that the rocker assumes with the vertical. This means that the roadway of the bridge will be at constantly differing elevations as the span expands or contracts. If the adjoining span is fixed there will be a bump at every position but one of the rockers.

Why not adopt the sound principle that a rocker, to serve its purpose properly, must be a sector of a wheel; not merely a piece of metal with ends rounded to suit the designer's fancy?

Texas Tower No. 4, 1961

Texas Tower No. 4 was a pioneer. At the time of its collapse with twenty-eight lives lost, on January 15, 1961, no framed structure had ever been placed in exposed water as deep as 185 feet. What's more, other offshore platforms had been placed in relatively sheltered areas of the Gulf of Mexico, but never in the waters of the North Atlantic.The mission of the Texas towers, however, unlike that of the Gulf platforms, was not to hunt for oil, sulfur, or natural gas. Instead, the towers served as artificial islands for Air Force radar protecting the northeastern United States from Soviet attack. Five towers had been planned in all, although only three were constructed. Tower No. 1 had been planned for the Maine coast, but the Air Force decided it was not needed, and it was never built.

Tower No. 2, the first to be completed, was set into the rocky shoals of the Georges Bank, in 56 feet of water about 160 miles southeast of Boston. Tower

No. 3 also rested on solid rock in about 80 feet of water southeast of Nantucket Island. Tower No. 5 was to have been located in 130 feet of water, some 200 miles east of Boston on Browns Bank. It was like the first tower, however, in that plans for it were scrapped before construction began.

Tower No. 4 was located 70 miles east of Ambrose Light, off the New Jersey coast. It was in the deepest water, and also was most exposed to hurricanes and other storms. Although it had been designed to withstand waves 35 feet high, it had been battered by seas running twice that high. What's more, investigations showed that it had not been designed properly in the first place, and that damage suffered while it was being moved into place had reduced its ability to withstand the North Atlantic.

The failure of Texas Tower No. 4 helped designers build better structures—platforms for exploiting North Sea oil. More recently, the oil companies have turned again to the North Atlantic, where an exploratory platform failed off the coast of Newfoundland in February 1982 with a loss of eighty-four lives. A comparison of media coverage of the two events shows far more surprise and outrage over the 1961 incident, though. Looking back, it is clear that the engineers who designed Texas Tower No. 4, and their client, the United States Air Force, had been rather cocky about their handiwork. The public, in turn, was not used to having structures fail so spectacularly.

Here's how ENR first reported the Texas Tower tragedy, in its issue of January 19, 1961:

Repairs Too Late

Hurricane-weakened tower destroyed by wind, seas.

A half-million-dollar contract for repairs to Texas Tower No. 4—a radar island in the Atlantic, 80 miles southeast of New York City—came too late to save the tower from being destroyed by wind and high seas on January 15.

The tower was badly damaged last September by Hurricane Donna. And in October a contract for repairs to tower legs, crossbracing and decks was awarded to J. Rich Steers. . . .

But as late as January 6, a survey made by the contractor showed the legs of the tower to be structurally deficient.

The tower, which was erected by the Steers-Knudsen combine in 1957 at a cost of $20 million, was designed by Moran, Proctor, Mueser-Rutledge of New York to withstand lateral forces exerted by the simultaneous action of 35-ft waves and 125-mph winds. In spite of this, both Donna and the more recent storm proved too much for the structure.

An appeal for help was heard early Sunday afternoon in a report that said the tower was swaying violently. At 7:33 p.m. a Navy ship six miles

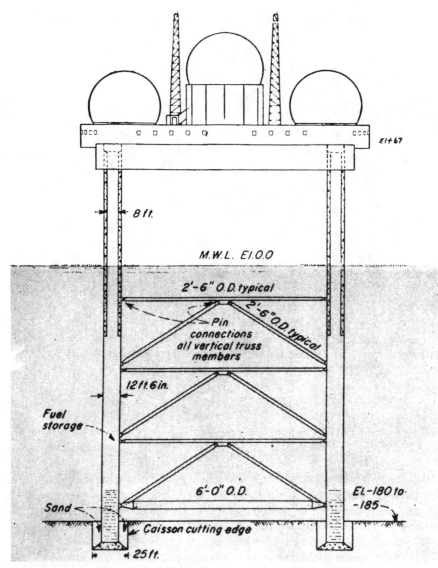

Figure 8-6 The legs of Texas Tower No. 4 were braced by trusses at four levels. They rested on sand 25 feet beneath the ocean bottom and were partially concreted. *(U.S. Navy.)*

distant lost both radio and radar contact with the tower, and it is believed that the tower collapsed at that time.

Air Force officials were unable the next day to explain what had happened to the tower or to say why the deck, which was floated into place during initial construction, should have sunk, even if the legs buckled.

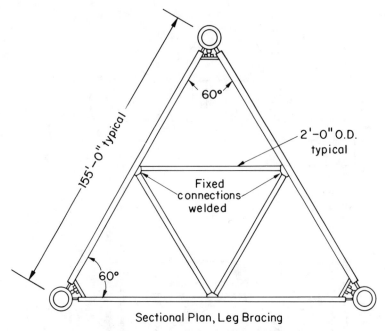

Sectional Plan, Leg Bracing

Figure 8-7   This plan shows how the horizontal leg braces of Texas Tower No. 4 were themselves braced at their midpoints. The braces were welded at the mid-points and pinned at the legs. *(U.S. Navy.)*

Despite its numerical designation, Tower No. 4 is actually the third and last offshore radar station erected under a 1954 plan for five such towers. It was also erected in the deepest water—185 ft. Its legs, heavily cross-braced, were 288 ft long and 12 ft 6 in. in diameter. Tower No. 2, set on Georges Bank, 160 miles east of Cape Cod, is in 56 ft of water and is supported by 10-ft-dia legs, which are unbraced. Tower No. 3 is on Nantucket Shoals, 80 miles southeast of Nantucket Island. It is supported in 80 ft of water by 14-ft 6-in.-dia legs, also unbraced. Tower No. 2, first of the units to be erected, was badly damaged by storms during its construction in 1955, but neither of the first two units has been badly hit since.

The demolished tower and its two counterparts were quite similar in design, except for the differences in leg bracing made necessary by the deeper water at the site of unit No. 4. However, there is one important difference in the sites. Tower No. 4 was founded in sand; the other two towers are seated on rock.

The Air Force moved quickly to find out what went wrong—and to squelch publication of all details of the inquiry, on national security grounds—even though the towers' designs had not been classified in the first place. On January

16, the day after the collapse, the Air Force put Major General James C. Jensen in charge of the investigation into what went wrong. Jensen immediately ordered that the other two towers be inspected.

The key questions: Why had the tower not been adequately designed to withstand the high waves and winds common to the North Atlantic, and why had not the Air Force totally abandoned it after storm damage the previous fall? Instead, the Air Force had reduced the tower's crew from a normal seventy-five to only fourteen—although twice that number were aboard when the tower failed.

It took about 2 weeks for public pressure to pry details loose from the Air Force investigation. On February 2, 1961, ENR reported the story this way:

Broken Lower Brace Probable Key to Tower Collapse

A broken lower brace may have doomed the radar tower, which collapsed into the Atlantic 80 miles southeast of New York on January 15 with the loss of 28 lives. This broken brace, not discovered until January 6, was the most serious of a series of mishaps that began in September, 1958—within a year after the tower was completed.

The nature and extent of the damage is supplied in a log of the repair operations undertaken, which has been released by the Air Force after a period of secrecy extending back to the time of Hurricane Donna last fall (ENR, Jan. 19, p. 23, and Jan. 26, p. 28). Most of the damage to Texas Tower No. 4, as it was called, occurred in the west face bracing between the two of its three legs which supported the bulk of the weight of the radar equipment.

The first mishap, in September, 1958, at the time of Hurricane Daisy, was the failure of bolts in the collars that connected the top panel of diagonal bracing to the tower legs in this west face. These collars and the top panel of bracing had been installed under water after the tower had been placed. They replaced a set of pin-connected bracing, like that in the lower panels, which unexpectedly had to be removed in order to float in the superstructure deck prior to its raising to the top of the tower legs. In removing the bracing it had been dropped and lost, so a new set had to be fabricated. Collar connections were adopted as easier to make under water than the original pin connections. Because of high seas, replacement of the collar bolts was delayed, and the work was not completed until May, 1959.

Between August and November 1959 the tower personnel noticed excessive movement in the platform, and a project was approved to tighten the bolts and do other repairs that inspection might reveal as necessary. One of these inspections, on Feb. 8, 1960, showed that the pins connecting the diagonal braces to the horizontal struts at the minus 25 and minus 75 levels on the west side of the tower were worn to such an extent that a maximum movement of 1 in. was possible. The collar connections were found to be tight.

To stiffen the tower against sway from these loose pins, it was decided to install a panel of X-bracing between the legs above the water line. This was accomplished by August, 1960, and before Hurricane Donna struck the tower with winds that were clocked at over 100 mph and with waves that carried away a maintenance bridge 65 ft above the normal level of the sea. This bridge, which was necessary to service the divers, could not be replaced until November.

The known damage from Hurricane Donna was further loosening of the connections of the diagonal bracing to the horizontal struts at the minus 25 and minus 75 levels, and wear and loosening of the connections in the new X-bracing above the water level.

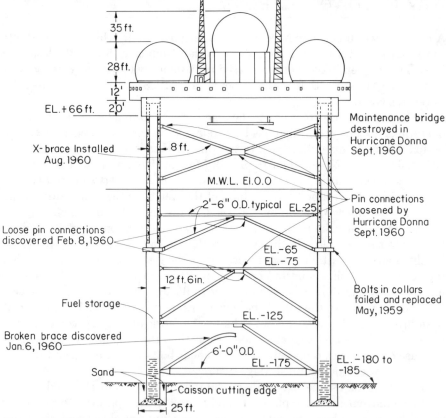

Figure 8-8 The repair log on Texas Tower No. 4 revealed 2 years of loose connection trouble in this west-facing framing, culminating in discovery of a broken member in the lowest panel of the bracing between the columns. (*ENR notes on a U.S. Navy drawing.*)

An inspection deeper down was not made until Jan. 6, 1961, when the broken brace at the minus 175-ft level was discovered. The decision was then made to evacuate the tower by February 1, and to postpone repair operations until better weather next May. A vicious winter storm struck the tower on January 15, and it collapsed.

These are believed to be the basic facts that an Air Force investigating board has to go on in determining the cause and manner of failure. Involved also in the investigation are the Navy's Bureau of Yards & Docks, which was the Air Force's contracting agency for construction of the tower; Moran, Proctor, Mueser & Rutledge, New York, and Anderson-Nichols & Co., Boston, the consulting engineers; and J. Rich Steers, Inc., New York and Morrison-Knudsen Co., Boise, Idaho, the contractors. The tower was fabricated by Continental Copper and Steel Industries, South Portland, Me.

By April, the Air Force had completed its investigation and had begun court martial proceedings against the officers who were responsible for leaving men on the platform after it was weakened in the fall 1960 hurricane season. The Air Force report did not contain many details about the actual design of the tower itself, however.

Instead, the Senate Armed Services Committee's Preparedness Subcommittee, chaired by Senator John Stennis (Democrat, Mississippi) was left to hold hearings on the tower's design and construction. The hearings were noteworthy for their frank testimony—particularly on the part of Leon DeLong, whose firm had built many offshore platforms, and who had bid unsuccessfully on the Texas Tower project. ENR covered the testimony in its issues of May 11 and May 18, 1961:

DeLong Sounds Off on Texas Tower No. 4

Senate investigators of the tragic offshore radar [station's] collapse in January heard [in May 1961] from a man whose name is almost synonymous with Texas towers.

Leon B. DeLong told the Preparedness Subcommittee of the Senate Armed Services Committee that he would have designed and built the ill-fated Texas Tower No. 4 differently. His Delong Corp. has put up half a hundred offshore towers in waters as deep at 210 ft during the past 20 years.

He would like to have built Texas Tower No. 4, too. He bid on it, in fact, in a joint venture with Raymond International. But they based their bid on an alternate design and method of construction. And they bid too high.

Mr. DeLong testified in response to a subpoena as the committee tried to

Figure 8-9   L. B. DeLong (below, left) shows how he would have built Texas Tower No. 4. An actual model of the tower is shown above.

establish whether design or construction slip-ups contributed to the eventual failure of the structure. And in his testimony he differed sharply with Capt. John J. Albers (CEC) USN who had testified the day before. Captain Albers was contract officer during design and the taking of bids but was not responsible during construction.

Captain Albers agreed with Mr. DeLong that the eventual collapse was traceable to breaks in two column connections of braces during construction [ENR, Feb. 2, 1961, p. 23]. And he conceded that something should have been done to remedy the defects. But he called the design and construction basically sound, called the collapse "more an act of God than of man."

Both men also made clear that they rate Moran, Proctor, Meuser & Rutledge, consultants on the tower with Anderson-Nichols & Co., high among the world's experts on marine structures.

But Mr. DeLong said he wishes he could have got them and the Navy's Bureau of Yards and Docks (which built the tower for the Air Force) to strengthen their design and change their construction method.

Ironically, the DeLong man who carried the fight for changes in Texas Tower No. 4 was unable to appear at the committee hearings. He was Mr. DeLong's chief engineer, George E. Suderow. Mr. Suderow died April 29, 1961.

In restating his firm's objections to the chosen design last week, Mr. DeLong criticized the pinned connections it had below water level. He insisted, as he said Mr. Suderow had insisted, that the structure should have been fully welded below water level to assure rigidity.

In recalling DeLong objections to the adopted erection methods, he said they exposed tower members to unpredictable stresses and hazards that could have been avoided by following tested techniques such as those his firm has been using since 1949.

Major hazards were present at two stages of the erection, he claimed. The first occurred in the method (never used before) of floating the three-legged substructure assembly in a horizontal position to the site and there upending it to stand in vertical position on the ocean floor. Tilting the assembled structure imposed stresses that could not be calculated, the witness observed.

The DeLong scheme would have floated the assembly in vertical position, as ... [was] on all ... other towers, including Texas Tower No. 2, off Nantucket.

Further great danger of damage came when the 4,000-ton permanent platform of Texas Tower No. 4 floated into position between the legs to be jacked to its final elevation, 67-ft. above the sea. Positioning and raising a close-fitting platform of this size and weight in the open ocean, before the three long legs had been embedded in the dense sand bottom, induced additional unknown stresses in the underwater framing, the witness said. It exposed the 12½-ft-dia tower legs to possible jumping by wave action on the heavy floating platform, said Mr. DeLong.

His plan had proposed a temporary 400-ton working platform on the tower until its legs were permanently embedded in the ocean floor.

Testimony presented last week shed new light on the damage during construction, damage to which collapse of the hurricane-ravaged tower has been traced.

In the tower's fabrication ashore, the top tier of three tiers of K-bracing between the tower legs was left off so that the tower's permanent platform could be floated in and jacked up. This meant less bracing for the structure, and increased stresses as it was tipped up at sea, Mr. DeLong noted. It also caused the initial tower trouble. Here's how:

Diagonals of the upper tier of K-bracing were pin connected to each tower leg ashore and lashed against the legs for the tow to the site, 85 miles off New Jersey. It was a stormy five-day voyage and lashing loosened on two of the diagonal braces. Swinging free, they damaged their connections to the tower leg. Substitute connections had to be installed under water at the site, after the tower was standing erect.

Both major witnesses at last week's hearings—Mr. DeLong and Captain Albers—agreed that Texas Tower No. 4 could not have been restored to its original designed strength at the site after the damage during towing had occurred. It would have had to go back to its home harbor for repair.

Probers Hear Tower Failure Was . . .
A Case of Too Little Too Late

The congressional probe in the collapse of Texas Tower No. 4 last week uncovered design conflicts, construction disagreements, and performance variances. The testimony left the Senate Preparedness Subcommittee of the Armed Services Committee in a quandary as to just how well the project was conceived and carried out.

Because of impending court-martial proceedings by the Air Force over the loss of the 28 lives in the disaster, the Senate committee is steering clear of this issue. But it wants to know just why the tower collapsed and who is to blame. The senators also want to know how safe Towers No. 2 and 3 are.

One immediate point bothering the senators is why the firm that designed the towers for the Navy—Moran, Proctor, Meuser & Rutledge—has been given a $200,000 contract to evaluate the present strength of the two towers that remain. Some congressmen don't think it quite proper that the firm should evaluate its own work.

When the hearings drew to a close, there was little doubt that Tower No. 4 was plagued with construction problems from its very beginning.

Leon B. DeLong told the committee that he did not consider the design of the tower adequate for its purpose, nor did he like the construction method used [EN, May 11, 1961, p. 18].

E. G. Rau, vice president and chief engineer for J. Rich Steers, Inc., told the senators that his company did not approve of the method used to tow the partially assembled tower to its construction site, as laid down by the designers. The tower suffered damage during its tow to the site, and repairs had to be made there. Other witnesses testified that they did not believe the towing damage could have been adequately repaired at the on-site location.

Alan Crockett, of Marine Contractors of Boston, told the senators that his firm had made three underwater surveys of the tower. The first was made in November 1958 when it was found that underwater collars on the structure had worked loose. In June 1959, the second underwater inspection showed that T-bolts fastened to the collars had corrected this situation.

In February 1960, Marine Contractors made its third inspection and found considerable deterioration in the pin connections of the underwater bracing to the tower legs.

Moran, Proctor, Meuser & Rutledge then called for emergency repairs to be made on the tower before the August hurricane season started. These were accomplished early in August 1960. In September, however, Hurricane Donna caused further severe damage.

After the Donna damage, all further underwater inspections were made by J. Rich Steers, Inc. Following the damage done by Donna, the senators were told that the Air Force wanted an evaluation made on the remaining strength of the tower. Steers hired Moran, Proctor, Meuser & Rutledge to handle the job on a subcontract basis. The two companies agreed verbally on the matter on Oct. 3, 1960. But it was not until Jan. 4, 1961, that a final confirmation was made. And the study was never accomplished, the committee was told.

On Jan. 7, 1961, an underwater inspection made by Steers revealed that one diagonal on the lowest underwater panel was broken. At this point, Steers was supposed to install wire cable bracings to substitute for two upper panels on the two shoreward legs of the tower. This was never done, however. When the lower diagonal was found to be broken Steers said it could not perform all repairs to the tower under its present contract. On January 12, contract negotiations were started to work out the cost difference. The tower failed January [15]. . . .

Theodore M. Kuss of Moran, Proctor, Meuser & Rutledge told the Senate committee that, even if the cable bracings had been installed, the tower would only have been about 55% as strong as its original designed strength.

Further complicating the picture, Given A. Brewer of Brewer Engineering Laboratories, Inc., Marion, Mass., reported that his firm had conducted motion studies on the tower between the fall of 1958 and the winter of 1959.

It was found, Mr. Brewer testified, that there was a plus or minus 3-in. sideways movement of the tower platform and a twisting, rotational motion of ⅒ of a degree. This was far above the design tolerance, but the bracings were not preventing the movement.

Mr. Brewer also said it was found the tower had a design frequency of 37 cycles per minute, but was actually achieving only 19. This, too, pointed to improper functioning of the bracings.

While the tower was designed to withstand 125 mph winds with 35-ft-high breaking waves, Mr. Brewer's study showed that waves only 10 to 12 ft high caused more tower motion than waves in the 30-ft-high range. Reason: The smaller waves have about a 155-ft wave length, allowing for two waves to break simultaneously on different sections of the tower; the bigger waves have longer wave lengths so that the tower is only battered by one wave at a time.

The hearings concluded with testimony from Theodore M. Kuss and Philip C. Rutledge of the firm that had designed the tower in the first place, Moran, Proctor, Meuser & Rutledge. Kuss testified that he had told the Air Force on April 1, 1960, that "the loose pin connections" were a "very serious matter . . . which will tend to worsen at an increasing rate with time."

In that report, made to the Air Force nearly 10 months before the disaster, Kuss explained, "the looseness induces impact stresses in the pins and pin plates, which are greater than for the non-dynamic design assumptions and will become increasingly greater as the play in the joint enlarges."

As his testimony made clear, the Air Force had realized by August 1960 that extra bracing added to the above-water section of the tower's legs had not been adequate to stop the movement in the pinned joints below.

Designer Rutledge refused to blame the construction contractor for the problems, however. "With some minor deficiencies," he admitted, "the tower was constructed properly and in accordance with specifications."

The final Senate report found plenty of blame to go around—for the designers, the contractors, and the Navy, which had acted as construction agent for the Air Force. Clearly, testimony showed that the tower should have been towed back to shore for repairs when damage occurred during the original erection process in 1956. But that was near the height of the Cold War, and the tower was needed to help protect the country.

Senator Stennis summed up his reactions this way: "It is an amazing series of events to me. From the time it was upended [during the erection process] until it fell there was never a time, except at short intervals, when . . . the tower came up to anything like its intended design strength."

In the wake of the failure of Texas Tower No. 4, designers increasingly turned to welded connections rather than pinned structures. Designers also learned to be ever vigilant for incipient failures in offshore structures. In March

1981, an $11 million British study was issued, pointing to potential problems in welded, large-diameter tubular steel joints used in many North Sea rigs. The joints fail under the combined stress of continuous movement, caused by wind and waves, while immersed in corrosive ocean water.

British and Norwegian investigators claim that this type of failure caused the collapse of a giant North Sea rig being used as an offshore hotel, the Alexander L. Kielland, in March 1980. The accident cost 123 lives.

Alaska Pipeline Weld Frauds, 1975

By July 1975, the 798-mile-long Alaska Pipeline was about half finished and 5 miles of pipe was being placed every week. Two sections of 40-foot-long pipe would first be welded together into 80-foot lengths with automated equipment. The joined lengths would then be transported to the pipeline site and welded in the field into the rest of the line.

Alyeska Pipeline Service Co., which built the line, had mandated stringent quality-control procedures for the field welds. After all, the company reasoned, the line was extremely visible politically and thus was vulnerable to public pressure. And harsh climate along with remote working sites would make errors inevitable—and hard to check.

According to plans, each weld would be checked visually by trained inspectors. After passing visual inspection, each weld would be radiographed to detect hidden flaws—incomplete penetration and fusion, slag inclusion, gas pockets, burn-through of the pipe, hollow weld beads, and hidden cracks.

The x-ray source, an electric-powered device that rode inside the pipe with its own gasoline generator, would automatically find each weld and x-ray it from the inside. Film was held in place on the outside of each weld in a beltlike, flexible cassette. The machine would then travel to the next field weld and so on, doing about thirty welds along a half-mile stretch at a time. Each exposure would take about 2 minutes.

For areas of the pipeline where the automated machine couldn't go, or for partial inspection of repaired welds, a gamma-ray machine was used to photograph as much as a fourth of the circumference of a joint at one time. To make sure that radiographs were taken of every joint, and that no duplicates were passed in for good joints, metal tags uniquely identifying each welded joint were attached to the pipe and x-rayed along with each weld.

As an added check, Alyeska used a computer to examine each radiograph along four dimensions that would uniquely identify the joint, just as a fingerprint identifies a person.

Bad welds would be repaired if, for example, radiographs showed only a small gas bubble just beneath the surface of a weld. Then the weld material

Figure 8-10   Technicians of a radiographic crew place a film cassette—a flexible belt in which the film is shielded from light—around a girth weld joining two sections of the Alaska Pipeline. The belt contains two strips of film, each about 6 feet long, to cover the circumference of the 48-inch pipe. The film was processed in a mobile darkroom in the field. *(Alyeska.)*

Figure 8-11   This gasoline-powered x-ray crawler stopped automatically along the inside of the Alaska Pipeline to radiograph the welds. *(ENR File.)*

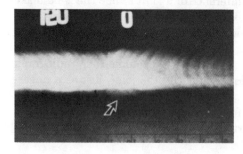

Figure 8-12   This radiograph of a weld in the Alaska Pipeline reveals porosity in the weld (arrow). *(Alyeska.)*

would be ground away and a new bead laid into place. If a crack was found, however, the whole weld would have to be replaced at a cost of about $2000. Most of the defects Alyeska was finding in July 1975 were small gas pockets at the bottom of welds, where the welders were completing their work.

If a defective weld failed a second time, after repair, the whole section of pipe would have to be cut away and replaced; federal regulations do not allow more than one repair attempt, for fear the pipe itself may become too brittle after heating and reheating for the welding process.

The whole inspection process seemed immune to frauds—that is, until Peter Kelley, a former employee of one of the companies hired to do the inspections, claimed he was fired for refusing to falsify radiographs.

Kelley sued his former employer, Ketchbow Industries, a subsidiary of Houston Gamma Ray. In the suit, he testified he had personally falsified thirty radiographs. One problem was that the x-ray equipment often broke down. As a result, the x-ray teams had trouble keeping up with the welders. The welders, in turn, were under immense pressure to keep up the construction pace. Indeed, the five construction organizations—each working on a separate section of the pipeline—were set into competition with one another. Alyeska's project manager, Frank C. Moolin, Jr., was intolerant of delays on the $7.5 billion project, and frequently fired managers who couldn't keep up the pace on various line segments. Moolin was also intolerant of poor quality, however, and had Kelley accompany Alyeska investigators to check the welds he had claimed had fake radiographs. When the inspection turned up welding defects, Moolin ordered reinspection of the radiographs of all 30,800 field welds made up to that time.

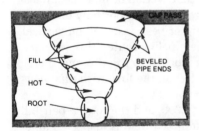

Figure 8-13 Here is how a pipeline field girth weld is made:

Mainline welding in the field is generally a two-step operation, involving front-end, or initial welding, crews and firing-line, or finishing, teams.

With the 80-foot-long, double-jointed pipe section suspended from a sideboom crawler tractor, a four-man front-end welding crew clamps it to the previously welded section with an internal alignment device. After the beveled pipe ends are spaced and the joint area preheated, the welders, one on each pipe quadrant, make the first, or root, weld around the joint. When the root pass is completed, the clamp can be moved to the next joint. Then the weld is ground, if necessary, to remove impurities and a second bead, or hot pass, is made.

A two-man firing-line team completes the weld by making repeated fill passes, applying one on top of the other and grinding in between where required. A final weld, called a cap pass, completes the joint for a total of six or seven separate passes, each taking about 12 minutes. A shelter erected during this operation protects the weld from rain, wind or snow, which could impair weld quality.

If the Alyeska quality control inspector, who visually checks each weld pass, approves the weld, it is then radiographed for internal irregularities. About 60,000 field welds are required for the entire 800-mile pipeline. (*ENR.*)

This audit of the inspection records cast doubt on about 1 weld in every 8—a total of 3955, by the time all audits were finished. Those activities were still in progress when ENR published an interim report in the issue of October 23, 1975:

Alyeska Probes Possible Pipeline Weld X-Ray Defects

The intensity of construction of the trans-Alaska oil pipeline, racing toward a target of 50% completion by early November, may be contributing to a failure in quality control.

A three-month investigation by Alyeska Pipeline Service Co., Anchorage, the pipeline owner, has uncovered falsified X-rays of pipe welds and defects and deficiencies in about 8% of all the manual welds in a 150-mile section of pipeline. A random audit by Alyeska of X-rays of 293 manual welds in a segment of pipeline running south from the Yukon River to a point about 60 miles southeast of Fairbanks has revealed that 20 of the mandatory X-rays were falsified, 175 welds were misjudged as satisfactory and 188 X-rays were of such poor quality they need to be redone.

In another test of 400 weld X-rays in the same section of pipe, using a computer to detect similarities, Alyeska also found 40 duplicates. According to Frank C. Moolin, Jr., Alyeska's senior pipeline project manager, it will recheck each of the 3,748 welds completed in that section of pipeline, almost two-thirds of which is buried. Similar investigations are reportedly under way on the rest of the 260 miles of pipe that has either been installed on vertical support members or buried along the 798-mile pipeline route. Pipe sections are mechanically welded in pairs before being trucked to the site, but there are an estimated 13,000 manual welds completed on the line, with pipe now being placed at a rate of about 5 miles per week.

The cost of replacing each weld is about $2,000, and the total repair bill is estimated to be at least $500,000. Every completed weld is inspected and X-rayed and an average of 25% are rejected and either repaired or replaced, according to Alyeska spokesmen.

Pipeline welders agreed to triple their welding speed to help increase productivity in August, but Moolin asserts this has actually improved the quality of manual welds and that reinspection and repairs will not delay completion of the pipeline, now set for mid-1976.

X-ray tests are made by EXXAM Co., Tulsa, and Ketchbow Industries, a subsidiary of Houston Gamma Ray, Inc., Houston, which is responsible for that section of pipeline where some X-ray records and welds are suspected of being defective. Quality control is supervised by Alyeska, officials of the state

Figure 8-14 "Get all you can before [it's] taxed too" reads the message on this welder's hood. The philosopher is welding a section of 48-inch pipe. The coating on the pipe near the weld is asbestos, to protect from scratches that could allow water—and eventually corrosion—to attack the metal. *(Alyeska.)*

pipeline control office and the federal Department of the Interior and by Bechtel, Inc., the quality assurance contractor for the pipeline. Moolin says there have been firings, but Alyeska has no plans to replace Ketchbow.

The issue quickly grew in proportion. Although replacing *every* weld for which there was any doubt would have cost $8 million for the repair work alone, the resulting delays would cost about $50 million more. ENR put it this way, on November 10, 1975:

Welding, and Welders, May Be the Key to Quality

Welding is one of the most basic yet most vital aspects of building the trans-Alaska oil pipeline and it may turn out to be the most troublesome. The 798-mile pipeline is designed to withstand seismic, climatic and geographical extremes, but a number of senior Alyeska officials privately say that welding problems, and specifically the welders themselves, may pose the greatest threat to the tight timetable for the project and to the ultimate integrity of the pipeline itself.

Welding specifications are probably the strictest of any pipeline project

Figure 8-15 Welders join two sections of the Alaska Pipeline for burial. *(Alyeska.)*

in the world and there are at least four stages of private, state and federal quality control to enforce them. Welding techniques, on the other hand, have changed relatively little in recent years and except for improved electrodes and several semiautomatic prototypes in limited use on the project, the majority of pipe connections are made using conventional stick-welding techniques. "Welders have been running on the ragged edge of capability in this process," according to William Wilson, pipeline project engineer for the U.S. Department of the Interior. "They are making sound and ductile welds, but the metallurgy of pipes has been improving and changing." In some cases the welders' union has vigorously opposed improved equipment and techniques because fewer welders would be required.

The 40-ft-long, 48-in.-dia pipe sections were joined in 80-ft sections using an automatic welding machine with a submerged arc that completes the bead in three external passes and one internal pass. External welds are completed manually in six or seven passes depending on the pipe thickness specified for the pressure and stress at different locations. Alyeska did stipulate gas metal-arc (Mig) welding process for some critical joints to minimize the possibility of cracking under seismic stress and in arctic temperatures as low as −60 F.

Every internal and external girth weld is X-rayed to detect hidden flaws and tested to assure hardness and impact resistance to 20 ft-lb at -50 F. The pipeline is designed to withstand an earthquake registering up to 8.5 on the Richter scale. It can withstand an axial force of 2.5 million lb and lateral deflection force of 450,000 lb before wrinkling.

Despite the safeguards, quality control has been one of Alyeska's major embarrassments on the project. An investigation of the X-rays of all 3,748 welds in a 150-mile section of completed and partially buried section of pipeline revealed that 379, or about 10%, were "misinterpreted" and some of those welds may have to be cut out and replaced. Another test uncovered 52 X-rays that may have been falsified, according to Alyeska. There will be about 100,000 [field- and shop-]welded joints on the completed pipeline.

Welders are an elite group on any pipeline and they are among the highest paid workers on the Alaska project. However, their performance has been spotty and an average of 25% of manual welds are immediately rejected. according to Alyeska. The figure is sometimes as high as 40%, "depending on the weather and mood of the pipeliners," says one federal official. The reject rate for automatic shop welds was 5%.

Despite a no-strike contract provision, welders have staged at least two major walkouts. Welders usually work seven 11-hour days in nine-week stints, earning $13.50 to $17-per-hour base pay that adds up to about $1,500 per week including overtime. Some estimates put Alyeska's total welding wage cost for the two-year project at up to $150 million and the cost of wages, equipment and possible repairs at 6% of the total cost of the project.

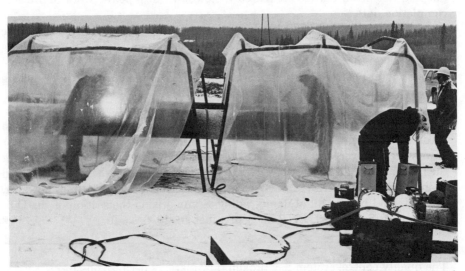

Figure 8-16 These portable shelters protected Alaska Pipeline welders from the cold and also protected welds from contamination when necessary. Here, the welders are working on 18-inch pipe used to help support the main pipeline itself. *(Alyeska.)*

Alyeska ultimately identified 3189 welds or weld radiographs with problems—28 cracks, 110 duplicated x-rays, and 360 missing records among them. Although the firm had spent $4.5 million on its audit by mid-1976, the Interior Department decided to look at the problems itself. Interior hired the accounting firm of Arthur Andersen & Co. to conduct first a spot check, then a complete audit. By July 1976, some 3955 questionable welds had surfaced. A congressional subcommittee investigating the project was calling the breakdown of quality control on the pipeline "almost total." And federal regulators were feeling the political heat.

One amazing revelation was that of Cesar DeLeon, acting director of the Department of Transportation's office of pipeline safety operations. DeLeon testified before the House Subcommittee on Energy and Power headed by Representative John D. Dingell (Democrat, Michigan) that the first he had heard about the problem was in March 1976—although trade press reports in ENR and elsewhere had been providing full coverage for at least 8 months before that, since August 1975. The DOT's Pipeline Safety Board had not stationed inspectors in Alaska. Instead, the board made three or four inspection trips a year. The inspectors concentrated on looking for evidence of bad taping—a source of possible corrosion after the pipe is buried.

The Interior Department, which had overlapping responsibility for the pipeline, kept six inspectors on the project. Only sixty stop-work orders had been issued by the inspectors in the 2 years they had been on the job.

Congressional testimony hinted—but never conclusively showed—that Interior had been aware of the problems for at least a year (since spring 1975) but had not acted because it feared a slowdown in pipeline work and a late completion date.

In the end, Alyeska did not have to dig up more than 1100 questionable welds in buried pipe. Instead, Alyeska proposed a new method for analyzing the likelihood that a slight flaw in a weld would cause a rupture under normal service conditions. The National Bureau of Standards approved the "fracture mechanics analysis" technique in November 1976.

Trouble flared again in January 1977 when careful checks of Alyeska records showed that nineteen lengths of shop-welded pipe had left the preparation yards without being checked (and in some cases without being repaired) after flaws were discovered in them. The nineteen welds had not been x-rayed after the initial flaws had been discovered. X-rays, purporting to show that they had been reinspected, were found to have been falsified. By that time, however, Congress had had its fill of name-calling. Summarizing the section of the Dingell Committee's report, ENR on September 16, 1976, said:

The quality control system has broken down largely because on-site inspectors felt they had little backing from above, either from the companies or federal officials. "We were regaled with horror stories detailing the threats of physical harm and abuse laid upon the quality control inspectors by the work force," the staff report said.

"The most dramatic threat involved a quality control inspector, who, in the face of warnings of retaliation if he shut down a certain operation, did do so. The next morning he found in the front seat of his vehicle a stick of dynamite with his name written on it." The staff admitted, however, that though they heard the story from several "seemingly unrelated sources," they had been "unable to identify the name of the inspector or to find out what had actually happened, if anything."

INSUFFICIENT OVERSIGHT

The staff attributed the problems in large measure to insufficient oversight by the federal government, in part attributable to inadequate meshing of separate monitoring and inspection programs by the Interior and Transportation departments. Michael Barrett, counsel for the committee, believes the line's current problems are a direct result of the atmosphere in which the whole project was begun. "The Interior Department interpreted its mission as expediting. That being the case, everything else flowed right along." The committee expects to release a separate report focusing on the government's actions perhaps as early as the week after next.

The report released last week by DOT paints a slightly different and generally more optimistic picture of the pipeline's status. But it does offer some support for the staff findings on the weld problems. In the course of a memorandum describing a meeting between deputy transportation secretary John Barnum and officials from Interior and some of the companies involved, William Wilson, vice president and project manager for subcontractor

Figure 8-17 These saddle-shaped blocks are concrete, designed to anchor the Alaska Pipeline to the river bottom. *(ENR.)*

Figure 8-18 Above-ground sections of the Alaska Pipeline typically are insulated to keep the oil warm and flowing, and taped to prevent corrosion. Government quality-control inspectors looked for errors in insulation and taping, rather then weld problems. *(ENR.)*

Mechanics Research Inc., is said to have cited continuing problems this year with "welding procedure aberrations." He attributes this to the cost-plus-fixed-fee nature of the project, which he is paraphrased as saying "does not foster proper disciplining of the welders." Other officials for subcontractors echoed that complaint.

But representatives of the welders' and radiographers' unions charged that workers were hired who were not qualified to do inspection and interpretation of film, causing delays.

At a hastily called press conference late last week, Barnum said, "I'm satisfied that the welding is being done adequately this year." According to him, the subcommittee thinks "that virtually everything being done wrong in 1975 is being done wrong now. That has not been our finding, and we disagree." He also said, 'We don't have any direct knowledge that there has been any intimidation of the quality control people."

Although there were many complaints in congressional testimony about the competence of the welders themselves (from the United Association of Plumbers and Pipefitters Local 798, Tulsa), they had been carefully tested and certified by the local before being allowed to come to Alaska. Evidence was strong that they intimidated inspectors, caused racial disturbances in construction camps, and refused to allow more automated equipment to be used in the field. But, as the good performance of the pipeline has proved, the welders made few mistakes that weren't uncovered. And the mistakes that were found could be attributed to the complexity of the project and the poor working conditions.

Nevertheless, the association of poor quality with welding in the minds of the general public spurred the American Welding Society's certification programs for welders and for inspectors. The program for welders—which had begun in 1972—was expanded. The certification program for inspectors began in 1976. Thanks in large part to the Alaska Pipeline fraud, interest ran high. In the first year of the program more than 1600 people signed up for the certification tests; 900 passed to become certified welding inspectors.

Problems of inspector intimidation continue to plague large projects, however, especially nuclear power plants. Perhaps, as many welders charge, inspectors are overzealous. But we won't know for sure, unless another disaster strikes.

Formwork Failure on a Cooling Tower, 1978

On April 27, 1978, the worst construction accident in U.S. history sent fifty–one men to their deaths. They had been working on a concrete cooling tower for a new power plant near St. Marys, West Virginia, and were standing on a movable formwork system almost 170 feet above the ground when the entire form suddenly peeled away from the newly placed concrete of the tower. No one survived to explain exactly what had happened.

ENR reported the accident in the issue of May 4, 1978:

Form Collapse Kills 51 on Cooling Tower Job

A jack-up formwork system atop a powerplant cooling tower in West Virginia collapsed last Thursday sending 51 workers plummeting 168 ft to their death in one of the world's worst construction tragedies. By Saturday federal Occupational Safety and Health Administration (OSHA) investigators "virtually ruled out" any fault in the ganged jump forms themselves and were concentrating on the concrete, the hoist used to raise it inside the tower, the method of jacking the formwork and the design of the concrete structure.

Figure 8-19　If the tower at St. Marys, West Virginia, had been completed without incident, it would have looked something like this one, which is being topped out at the John E. Amos plant of American Electric Power. *(Research-Cottrell.)*

Workers were placing a 5-ft lift of concrete at the Pleasants Station near St. Marys when the interior work platform peeled away "like someone opening a can," said one witness. A number of men leaped into a safety net outside the tower, but it along with the exterior platform and tons of concrete were pulled inside and fell in a jumbled mess.

The accident is believed to be the second most fatal construction failure ever in North America, and perhaps in the world. It trails the first collapse of the cantilever truss bridge across the St. Lawrence River at Quebec in August, 1907, which took 74 lives [*Engineering News,* Sept. 5, 1907, p. 258].

WELL TESTED METHOD

The tower was designed and under construction by the Hamon Cooling Tower Division of Research-Cottrell, Inc. (R-C), Bound Brook, N.J. According to R-C president Dennis Carlton-Jones, it was using the same type of patented formwork used successfully on 36 towers completed by the company over the past seven years, including an adjacent one on the same site. It has stopped work on three other towers elsewhere until the probe of the St. Marys incident is completed.

The company holds a $12-million subcontract on the pair of 430-ft-high towers near the Ohio River at St. Marys. Prime design-constructor on the $677-million, coal-fired powerplant for Allegheny Power System, Inc., New York City, is United Engineers & Constructors, Inc., Philadelphia. Work started there in May, 1974. The first 626-Mw unit was due to go on line next March and a second one a year later.

The cooling tower's lattice base of diagonal columns is 367 ft in diameter. Above that, the solid wall diminishes in thickness as the tower tapers and then flares out. It was about [8 in] thick at the 29th lift, where the concrete crew was working when the collapse occurred. OSHA regional administrator David Rhone says that is the narrowest point of the hourglass shape, and the wall was just starting to angle out again. Contractors' spokesmen declined to release any dimensions or other details after the accident. And they would not disclose the strength or type of concrete mix, one saying that "it would serve no useful purpose." But the mix on cooling towers is typically high strength (as much as 5,400 psi) and contains a high early strength additive.

Figure 8-20   Jump forms atop the St. Marys structure tore loose, pulling work platforms and concrete down inside the tower. *(United Press International.)*

Figure 8-21   Wreckage 168 feet below the top of the St. Marys tower being picked apart by investigators looking for clues. The state of West Virginia objected to the site being cleaned before it could make its own full investigation. *(United Press International.)*

As on other R-C projects, the forms at St. Marys were generally raised hydraulically on a one-day cycle and bolted to anchors cast into the last two lifts placed. Last Thursday, however, they were secured to a lift that was 24 hours old and one below it that was placed 72 hours earlier because of a day lost to rain.

John Peppler, a laborer working at the base of the concrete hoist, said he had just sent a bucket up when the formwork started to give way and the loaded bucket came crashing down. As the platforms and formwork ripped loose, they brought down all the fresh concrete and most of the day-old lift below it. The three-day-old 27th ring, however, stayed put. The weather had been cold and rainy recently. But all last week temperatures were in the 60s during the day and in the 30s at night.

CONCRETE DEBATE

Workers at the site claim that the job was being pushed too fast and the top two lifts had not set sufficiently. One electrician said, "I don't care how much OSHA lies or the Secretary of Labor lies. It was green concrete. That's all it was. They jacked that up on green concrete."

But R-C's Carlton-Jones insisted that the cycle was the same as its other projects, adding, "They were ahead of schedule." Concrete cylinders from the job were tested on a daily basis by Pittsburgh Testing Laboratories, which did not report anything unusual. Tony Zitti, plant manager for the supplier, Criss Concrete Co., St. Marys, refused to discuss the mix.

However, Don Smith, president of laborers' Local 1085, which lost 18 men in the accident, said that the workers were paid for a full day's work no matter how long it took them to place a lift. He acknowledged that on the lift being poured, "That could have been cause for them to rush more than they should. But we'll probably never know what actually happened because they're all dead."

OSHA is doing its own laboratory analysis of the concrete and expects to have preliminary results this week, although investigators have had trouble gathering sufficient samples on the ground of the latest concrete placed. "This is the most critical part of our investigation," said Rhone. "We have some leads and we are developing them." OSHA's final report will take two to five weeks, officials said.

OSHA came in for some knocks by workers and labor leaders at the site for what they consider lax enforcement. The agency has inspected the project 14 times, four times in response to accidents that previously killed four workers. Officials said they found numerous violations, some serious. But the last OSHA inspection was in April, 1977, before work started on either of the cooling towers.

Work resumed on the site Monday, except for the second cooling tower, which will be shut down until investigators release it. Then, says laborers' president Smith, "It's going to be tough to get people to go back up there."

In the wake of the tragedy, OSHA issued its report. Unfortunately, the document listed so many possible causes that it was impossible to pin the blame on any one thing. The report was summarized in ENR on June 5, 1978:

Human Error Blamed in Cooling Tower Disaster

The Occupational Safety and Health Administration (OSHA) charged last week that failure to follow proper procedures caused the collapse of a jack-up formwork system on a powerplant cooling tower in West Virginia. The failure, killing 51 workers, was the country's worst construction accident ever [ENR, May 4, 1978, p. 10].

OSHA officials said the formwork was not adequately secured to the wall; they also cast doubt on the quality of the concrete. The agency did not identify exactly what precipitated the failure, but interest centers on a hoisting cable that was pulling a concrete bucket up to cathead crane No. 4, the point where the progressive failure started.

With the investigation continuing, criminal charges are expected soon. Eula Bingham, assistant labor secretary in charge of OSHA, said,

> If proper tests had been conducted on concrete prior to removing forms, if the scaffold formwork system had been properly secured to the tower, and if beam sections supporting the concrete lifting system atop the tower [the cathead] had been anchored and maintained to support the maximum intended load, this tragedy would never have occurred.

Aside from Bingham's broad explanation and responses at a press conference, OSHA officials declined to discuss details. One investigator said they knew several days before there would be criminal charges coming "and everyone stopped talking."

The National Bureau of Standards (NBS) still is conducting exhaustive tests of the concrete, and a source close to the probe says that may be a root of criminal action. One investigator, though declining to be specific about the mix, said its compressive strength was less than the 5,400 psi ENR earlier suggested and that it contained no accelerator or curing compound.

The only major analysis not completed is a Bureau of Mines evaluation of the hoisting cable that may have snapped, according to an OSHA spokesman. This is an attempt to determine the cable's condition before the accident and the bucket's location when it gave way. A laborer working at the base of the hoist said he had just sent one of the 2,500 lb. buckets up when the formwork gave way and the loaded bucket crashed down.

"We're still seeking what triggered the collapse," said Sid Levalds, OSHA's St. Louis area director, who participated in the probe and the press conference. "But we have enough evidence to support what we announced today."

OVERLAPPING CITATIONS

Based on the findings so far, OSHA issued 10 citations for "willful violations" and six for less severe "serious" ones to Research-Cottrell, Inc. (R-C), Bound Brook, N.J., whose Hamon Cooling Tower Division designed and was building the tower with its patented jump form system. Not all the citations relate directly to alleged causes of the collapse.

It also issued two serious citations to the prime design-constructor on the Allegheny Power System coal-fired . . . station, United Engineers and Constructors, Inc., and to the company testing concrete for R-C, Pittsburgh Testing Laboratory. Those citations are identical to each other and to two of the willful citations R-C received: not making tests on the concrete prior to removing the forms and not properly instructing each employee. Bingham said that "proposed penalties vary due to the extent of the employer responsibility. . . ."

One of the willful violations charged to R-C was "for not making a thorough inspection of all wire ropes at least once a month and keeping a proper record of all inspections."

Many of OSHA's findings are based on a report by S. Ty Looney, president of Safety Consultants, Inc., Richmond, Va., who was the principal outside evaluator of the physical evidence, supported by testing done by NBS and the Bureau of Mines.

OSHA proposes the maximum penalties of $10,000—for each of the willful violations with which it charges R-C. It asks the maximum of $1,000 for only one of the R-C's alleged serious violations, lesser amounts in all other instances. The total fine proposed against all three companies is $108,300.

Bingham defined a serious violation as one that could cause death or serious injury, but where "the employer did not know, or could not have known with reasonable diligence, of the existence of the hazard." A willful violation, she said, is an "intentional and knowing" act, or else where "even though an employer was not consciously violating the act, he was aware that a hazardous condition existed and made no reasonable effort to eliminate the condition."

The law prescribes criminal sanctions for a willful violation of a standard resulting in death. In its seven years of operation the agency has initiated criminal charges in about 10 instances. Asked if it was considering doing so in this case, Bingham said, "We will be making the statement by our action fairly soon."

TENUOUS GRIP

The R-C jack-up formwork system is supported by cast aluminum jump beams, each of which is secured to the wall by two bolts cast in each 5-ft concrete lift. At the point where workers were placing concrete, about 170 ft

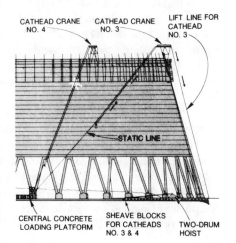

Figure 8-22 The St. Marys failure started at Crane No. 4, as the hoisting line brought up a bucket loaded with 2500 pounds of concrete. *(ENR.)*

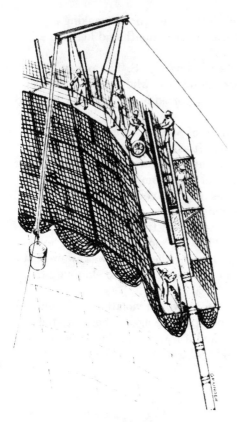

Figure 8-23 The St. Marys formwork was partially anchored in two lifts of concrete. *(Occupational Safety and Health Administration.)*

above the ground when the Willow Island disaster occurred, the wall was 8 in. thick . . . and the jump beams were on about 8½-ft centers. The tower was tapering toward the narrow point of its hourglass shape.

The jack beams have protrusions on them and the system, with its four work platforms both inside and out, is raised hydraulically much as an automobile bumper jack works. The 15-ft jack beams are leapfrogged up the inside and outside walls by hand. They are staggered in height by 5 ft inside and out. Normally, after a day's lift is poured, one third of the beams are moved up, the system is raised 5 ft and carpenters set forms to cast another lift the following day.

Since the beams are not connected end to end, those carrying the weight of the entire formwork system are theoretically one-third secured to the previous day's pour, one-third to two-day old concrete and the other third to three-day-old concrete. Owing to a day lost to rain, however, when the Willow Island collapse occurred the lowest beams were tied to a four-day-old lift.

But Bingham says the investigation "shows the company recently had been unbolting the bottom bolt on the lower beam before subjecting the formwork to the load of a new pour of concrete." That means that in the case of the two beams at the point of collapse, the OSHA report shows, the inner one was tied only to two bolts in the previous day's pour and the outer one was secured to those bolts plus only one in the top of the two-day-old lift below. . . .

In addition, OSHA charges that the four separate beams supporting the legs of each cathead atop the formwork were not adequately fixed to the wall. Says Bingham, "With poorly anchored and maintained support legs, missing bolts, and uncertain concrete, there were clearly present the ingredients for a disaster."

An engineer who until three and a half years ago was a top designer for R-C agrees in principle. Marvin Warner, now head of the architectural section at the Fermi Laboratory in Batavia, Ill., says the formwork was designed "very conservatively" and the erection procedures were laid out explicitly. But, he says, "If those lower bolts were left out, that was not the intent of the design."

SEEKING THE TRIGGER

That still leaves in question what exactly triggered the fatal collapse. And the investigators seem to point at either the action of the concrete bucket or the hoisting line itself.

Says one engineer close to the investigation, "If everything else was OK, it would have been SOP. You could have dropped that bucket 40 times without anything happening. But when you shock-load the formwork in an unstable condition, you start things happening." According to OSHA's Levalds, the break occurred abruptly at cathead No. 4, and the formwork [peeled] off inside moving in both directions and the collapse ended in about 30 seconds virtually 180 deg from the starting point.

The hoisting rig in question was one of six, each with a concrete bucket riding on a static line secured at the central loading platform on the floor below and the catheads above (see drawing). From the cathead, laborers distributed the concrete in mortar buggies. Three, two-drum hoists each operated a pair of hoisting lines. Bingham emphasized that the operators of the hoists, at the base of the tower, could not see the catheads and were dependent on phone communication.

Human error seems to get the blame from everyone who has probed the incident. George H. R. Taylor, executive secretary [of] the AFL-CIO safety committee says that he and the safety directors of each union representing workers on the job basically agree with most of OSHA's findings.

But he adds, "Research-Cottrell is so damn secretive about their patented method that the carpenters don't know a thing about what the laborers are doing. They do not have a real team operation."

By coincidence, the same issue carried a report of an unrelated construction accident that killed two workers at a cooling tower being built for the Byron, Illinois, nuclear power plant of Commonwealth Edison (ComEd). The workers died when the precast, X-shaped lattice that was to support the tower collapsed as it was being erected. Each lattice was 74 feet high and weighed 86 tons. Although this accident occurred for an entirely different reason than had the St. Marys failure, and although the companies involved were not the same—the ComEd tower was being built by Ecokel of Cincinnati—the second failure served to focus even more attention on Research-Cottrell.

In July, Research-Cottrell sued Criss Concrete Co. of Parkersburg, claiming that the concrete it had supplied to the project "contained improper ingredients and quantities of admixtures ... as to seriously slow down the curing process normally expected" (according to the firm's attorney). The company also sued the concrete testing firm, Pittsburgh Testing Lab. But Criss's own tests showed the mix was adequate.

By September, OSHA had examined hoisting equipment used in the project, and was focusing attention on a snapped cable that had been hoisting a concrete bucket at the time of the collapse as described in the June 15 OSHA report. Research-Cottrell was clearing the site (under the objections of West Virginia officials who were nervous about the possible destruction of evidence) but had not resumed construction there, or at three similar tower projects elsewhere.

Work was resumed on the project in the summer of 1979. Research-Cottrell had replaced the cathead system with separate cranes for bringing concrete to the top of the tower. A federal grand jury investigated the possibility of filing criminal charges against the firm at about the same time, but ultimately decided that such charges were not justified.

One recurring theory is that field repairs and changes to the formwork system had not been properly made. Because of the form's complexity, some structural members that would seem to be in tension, for instance, were in fact in compression—and vice versa. That point has not been firmly proved to this day, however, as continuing civil suits have made it difficult to obtain information.

The January 22, 1981, issue of ENR summarized the final report of the state of West Virginia, which complained about the same thing:

State Cooling Tower Probe Blasts OSHA, Cites Human Error

After a frustrating two-year inquiry into the fatal cooling tower accident in 1978 at Willow Island, W.Va., a state commission has attacked the federal government's refusal to provide critical evidence it had about the accident.

The commission's report also criticizes the failure of the Occupational Safety and Health Administration to enforce its own regulations and "the responsible parties in the private sector" for failing to observe OSHA regulations.

In addition to the lack of site inspections by OSHA, and the unresponsiveness of the federal government and contractors, the commission concludes that human "errors of judgment" were "the root causes of the disaster."

The report makes several recommendations. Chief among them are: strengthening OSHA's enforcement powers; creating a state office in West Virginia for investigating industrial accidents; increasing OSHA's responsibility for ensuring safe working conditions at an accident site when work resumes; further federal and state investigations into the accident focusing on why the accident occurred and who is responsible; and establishing federal regulations "authorizing mandatory curing times and load tests for elevated concrete construction before removal of forms."

The commission praises OSHA's two "public reports on the causes" as "technically superb." But, the commission expresses strong disappointment at the government's uncooperativeness during the state probe. The report says that the commission "is of the opinion that OSHA was not fully cooperative; and the commission is not certain whether it has, to this day, received all the information to which it is entitled."

OSHA refused to comply with five requests from the commission for information the agency had collected about the accident on the grounds that disclosure of any data about the accident, the design or the construction of the cooling tower might prejudice the rights of individuals involved in the Department of Justice's criminal investigation of the accident. However, Justice concluded that there was not sufficient evidence to initiate prosecution. The report states that " . . . even after criminal prosecution was abandoned . . . OSHA was not candid."

The report suggests that when federal officials became aware that OSHA might be criticized in the report, "OSHA suddenly made available a new report disclosing additional facts."

The commission was also critical of the number of qualified federal safety inspectors in West Virginia. At the time of the accident, says the report, there were only 14 OSHA inspectors in the state and just seven were for construction projects, a number the commission regards as "absurdly low." Even though the OSHA staff in West Virginia was increased by 40% in the two years following the accident, the commission says that number is "still grossly inadequate."

One interesting lesson that has occurred in the meantime was the failure of jack-up formwork while building a cooling tower for the Washington Public Power Supply System (WPPSS) Unit 5 at Satsop, Washington. Two workers were killed and a third seriously injured when one 30- by 6-foot steel form pulled away from newly poured concrete. Thanks to one lesson learned at St. Marys—that all the forms would progressively fail if they were tied together— the WPPSS forms were assembled separately, in sixty sections.

The incident was described in the ENR issue of March 19, 1981:

Cooling Tower Deaths Laid to Form Hookup

Last week's failure of a section of jack-up formwork that killed two workers and seriously injured a third building a cooling tower for the Washington Public Power Supply System's unit 5 at Satsop, Wash., was due to improper installation of one of four rods used to secure the gang form to the concrete, early investigations indicate.

"Whatever controls the contractor had in place to check those bolts were not enough," says a WPPSS official, who questions the adequacy of a design safety margin in which the failure of one bolt could bring down the 30 X 6-ft steel form.

The three men involved in the accident were standing on a walkway attached to the form while it was being jacked up for the next lift. Four steel rods threaded through coil inserts embedded in the concrete are used to hold the form in place at that stage. A fourth worker escaped injury by jumping to rebars placed for the next lift before the gang form broke loose and fell 70 ft to the ground inside the tower shell.

Early reports from the tower builder indicate that one of the four rods was not properly inserted through the coil, leaving only the concrete to hold the rod in place. When that failed, another rod snapped and most of the form came down, say investigators. Heinz Treuberg, site manager for the Tampa, Fla.-based cooling tower division of Zurn Industries, Inc., Erie, Pa., says no concrete failure was involved.

Zurn holds the design-construct contract for the cooling tower, which is identical to one it built without mishap for unit 3 at the Satsop site. Designed and supplied by Ewing-Records Associates, a division of the Burke Co., Converse, Tex., the forms are paired on the inside and outside of the shell around its circumference. Each of the 60 gang forms used is attached to the tower concrete independently and there are no connections between forms.

Hyatt Walkway Collapse, 1981

Flamboyant architecture found a home in American hotels of the 1970s, thanks in large part to the Hyatt chain. Soaring lobby atriums and slender suspended walkways became a trademark of sorts, and have been widely copied. Although the walkways look like daring engineering wonders to most members of the public, they generally are extremely simple to design. "They might well be course projects for undergraduate engineers," said an ENR editorial published on July 23, 1981.

On July 17, 1981, the walkways failed at the Hyatt in Kansas City, Missouri; 113 persons eventually died from injuries sustained as they fell with the walkways or were crushed underneath. More than 180 were injured, many of them badly maimed for life.

The accident's cause—improperly built hanging supports for the walks— was quickly determined. But responsibility for the error has been harder to pin down. More than 100 separate suits were pending by mid-1982. ENR discussed the disaster in the issue of July 23, 1981:

Hotel Disaster Triggers Probes

The first investigators have moved into the Hyatt Regency Hotel in Kansas City, Mo., to take samples and to search the debris of the two concrete-and-steel pedestrian bridges that fell into the hotel's crowded lobby last Friday. . . .

Speculation was still rife about the cause of the accident, and none of the principals connected with the hotel would commit themselves to a theory.

Investigations into the collapse's cause have been promised by:

· The hotel's owner, Crown Center Redevelopment Corp., a wholly-owned subsidiary of Hallmark Cards, Inc.
· The facility's operator, Hyatt Hotels Corp.
· Eldridge & Sons Construction Co., the Kansas City-based contractor for the building.
· The City of Kansas City.
· The hotel's joint venture architect, Patty Berkebile Nelson Duncan Monroe Lefebvre Architects Planners, Inc. Three local firms make up that joint venture—Patty Berkebile Nelson Associates Architects, Inc.; Duncan Architects, Inc.; and Monroe and Lefebvre Architects, Inc.

Representatives from the hotel's structural engineer, Gillum Colaco Associates, St. Louis, also visited the hotel soon after the collapse. James L. Stratta, the Menlo Park, Calif., failures expert who was called in by the city to investigate the Kemper Arena collapse in 1979, is also investigating the disaster.

The Hyatt Regency is part of Kansas City's Crown Center Urban Development Complex. Its four-story open lobby connects a 40-story, 733-room hotel tower and a four-story wing of meeting rooms and restaurants.

Figure 8-24 Falling walkways caused havoc in the atrium lobby of the Hyatt Regency Hotel in Kansas City. *(United Press International.)*

The lobby was crossed by three 120-ft-long open walkway bridges, one each at the second, third and fourth levels. The fourth-level walkway was directly over the second, and the third-level walkway was slightly off to one side.

Each of the walkways was held up by six steel rods, 1¼ in. in diameter and suspended from the ceiling. The rods supported four 30-ft-long, 18-in.-deep steel I-beams connected end to end along each outside edge of each walkway. The beams in turn supported a concrete deck. The sides of the walkways were short glass walls topped with wooden handrails.

The threaded ends of the supporting rods were tied to the steel beams by nuts. The rods holding up the second-level walkway were attached to the fourth-level walkway rather than directly to the ceiling. The walkways were attached to the balconies at either side of the lobby with steel plate connections. One walkway end connection was bolted, the other had an expansion joint.

When the collapse occurred, between 1,000 and 2,000 people were crowded onto the floor of the lobby and onto the three bridges spanning it to watch and participate in a dance contest. Witnesses report that they heard a loud crack as the fourth level bridge buckled into three sections shortly after 7 p.m. The bridge fell onto the second-level bridge, collapsing it and dumping 64 tons of debris and the spectators from both walkways onto the dance floor.

There is also speculation that the crowded second-level bridge pulled the fourth-level bridge down with it.

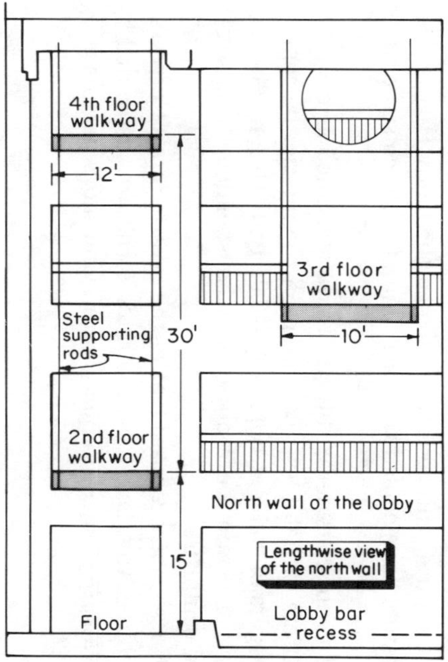

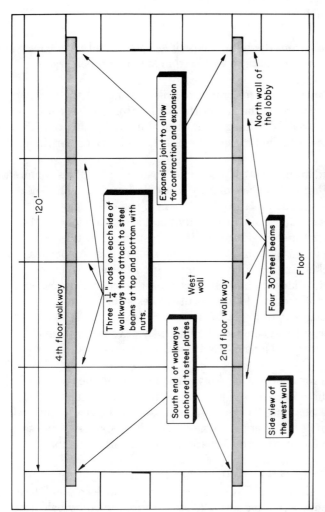

Figure 8-26 This side view of the west wall at the Hyatt shows how the walkways were held along their entire 120-foot length. (Kansas City Star.)

Figure 8-25 This lengthwise view of the north wall at the Hyatt shows how the walkways connecting corridors at the second-floor and fourth-floor levels were suspended from the same rod system. The third-floor walkway was hung separately. (Kansas City Star.)

391

The whoosh of air from the falling mass knocked several people over and flying shards of glass injured others. Water from snapped pipes began to spread across the lobby floor.

It took more than 12 hours for cranes to finish lifting out the wreckage of the two bridges and to remove the last of the bodies from underneath.

The steel support rods still hung from the ceiling, indicating that they failed where they were attached to the fourth-level walkway rather than at ceiling level.

Pat Foley, president of Hyatt Hotels, told reporters at a press conference the day after the collapse that the walkways were designed to hold dense concentrations of people such as the ones they held the evening of the collapse. Foley also said that the Kansas City hotel is the only one in the Hyatt chain with structures similar to the three suspended bridges.

The architectural consortium has hired Failure Analysis Associates, Palo Alto, Calif., and Packer Engineering Associates, Inc., Chicago, to probe the collapse, and both firms already have engineers on the scene. Spokesmen for the two firms could not provide details about the tests they would perform or what parts of the bridges were to get the most scrutiny.

The owner, operator and contractor apparently have not brought investigators to the site yet. None of the three could be reached by press time for confirmation.

A spokeswoman for Kansas City Mayor Richard L. Berkley says that the city will wait until the project's principals have announced plans for their investigations before planning its own. The first area of the city's probe will probably be the Hyatt's building permits, she says. The spokeswoman says the mayor is pleased so far with the impartiality of the other planned investigations.

Dramatic atriums have become the hallmark of most Hyatt hotels over the past decade, ever since John Portman transformed modern hotel design with the Hyatt Regency Atlanta and its 22-story atrium lined by balconies that lead to the guest rooms.

By now, many different architects have designed the many Hyatts, and even other hotel operators have copied the idea. Therefore, each structure varies widely.

The atrium itself is not considered difficult to design. The biggest concern of most operators is that guests can jump off the interior balconies.

In any case, managers of some of the nation's 59 Hyatt Regency hotels are reportedly ordering inspections of walkways and suspended structures, including artwork and sculptures.

Donald Deporter, regional vice president of the Hyatt Hotels Corp., says he has ordered an architect to take a look at a ramp structure suspended by steel beams at the Hyatt Regency in Illinois Center, Chicago, where he is general manager.

The Kansas City hotel remains closed indefinitely while the debris is being cleared up and the necessary repairs made.

It didn't take long for investigators to focus on the problem. From the ENR issue of July 30, 1981:

Hyatt Walkway Design Switched

New evidence turned up last week that connections in the walkway bridges of the Kansas City Hyatt Regency hotel were changed from the original scheme. The change would have doubled the stress on one of the structural elements that eventually failed as the walkways collapsed July 17. Who made that change and whether other parts of the design were changed to compensate for it are still mysteries.

Also last week, the one remaining walkway was removed by the hotel's owner when it was discovered that its beams had deformed. . . .

DRAWINGS RELEASED

The two 8.7-ft-wide walkways that collapsed during the July 17 "tea dance" were at the second and fourth levels. The fourth-level walkway was suspended from the ceiling by steel rods and the second level was suspended by rods from the fourth level. A 10-ft-wide walkway at the third level was suspended about 13 ft to one side.

According to the structural and architectural design drawings released by the city last week, the walkway floors were held up along each edge by four 16-in.-deep, wide-flange sections laid end to end to cover the full length of the bridges—roughly 120 ft. At one end, the bridges were attached to atrium balconies with fixed joints that are not detailed in the city's set of plans. The other end, however, is shown as a 1-in.-wide expansion joint.

The ends of the four edge beam sections along each side of each bridge were welded to transverse box beams. The box beams supported the bridges at three evenly spaced points, dividing the 120-ft bridges into four 30-ft spans.

Each box beam was built up from two steel channels (*ASTM* designation MC 8 X 8.5) welded together. Each end of each box beam was suspended from a 1¼-in. steel rod passing through a hole drilled through the box beam's welded seams. These rods, six of them in all for each walkway, and the balcony connection at either end of each bridge, were what held the walkways up.

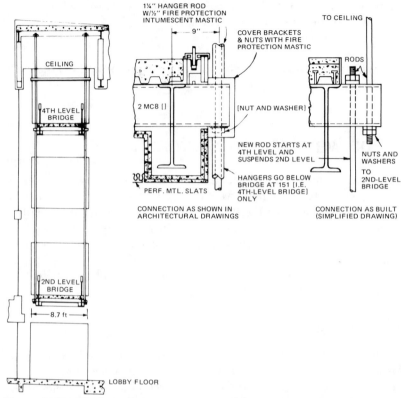

Figure 8-27   The design drawings of the Hyatt Hotel imply a single rod from ceiling to second level (left and center), but the suspension was actually built with two rods (right). As a result, the entire weight of both walkways was held by the nuts screwed onto the lower ends of the upper rods (far right in drawing). *(ENR File.)*

Within each 30-ft stretch of walkway, three 8-in.-deep, wide-flange transverse beams added stiffness to the floor. The floor itself was constructed from a 1½-in. ribbed metal deck and 3¼ in. of light-weight concrete.

STRESS DOUBLED

A detail in the architectural drawings indicates that at each support point a single rod would have passed from the ceiling, through the fourth-level box beam, and on to the second-level box beam. A nut and washer under each box beam were to have held the weight of the floors.

But the rod connections were not built that way. Instead, one rod from the ceiling was fastened with a nut and washer underneath the fourth-level box beam. Another rod a few inches to one side suspended the second-level bridge from the fourth-level beam.

The change would have doubled the stress around the nut under the fourth-level beam. In the original design, that nut would have supported only the weight of the fourth level. But the as-built connection supported both the second and fourth levels.

Photographs of the Hyatt debris show that these nuts actually did pull through the box beams during the collapse. Whether that failure caused the collapse or was merely one of its results, however, remains to be seen.

DENIES MAKING CHANGE

Jack D. Gillum, of the St. Louis consulting engineering firm Jack D. Gillum & Associates, is the structural engineer of record for the hotel. His office designed the hanging walkways.

But Gillum claims that the rod-to-beam connection used on the sky bridges was not the one he designed. "That detail was not what was on our drawing," he told ENR in an interview last week.

Gillum says he did not approve the switch, and he declines to say who did. He also says that his firm did not inspect or supervise construction of the Hyatt.

James D. Dawson, spokesman for the hotel's owner, the Crown Center Redevelopment Corp., will not say who changed the design, who approved it or why. Lawyers representing the Hyatt's contractor, Eldridge & Son Construction Co., Inc., and its architect, Patty Berkebile Nelson Duncan Monroe Lefebvre Architects Planners, Inc., also will not say who changed the detail.

According to Kansas City Public Works Director Myron D. Calkins, the city would not necessarily have reviewed the connection change.

Calkins says that once the city approves the structure as complying with the Uniform Building Code, only major alterations of the structural scheme would require a reapproval. In the case of the changed connection detail, the bridges were still supported by the same kind of rods attached in virtually the same places, he says, so the altered design would not have triggered another city review.

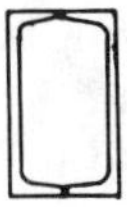

				Flange		Web thick-		Axis X-X		
	Designation	Area A	Depth d	Width b_f	Average thickness t_f	ness t_w	$\frac{d}{A_f}$	I	S	r
		In.²	In.	In.	In.	In.		In.⁴	In.³	In.
	MC 8×8.5	2.50	8.00	1.874	0.311	0.179	13.7	23.3	5.83	3.05
	MC 7×22.7	6.67	7.00	3.603	0.500	0.503	3.89	47.5	13.6	2.67
	×19.1	5.61	7.00	3.452	0.500	0.352	4.06	43.2	12.3	2.7

Figure 8-28 The box beams of the Hyatt were built up from channel sections called for in the plans, and had side walls 0.179 inch thick. *(ENR.)*

EFFECT UNKNOWN

Whether the design change impaired the ability of the bridges to carry their design live load of 100 psf is still not clear.

Gillum says his office is now determining what the stresses on the bridges would have been in both the as-designed and as-built versions, based on the way they were actually used. That apparently would require some estimate of the dynamic impact of people dancing on the two bridges, suspected as a collapse cause.

When Gillum's firm designed the bridges, "We were never aware of this use," he says, adding that the bridges were designed as corridors. "There is no problem in our design," Gillum insists.

But detailed testing remains to be done. Gillum says he still needs to know the quality of construction, welding quality and the grades of steel used, information that was difficult to get last week.

THIRD BRIDGE REMOVED

It is also possible that neither the vibrations from dancing nor the design change were prime causes of the collapse, according to other evidence discovered last week. Two engineers hired by Schnider, Shamberg & May, a Kansas City, Kan., law firm representing some of the injured and their families, found that the one remaining walkway in the hotel showed deformation similar to that experienced by the walkways that failed. That deformation occurred in a joint unlike the altered connection of the other walkways. According to Lynn R. Johnson, an attorney with the law firm, the deformation had occurred over a long period of time.

The two engineers, Lee Lowery, a professor at Texas A&M University and Rex Paulsen, with the Denver consulting firm Fay Engineering Co., examined the points where steel rods held up the third-level bridge's box beams.

"Dr. Lowery saw deformation in each of the box beams," Johnson claims.

Johnson says that all of the box beams were bowed out along their sides—which were only 0.179 in. thick if built according to the original design drawings. Their 0.311-in.-thick bottom walls were deformed as much as ¼ in. where the nut and washer pulled up on the box beam to take the weight of the bridge. Because there was no walkway suspended from the third-level bridge, the connection was simpler than the one linking the other two bridges.

"We gave Hyatt a letter concluding the walkway was very unsafe and should be shored up or supported," Johnson says. "Instead, they removed it." Crown Center spokesman Dawson says they did so under advice from their consultant, James L. Stratta, a Menlo Park, Calif., structural engineer.

Johnson sees the deformation of the uncollapsed bridge as evidence of a failure that had been progressing for some time. "I don't think movement of

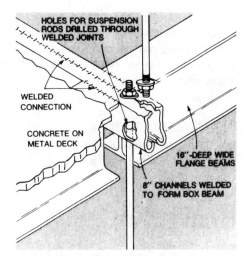

Figure 8-29 This drawing shows more clearly how the Hyatt failure occurred. The failed box beams supported wide-flange beams along the edges of suspended walkways. *(ENR.)*

people had anything to do with it, other than to trigger what was inevitable," he says of the collapse.

ENGINEERS ON SITE

Besides Gillum, Lowery, Paulsen and Stratta, investigators also include Failure Analysis Associates, Palo Alto, Calif., and Packer Engineering Associates, Inc., Chicago. Those two firms were hired by the architect. Edward O. Pfrang and Richard Marshall of the National Bureau of Standards have been in Kansas City giving the city technical advice. The contractor has also had engineers on the site, but the firm's lawyer, Robert A. Babcock, would identify them only as "a reputable firm."

All parties denied having approved the change in the walkways' suspension. But the *Kansas City Star* published a steel fabricator's drawing in mid-August, showing that all of the project's principals knew of the design change that doubled stresses on the support of the fourth-floor walk. ENR discussed the findings in its August 10, 1981, issue.

The newspaper's drawing, a shop drawing from the Havens Steel Co., Kansas City, shows the altered design. The shop drawing was stamped and initialed by the hotel's architect, Patty Berkebile Nelson Duncan Monroe Lefebvre Architects Planners, Inc.; the structural engineer of record, Gillum-Colaco; and the contractor, Eldridge & Son Construction Co.

Although the shop drawing may not have been the one on which the design change was first proposed and okayed, the initialed approvals indicate that all three parties were at least aware of the new design before construction began. None of the three firms had previously admitted this knowledge.

Meanwhile, ENR itself was getting many letters from readers, pondering how the structure could have been built as designed in the first place. From the issue of September 17, 1981:

Hyatt Puzzle

I have been following the Hyatt hotel accident from the start, but I wish you could explain one thing to me. In your July 30 story [ENR, July 30, 1981, p. 11] you stated that there was supposed to be one 1¼-in. rod that was suspended from the ceiling through the fourth level and to the second level.

What I want to know is, how can you put a nut and washer in the middle of a bar unless it is an all-threaded rod?

Being an ironworker for 27 years I have seen many things changed from what the blueprints had on them, but they are still standing. Sometimes what they put on paper will not work.

Robert G. Stevens   *Newark, Ohio*

Your article fails to comment on the practicality—in fact the impossibility— of constructing a beam-to-rod connection as shown in the architectural drawings. There are two serious flaws to this design: How do you pass a 1¼-in.

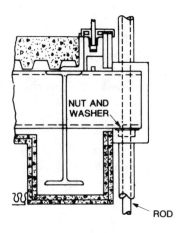

Figure 8-30 A close-up of the architectural plans of the Hyatt Hotel, showing a nut seemingly in the middle of a rod. *(ENR File.)*

steel rod, five stories long, through holes drilled in the box beam? And, wonder of wonders, how can you place a nut to fit the thread in the continuous bar unless the threaded portion of the bar is thicker than its body?

Nejad Enustun   *Lansing, Michigan*

It isn't possible unless you weld on a flange of larger size on which to place the threads so that a larger size nut can be slipped over the rod to the center section. It might not be desirable to do welding on a rod of this size because of stress considerations. It appears the contractor modified the design to get something he could do, but failed to think of the double load on the nut at the fourth-floor level.

Ellis Danner   *Emeritus Professor of Enineering,*
University of Illinois,
Sun City, Arizona

Unless the hanger rod was specially rolled with different diameters or the rod was made up of two sections welded together after assembly of the fourth-level beam and nuts, the nut would not be able to slip over the lower rod to fasten the fourth level.

Stephen M. Bull   *Bull & Palmer,*
Attorneys and Counselors at Law,
Orlando, Florida

A detail that begs a change cannot be completely without blame when the change is made.

John Peterson   *Department of Civil Engineering,*
Oregon State University,
Corvallis, Oregon

That, in turn, stimulated letters from many readers who noted that a sleeve nut could do the job—coupling the rod for the second-floor walkway onto the threaded end of the connection below the nut holding the fourth-floor walk. Readers also questioned the integrity of the beams the nuts were holding. From the ENR issue of October 15, 1981:

A Hyatt Puzzle Solution

I was surprised to see five letters to the editor concerning the Hyatt rod connection [ENR, Sept. 17, 1981, p. 9]. Each of the writers seemed to think the connection desired by the engineer was impossible.

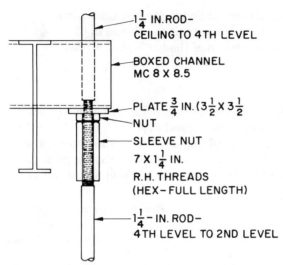

Figure 8-31 The task at Hyatt could have been accomplished this way—with sleeve nuts. But the builder evidently didn't think of it. *(ENR.)*

In my opinion, the intent was quite clear, but the detail was incomplete.

The desired result is easily accomplished through the use of a sleeve nut as shown in [Figure 8–31].

A sleeve nut develops the full strength of the 1¼-in. rod, according to the AISC 7th edition—in use at the time of the design.

On the sketch I have added a ¾-in. plate to distribute the load so there is no concentrated force right at the center line where the channels were welded.

I have used thousands of sleeve nuts with left hand/right hand threads in place of turnbuckles in order to develop the full strength of a rod on rack-supported buildings.

Recent engineering graduates do wonderful work with the computer when it comes to sizing members in a structure, but many of these young engineers are not at all good in understanding how forces act at connections. Since this is where so many failures occur, it would seem useful for educators to provide a one semester course: "Connections that won't fail."

J. Wayman Williams, Jr.

President,
Rack Structures, Inc.,
Hackettstown, New Jersey

The comments of Messrs. Enustun, Danner, Bull and Peterson are well taken. One solution to installing the nut as shown is to cut the tension rod below the nut and splice it with a sleeve nut. Such a nut is shown on page 4–144 of the Manual of Steel Construction, Eighth Edition. This solution is a change from the drawings and subject to the same submittal and approval requirements as any other change.

James H. Trewin *Dallas, Texas*

The stress on the threads at the upper end of the coupler would have been twice that in the nut-on-threaded-rod detail, but the stress at the root of the thread in the rod would have been identical. For this reason, the coupled rod would have been satisfactory.

The major weakness in the connection seems to have been in the use of thin-web channels and the lack of stiffening on both the channel flanges and webs at the point of attachment. Published reports seem to indicate that the channels had begun to deform even on the single bridge that did not fail.

It is my hope that this incident, as tragic as it was, will not lead to gross overdesign of all elements or of an increase in required design loads as a "factor of ignorance" approach to the problem.

There has been no published evidence that the beams of the Hyatt bridges were underdesigned. Had they been, the persons on the bridge would have been given ample warning of the failure. Rather, it appears that a poor detail led to a sudden collapse. What we need is attention to detail, not an arbitrary increase in code loadings.

Donald A. Sawyer *Vice President–Engineering,*
Brown Steel Contractors, Inc.,
Newman, Georgia

So, the rod design was workable. But it would have been more sensible to connect the channels back-to-back instead of flange-to-flange. A stronger connection would have resulted.

Anthony P. Chrest *Senior Vice President,*
Carl Walker & Associates, Inc.,
Kalamazoo, Michigan

Several other readers also wrote in to say that a sleeve nut could have been used to accomplish the single-rod design in the Hyatt drawings.—Editor

The article regarding the Kansas City Hyatt Regency walkway bridges [ENR, July 30, 1981, p. 11] discloses a facet not addressed as a cause of the failure: The lack of any web stiffeners in the drawings (and photographs). Without web stiffeners the channel box is about the same as a 12-in.-thick column 30 ft. high. Could any structure be considered by code or designer without shear walls or web-stiffeners for three stories?

Lack of web stiffeners in construction grillage caused the collapse of the second Narrows Bridge in Vancouver, B.C., several years ago.

Web stiffening is such an elementary requirement that it is astounding to see obvious omissions.

A. J. Johannesen   *Portland, Oregon*

The Hyatt walkway design switch exemplifies the need for a strictly enforced change-of-design procedure including technical review and documentation. Technical people sometimes feel this procedure is a burden and does not apply to them. Then we see examples where the procedure was not followed.

Thomas Lewis   *Project Engineer,*
E. I. Du Pont de Nemours & Co.,
Buffalo, New York

The National Bureau of Standards built models of the connection areas, using the same materials as had been used in the actual failed pieces. The NBS report tiptoed around who might be at fault, however, lest it lose what little cooperation it had from the litigating parties.

By October, a revamped Kansas City Hyatt had opened for business, with the original three walkways replaced by a single, 17-foot-wide "causeway" at the second-floor level. Rather than being suspended, it is supported on ten stout columns 10 by 16 inches and 10 by 18 inches in cross section. The columns are arranged in five pairs, each supporting a transverse beam 16 by 33 inches, and longitudinal beams of the same cross section along the edge of the walk. The columns are spaced 30 feet apart across the 120-foot lobby.

If that seems like overkill, it is: The walk should support 200 pounds per square foot live load on its 6-inch-thick concrete slab. That's twice the load of the old walkway's original design—and in fact, twice the load expected of the lobby floor and corridors elsewhere in the hotel! Will codes be changed to mandate such support? Kansas City officials think yes, code officials think not. As of mid-1982, the situation remained unchanged from when it was first discussed in ENR on July 30, 1981:

Sky Bridges Not Addressed by Major Codes

"As a result of this experience, I would hope to recommend that the national building code groups revise their requirements specifically for sky bridges, as opposed to balconies, dance floors or fire escapes," says Myron D. Calkins, Kansas City director of public works. Calkins says that because sky walks are not treated specifically in the codes, an engineer must combine the recommendations for all similar structures to develop an ad hoc design live load.

Figure 8-32 In this sequence from NBS tests, the rod pulls through a replica of the box beam. The beam is on its side for ease of testing, and the rod is pulled from the right. *(National Bureau of Standards.)*

Representatives of the three major model code-writing groups say it is too early to propose any revisions to the codes, but they are considering the possibility of review pending the outcome of the Hyatt Regency Hotel investigations.

Currently, the three codes—the Building Officials Code Administrators (BOCA) code, the Standard Building Code (SBC) and the Uniform Building Code (UBC, in effect in Kansas City, Mo.)—all treat walkways in hotels as corridors serving public areas or as exit facilities, with a design live load of 100 psf.

"The code doesn't speak specifically to aerial walkways," says Vincent Bush, assistant technical director for the UBC. "We didn't think of it until the Hyatt collapse." But Bush adds that the 100-psf design load assumes a fairly dense crowd of people. In all three major codes, dance floors and public assembly halls also require a 100-psf design live load.

A spokesman for John Portman & Associates, Atlanta, the architect-developer who first designed a Hyatt atrium (but says the firm has no structures similar to the aerial walkway that collapsed), says Portman considers the codes adequate. "The safety factor actually makes it work out to about 200 psf," he says.

According to William J. Tangye, director of engineering services for the SBC, the structural elements are designed for anticipated use and live loads. "The fact that a walkway is suspended does not increase or decrease the design live load," he says.

But the codes assume people will be walking along a corridor, says Tangye. If the corridor is used for dancing or other uses, the codes allow local officials to adjust the requirements, he explains.

"The development of the model code tries to shy away from unique situations," says Kenneth M. Schoonover, manager of technical services at BOCA. The Hyatt may be a unique situation, he says.

Calkins says he believes the code makers will eventually review the codes. "If they don't," he says, "I will be requesting specifically that they do so."

The collapse also touched off investigation at many similar structures, including about sixty hotels. The results of most of them were never disclosed, but one investigation that was published proved disquieting, to say the least. It was printed in the December 10, 1981, issue of ENR:

Cantilevered Hotel Bar Closed for Major Repair

A structural collapse at the Hyatt Regency Chicago "was imminent" and could have reached the magnitude of last summer's Hyatt walkway collapse in Kansas City, according to a consultant to the City of Chicago. Last week the city ordered the hotel to close off and shore a suspended area it deemed dangerous.

At issue was a cocktail lounge approximately 130 X 30 ft, partially cantilevered and suspended by hanger rods from roof trusses. It sits directly above the hotel's main entrance and a grand ballroom a floor below.

Five other areas within the Hyatt were also under investigation, and while some have shown structural defects, no others presented as immediate a threat, says James Ratterree of Bevins Consultants, Inc., Chicago, hired by the city.

"The [lounge] collapse was just a matter of time," says the firm's president, William Bevins.

The problem, according to Ratterree, was that the support system for the cantilevered portion, which made up approximately half of the floor area, was "obviously exposed to loads that it hadn't been designed for." Hangers from roof trusses were welded to steel plates, which in turn were bolted to the floor system. Inspections revealed buckled steel plates in two cases and a partially-broken weld at one connection, Ratterree says.

The faults were discovered Wednesday by the Portland Cement Association's Construction Technologies Laboratory (CTL), Skokie, Ill. The organization had been hired by the hotel owner, Chicago Hotel Venture. According to Ratterree, CTL analyzed available data and suspected the hanger plates, bolted to the top chord of the floor trusses, could not adequately support their loads.

EXCESSIVE STRESS

CTL investigators found cracking in the 4-in. concrete floor around the hangers, which they believed indicated excessive stress on the supports, Ratterree says. The hotel immediately vacated and closed off the bar, and informed the city, says spokeswoman Mary Ann Josh.

CTL then removed the concrete by jackhammer to examine the connection of the hangers and steel plates to the top chord of the floor truss. "Both plates had buckled," Ratterree says. One immediate step was fabricating a pair of gusset plates for each weak joint and welding them to the connection and the hangers, bypassing the weak joint. Another was removing all furniture.

MORE SHORING

Later, a "belt-and-suspenders" assembly—steel rods hung from the roof trusses and slung underneath the weak joints—was installed as further shoring. Josh says repairs will be completed by New Year's Eve.

The investigation that uncovered this and other defects began last July 20, following the collapse of walkways at the Crown Center Hyatt in Kansas

City, Ratterree says. All Chicago buildings with exposed pedestrian walkways were reviewed by the city. Except for minor repairs required at one University of Illinois building, no other problems were found. A pedestrian bridge connecting the Hyatt's two towers needed shoring, says Ratterree, although it was never in danger of collapse. But it and several other areas of the hotel have had occupancy and use restrictions as a precaution.

Hotel architect-engineer A. Epstein and Sons, Chicago, could not be reached for comment.

Kansas City itself, after suffering two major construction failures in 2 years—the Kemper Arena and the Hyatt—hired the International Conference of Building Officials to do a "thorough review" of the way the city inspects construction projects.

As for the Hyatt failure itself: The courts were to decide whether the proximate cause was the improper detailing of support rods, or whether the walkways would have failed anyway, from transverse beams that were too weak. In various court documents the steel fabricator has said the structural engineer made the change, the engineer said it was the fabricator's idea, the contractor has blamed the engineer and the architectural joint venture, the construction manager has blamed the contractor or steel fabricator, and the architects have blamed the engineer or steel fabricator or both.

By mid-1983, settlements in two class action suits totaling $30 million had been approved by federal and county courts. Individual out-of-court settlements added another $33 million. The total was $63 million, or $13 million more than the structure cost to build in the first place.

The worst is yet to come: Another quarter billion dollars worth of suits are pending.

Perhaps that's the greatest lesson of all when disaster strikes: No matter whose fault it was, the lawyers always win.

Index

407

About the Author

Steven S. Ross, an award-winning writer and editor, is highly regarded for his journalism in a variety of technical areas. In 1969 he earned the B.S. degree in physics at Rensselaer Polytechnic Institute. After receiving the master's degree in journalism from Columbia University, Mr. Ross edited *Air and Water News,* an environmental newsletter published by McGraw-Hill, as well as several magazines, including *New Engineer, Boardroom Reports,* and *Direct.*

Mr. Ross has written on and consulted about quality assurance in many forums. He is a member of the American Society of Testing and Materials and was named a fellow of the American Institute of Chemists for his work in environmental monitoring. Among his other books are *Product Safety and Liability: A Desk Reference* (with the late John Kolb) and *The Toxic Substances Sourcebook.* In 1979 he helped organize and lead the first American multicompany quality control study mission to Japan.

Among the honors he has received for his writing and research are the Chairman's Award from the Private Practice division of the National Society of Professional Engineers, the Citizen of the Year award from the New York State Society of Professional Engineers, and a certificate of appreciation from the U.S. Environmental Protection Agency. He has been listed in *Who's Who in America* since 1976.

Today, Steven S. Ross is a member of the adjunct faculty at Columbia University, where he teaches courses in energy and environmental reporting. He is also director of special studies at the Environment Information Center in New York and an associate of McNamee Consulting Company.